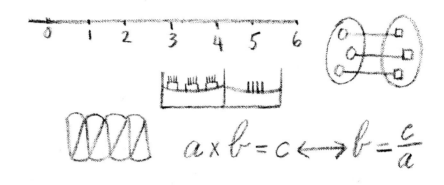

READING, MASSACHUSETTS · PALO ALTO · LONDON · DON MILLS, ONTARIO

TEACHING
MODERN MATHEMATICS
IN THE ELEMENTARY SCHOOL

HOWARD F. FEHR
Teachers College, Columbia University

JO McKEEBY PHILLIPS
University of Illinois Curriculum Laboratory

ADDISON-WESLEY PUBLISHING COMPANY

This book is in the ADDISON-WESLEY SERIES IN EDUCATION

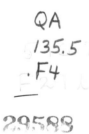

preface

In writing a book on teaching elementary school mathematics, one can proceed on one of two bases: First, one can try to produce a set of methods for teaching each of the myriad topics in a school program. Second, one can adopt a general point of view, presenting ideas which can be applied to the scope and sequence of any contemporary program. The first basis would result in a sort of handbook on ways to teach a topic, and would to a great extent repeat material given in teachers' manuals for existing series of textbooks. The second basis would take cognizance of the fact that the study of a curriculum, its organization, the underlying psychological and philosophical principles, and creative teaching techniques are fundamental to every teacher throughout his entire teaching career. This is especially so in the present era of flux, when new knowledge is demanding continuous change in both the content and the pedagogy of elementary school mathematics. For this reason, we selected the second basis as more suitable for either a preservice or in-service educational document on teaching and learning.

The word *structure* is currently used in at least two senses. It may refer to an ordered process of learning or it may refer to the axiomatic systems of modern mathematics. Since this is a book on teaching, we shall use the word in the first of these two senses. The purpose of this book is to show how elementary mathematics can be organized into a learning sequence and taught so as to build a structure of knowledge which can serve as a base for a wider and deeper knowledge of mathematics through subsequent study. Continual reference is made to sources illustrating in detail most of the skills, concepts, and fundamental principles that are enumerated. However, an abundance of suggestions and illustrations will be found in the text.

In contemporary teaching of elementary school mathematics, there are a number of innovations, some of them mathematical in nature, others pedagogical. It is common to refer to these as the "new mathematics" or the "new teaching of mathematics," respectively. We have concerned ourselves with both these aspects, devoting one entire chapter to mathematical innovations, and allowing the spirit of the entire text to reflect modern teaching techniques. In particular, the presentation of geometry illustrates both mathematics new to the elementary school and methods of teaching (including the use of scientific inquiry) new to many elementary classrooms. Since geometry is a new topic in almost all elementary school mathematics programs, special attention is given to the interpretation of the subject.

This book is intended primarily for a methods course for preservice elementary school teachers. Although it assumes a basic mathematical knowledge on the part of the reader, it gives a mathematical explanation for all ideas that are difficult or easily misinterpreted. References to mathematical treatises provide the reader with additional sources by which he may strengthen his mathematical foundation in the topics in which he instructs. The book can also be used for in-service courses for teachers who are reforming or updating their instructional practices.

Both of us have had many years of experience in teaching, consulting, experimenting, and critically studying the content and pedagogy of elementary school mathematics. We have taken cognizance of all major experimental teaching and writing projects in elementary school mathematics and have reflected here that which appears to us to be sound pedagogy and realizable content in Grades kindergarten through 6. We know how small an amount of knowledge exists on scientific pedagogy and on human learning in general, but where real evidence does exist, we have made use of it. It is, of course, impossible in a book of this nature to treat those general theories of education which pertain to all subjects in the curriculum. However, the last chapter attempts to focus several theories of learning on the subject itself, so as to give a fairly large overview of the process of learning elementary school mathematics.

New York H. F. F.
March 1967 J. McK. P.

on reading
and understanding

Clarity of written communication depends, in part, on agreement about what certain typographical schemes indicate. Such agreements need not be formal, or even spelled out clearly and enforced pointedly, but they should be understood.

In this book we shall be writing mostly about numbers. Numbers are mathematical entities. In writing about numbers we use the customary names for numbers. These names are called *numerals*. Numerals are linguistic entities. Here is an example of using numerals to write about numbers:

13 is prime; 21 is composite.

Sometimes we need to call attention to numerals and other specific marks or expressions. We have used three methods of doing this. One: we use *quotation names* for them. We form a quotation name for a numeral by enclosing the numeral in single quotation marks. Here is an example of the use of quotation names to write about numerals:

The '98' in '2^{98}' is smaller than the '2'.

A second way to refer to a mark (symbol) or expression is to write it *all by itself* on a separate line, or to separate it from the rest of a sentence by a colon. The following is an example of using a separate line to write about numerals.

We write the sum of two plus three or three added to two as:

$$2 + 3.$$

A third way is to *italicize* the numerals, marks, or expressions. We often use this third way when we introduce or define a new word or phrase or symbol. (We use italics for general emphasis also, but this use will always be evident, in context.) An example of the use of italics is the following:

A line containing points A and B may be named *line AB* (or *line BA*).

There are other ways of distinguishing references to numbers from references to names of numbers, but the three ways just described are those which are used in this book.

When you read textual material, the connotation of the symbols is usually evident from the context in which they appear. In general, it is more rewarding to read for meaning without conscious attention to typographical schemes. The real reason for this foreword is to communicate to the reader the interpretation the writers had in mind as they wrote. A well-defined procedure for differentiating a name from the thing it connotes should aid the reader to eliminate ambiguities. So we bid you read, and hope that by our procedure you will all the better understand.

contents

Chapter 12   Teaching Ratio, Proportion, and Percent

Chapter 13   Measures Extended; Coordinates; Graphs

new thinking about elementary school mathematics

Mathematics has always held a key position in the school curriculum because it has been considered knowledge indispensable to the educated man. In the elementary school, this knowledge consisted in large measure of computational arithmetic. No one would deny that this aspect of mathematics has played an important role in the education of all people, and today it is more important to basic education than ever before in the history of mankind. But there are major factors of life in this century that require us to examine anew the role that mathematics education is to play in the development of citizens for the scientific technological industrial society which we are in the process of creating. One factor is the explosion in mathematical knowledge, and new ways of conceiving of even the elementary ideas in mathematics. Another is the increasing dependence of scientific thought and of almost every career—professional, skilled, and semiskilled—on mathematical methods. The forces exerted by these two factors alone are now rebuilding the traditional framework of elementary school instruction. We have entered a period of modernization and improvement of the teaching of school mathematics.

1–1 PURPOSES OF MATHEMATICAL EDUCATION

Mathematical education, especially at the elementary school level, is not to be aimed directly or solely at producing future mathematicians. These years of schooling are intended for general education, the all-encompassing intellectual development of every school child, regardless of his subsequent ambitions in life. In this general education, the uses and applications of mathematics, the needs of future scientists and humanists, the understanding by laymen, the coordination of instruction in mathematics with that in the other school subjects, and the need for articulating elementary, secondary, and university study are the principal factors to be considered as a program in mathematical education is unfolded. Although we must necessarily consider maximum development of mathematical knowledge, we must also focus sharply on the purposes of teaching and the objectives to be gained for all children in the studies they pursue.

The general purposes of mathematical education are derived from four broad considerations:

1. Mathematics is a necessary component in the formation of a liberally educated person, but if an educated person is to understand mathematics, he must not be left a few hundred years behind in its content and conceptualization. We are indeed under obligation to eliminate outmoded and unimportant parts of mathematics and to replace them with more recent, more general, and more powerful concepts.

2. In the past, and to an even greater extent today, the usefulness of mathematics in practical matters has been the important factor in its vitality as a school subject. The rise of modern science and the creation of a technological society compel us to give increasing weight to utilitarian demands for more intensive teaching of mathematics. We now recognize that if mathematics had not been useful, it would long ago have disappeared from our school curriculum as required study.

Some mathematics reform during the last decade has been in the hands of pure mathematicians. This was good in a way, since it was necessary, as a first step to put our mathematical house in order, to make our mathematics correct and truly contemporary in concept and spirit. It is the lack of applications of this mathematics in many of the new programs that causes alarm, especially when weighed against the worth of this mathematics to a large segment of our youth.

3. Of great value to a limited but increasing number of students is sound preparation for subsequent study of mathematics. More

2

and more, high schools and colleges are presenting courses modern in content, form, and symbolism. In algebra, concepts and points of view developed quite recently have so enriched the subject that it is a completely different type of study from the algebra of 25 years ago. Geometry has been made greatly algebraic through the use of coordinates and vectors. For this and other similar reasons, modern mathematics *of a suitable sort* has been introduced into the high school, and the elementary school program must prepare pupils accordingly.

4. Even more important than the kind of knowledge to be provided is the type of mind we wish to produce. A desirable goal of formal education is to produce a person possessing freedom of the mind. Neither the pupil departing from the elementary school nor the future teacher graduating from the university must ever be a prisoner of his own acquired knowledge. He must have developed within himself abilities that enable him to dominate reality. It is not sufficient to have acquired a set of facts and procedures. For the student of mathematics, it is essential that he should have acquired the faculty of being able, by his own wit, to learn more mathematics, to solve new problems, to adapt his past knowledge to new knowledge and new points of view and, above all, to have been liberated from the shackles of authority.

In the elementary school, a formalistic logical study of mathematics does not provide a medium in which this freedom of the mind can be developed. Before any formal structure of mathematics can be understood there must be a host of experiences in doing mathematics in which concepts, manipulations, and relations are developed and applied. It is only after experiences of this type that mathematics as a study of formal structures makes sense.

1-2 GOALS FOR ELEMENTARY SCHOOL MATHEMATICS

There appear to be three major goals of education, and at the elementary school level they are of prime importance. The first is to learn how to read—to read in the broadest sense of the word: that is, to get and to interpret information acquired through the senses from the printed page, the radio, the TV screen, and word of mouth. The second goal is to acquire the ability to use this information to solve problems, to gain new knowledge, to deter-

3

mine responsible action. A third goal is to acquire an ability to gain esthetic satisfaction. This last goal is merely an application of the first two, for genuine appreciation or esthetic satisfaction comes about only with the ability to read paintings and sculpture, to interpret music and the dance, and to recognize as well as to develop skill in performance. When one uses all this knowledge in a successful search of an artistic, humanistic, literary, or scientific production, a desired esthetic satisfaction in the form of an emotional outlet occurs.

Hence the first goal of mathematics instruction is that children learn to *read* mathematics, that is to learn fundamental concepts that are basic to the understanding of the subject. They must learn to express these concepts, in words and later in symbols. They must come to see relations among these concepts. It is the grasp of these fundamental ideas that will permit children to construct, each child for himself, the fundamental operational facts in arithmetic and spatial relationships in geometry. All this knowledge is sometimes referred to as the "why" of mathematics, or the understanding of what mathematics is—why it works the way it does—what each idea means.

To understand why, however, is not sufficient for a good mathematical education. The child must also be able to *do* his mathematics. In the past the development of computational skill, usually through rote learning and drill on the algorisms, was the main goal of elementary mathematical instruction. Today most educators are agreed that this viewpoint must be changed. But these persons are also agreed that unless a child learns to compute skillfully, with ease and unhurried calm, he will be handicapped and frequently frustrated throughout the rest of his life. Hence a second goal is that children be able to *do* mathematics, to develop skill in handling mathematical symbols and concepts so as to obtain mature performance. These skills are indeed a tool, but a tool which must be thoroughly understood so as to free the mind of routine work and permit it to concentrate on new learning.

This leads to the third goal of mathematical instruction: to develop the ability to solve problems. All new learning can be conceived of as problem-solving. A problem is a situation in which a desired outcome is sensed or known, but the intellectual means to the goal are unknown to the child. The solution of problems has been discussed at great length in the literature, and in all these

4

treatises there is agreement that the child must bring to a situation (1) all the concepts and skills he has already learned, (2) an awareness of the new elements in the situation, (3) an organizational ability so that he can use this knowledge to solve the problem. If concepts are well established by going from physical situations to mathematical ideas and then back to physical situations, and if all new learnings are directed discoveries of ideas and methods, then the third goal will be attained more easily and surely than it would if the student had had to learn by means of authoritative and rote teaching. The great complaint of arithmetic teachers in the past was that "the children can do their computations, but they cannot solve problems." The above discussion should reveal why this desired goal was seldom attained.

These three goals are necessary and sufficient for the purposes of mathematical education. Each is as important as the others for general or liberal education. To neglect one in favor of the others would result in an inadequate education. Therefore correct and meaningful concepts organized into a structure of knowledge, skill in operating with these concepts through appropriate symbolism and processes, and the ability to apply this knowledge to solve problems (one type of problem is to learn more mathematics) should be uppermost in the mind of each teacher as he instructs each lesson in mathematics.

In each of these goals, there is implied that whatever is taught in the mathematics lesson should be related, when possible, to instruction in other subjects, especially science. There are a number of new science programs, recently introduced into the elementary school, for which the central thesis is "all good science teaching makes a difference in the way people live." To realize this objective, pupils must use mathematics in carrying out and describing the results of their experiments. The mathematics is usually limited to the following topics:

a) whole numbers, fractions, and negative numbers,
b) scales of measurement,
c) measurements of distance, time, volume, weight, mass, temperature, area, and angles,
d) graphing of relations,
e) space-time relations.

All these topics can be introduced into the mathematical instruction, when needed, in an informal, experimental, naïve manner that will not interfere with the building of formal construction of these concepts at a later stage. The teacher should never hesitate to build strong relations between mathematics and the sciences.

1-3 A NEW WAY OF LOOKING AT ARITHMETIC

Arithmetic was, and to too great a degree still is, considered a necessary tool subject which can be learned through rote and drill. Today we are agreed that this is too narrow a purpose for instruction. Arithmetic is also to be looked upon as a "way of thinking," as an organized body of knowledge about number, having its own organizational structure and laws. It can be learned meaningfully, by first abstracting and making generalizations from the physical world, and by later making further abstractions from concepts that have been previously learned. The computational process then becomes a matter of developing a scheme for writing the names of the numbers and manipulating these symbols according to the structure and laws of the numbers they represent. When learned in this meaningful manner, arithmetic is retained longer, and applied more easily to the solution of practical problems.

The initial step in this type of learning is the study of sets of physical objects, that is, collections of individual things. Out of the comparison of different collections of objects, there emerge the first concepts of cardinal number (manyness) and of order. A way in which this learning can be fostered will be unfolded in the chapters that follow.

Several words will appear that were not in the study of arithmetic in the first half of the twentieth century, but these words are for the most part ways of making hitherto ambiguous ideas clearer and more precise.

1-4 GEOMETRY IN THE ELEMENTARY SCHOOL

In the United States, geometry scarcely existed as a study at the elementary school level before 1955. With the explosion in technology, space and the universe around us has taken on such added significance that a basic geometric knowledge must now become the possession of every citizen. Thus the elementary school is given an additional charge: to develop those concepts of space which are necessary and basic to liberal education. In the past this knowledge was limited to the measure of length of a segment, area of a surface, and volume of simple solids. Today, descriptions of space and figures of space are just as important as the measures, and so a new phase of geometry, called *nonmetric*, takes on significance for the elementary school program.

This geometry looks on a space as an infinite set of points, where the meaning of point is to be grasped intuitively at first. Then subsets of a space can be described as certain geometric figures, or an assemblage of figures. For example, a triangle is a certain set of three line segments. This geometry also uses some new names and symbols, and attempts to be precise and correct in its descriptions and uses. It is learned initially through observation and drawing, and speaking about sets or collections of points. By comparing figures according to their shape, position, size, and the way they are connected, we develop an informally structured body of knowledge about the space we live in that will enable children to describe and to solve practical problems of a geometrical nature. A way of building this geometric knowledge is described in this book.

1–5 UNIFIED MATHEMATICS

The reader will have noticed that basic to both arithmetic and geometry is the ideas of a *set* or collection of things. It is only natural then to think that in some way arithmetic and geometry are related, and indeed they are. You see this on a ruler with its geometric markings and the numerals assigned to these markings. Thus number, as used in measurement, helps us to express geometric relations of size. On the other hand, when a graph is drawn of a set of statistical data, we have an illustration of how geometry (a line figure) is used to help us understand arithmetic (a collection of numbers). Beyond this, there are times when a certain rule seems to work universally; for example, when we multiply the number of units in the base of a rectangle by the number of units in the altitude of the same rectangle, the product is the number of square units in the area of the rectangle. We write this $A = b \cdot h$. Here we are using variables (letters) and are already entering the field of elementary algebra.

For this and many other reasons, we now drop the word *arithmetic* as the title for the mathematics taught in the elementary school and use the word *mathematics* as best describing what we should be teaching. In fact, we must think of education as a process to be continued throughout life, and elementary school education forms the basis for all subsequent learning. There is thus only one mathematics, with various levels of depth and extension and various levels of abstraction and complexity. In the elementary school, we shall make a naïve study of number and space. Building on this knowledge in high school, we shall deepen our study of number through the study of algebra, and our study of space through a formal study of Euclidean geometry, and then unite space and number in the study of coordinate geometry and vectors. Thus what we teach in the elementary school must be correct and comprehensive. It need not necessarily be rigorous, formal, or of great difficulty.

1-6 AN OVERALL VIEW OF ELEMENTARY SCHOOL MATHEMATICS

Since the instructional program is to be a unified program of arithmetic and geometry taught in some systematic way so as to build a structure of knowledge in the mind of the child, it is necessary that the elementary school teacher understand not only the content of the particular grade he instructs, but the program of all six grades as a whole. The teacher can get a rather complete view through the study of this book. However, it is worth while to get a panoramic picture at the start and for this purpose there is outlined below the basic content of a program in mathematics designed for *all* children. Beyond this basic content, there is enriched treatment or extension of all the content which may be given to those children who are gifted or have special talent in mathematics. This outline is followed by a concise presentation of a structured development of the cardinal numbers, a development which will be spelled out in great detail in the next few chapters. Both the content outline and development of the cardinal numbers should aid the reader to grasp the purpose of the textbook.

1-7 BASIC MATHEMATICAL CONTENT

1. Sets: correct intuitive grasp of sets of physical and abstract elements

2. Mappings of sets: injections and bijections; that is, one-to-one matchings

3. The meaning of cardinal number: order; ordinal number sense; zero

4. Decimal-place system of numeration. (Any other systems are for enrichment only.)

5. Counting as a fundamental unary operation; other unary operations, e.g., adding 1, dividing by 3, etc.

6. Operations (binary): relation to operations on sets; what an operation is

7. Algorisms to carry out all operations developed to a mature level of performance

8. Elementary theory of numbers: factors; types of number; division theory; GCF; LCM; use of exponents

9. Various interpretations and uses of whole numbers

10. Fractions: various interpretations; fundamental principles

11. Operations on fractions: concepts related to physical world

12. Fractions and rational numbers: the real number line. Informal extension to negative numbers

13. Decimal notation for rational numbers: operations in decimal form

14. Theory of ratio, proportion, measure, and percent

15. Nonmetric geometry: physical recognition of geometrical configurations and their relations

16. Metric geometry: length, area, volume, coordinates, graphs

17. Problems in every aspect of the mathematical content that is taught

The program to be implemented in the elementary school will contain very little "new" mathematics, for the mathematics that is truly "new" is advanced, abstract, highly theoretical, and properly belongs in the university and graduate study. There will, however, be a great deal of mathematics new to the elementary school program. There will be new words and phrases, and much of the traditional arithmetic will be treated under new concepts. Among the new words and concepts will be found: sets; mappings or matchings; numeral as distinct from number; one-to-one correspondence; order; the symbols ' $<$ ', ' $>$ ', and ' $\neq$ '; binary operations; systems of numeration, including the binary system; greatest common factor; least common multiple; exponent; prime factor; composite number; ordered pairs of numbers; mathematical sentences; etc.

In geometry, while the idea of measure of length, area, and volume will continue to be presented in a contemporary mathematically acceptable manner, there will also be much study of space from a physical and intuitive viewpoint. There will be developed the meaning and concept of such nonmetric aspects of space as: point; sets of points; segment; ray; half-line; half-plane; region; simple closed curve; boundary; interior; space as a set of points; the usual figures. All this is to be learned by abstracting the ideas from the physical world, by using paper folding, geometrical models, examining the environment, drawing, and measuring.

The language used will be clear, clean, concise, and correct instead of, as has often been the case in the past, ambiguous, unclear, verbose, and sometimes incorrect. The emphasis will be on building an intuitive structure of related fundamental concepts through directed scientific inquiry. Each child must make his own mental construct of every mathematical idea he acquires. In helping him to do this, however, we must guard against the great danger of over-symbolization and over-abstraction at too early an age. Enthusiasm of the experimenters in the new programs is usually high, but the general overall accomplishments must always be tested, and weighed as to their value. Nevertheless, it is evident that, except for those things (usually linguistic entities) learned principally by imitation, all pure rote learning should be abolished, and in its place we must have learning by a scientific method, that is, by abstracting from observed phenomena, under guidance, the concepts and structure of number and of space. Let us now illustrate the way we shall do this.

The beginnings or foundations of arithmetic can be initiated in several ways, but in school we shall start with sets, groups, classes, or collections of objects. The name *set* is relatively immaterial at this stage, but the idea is all-important. Certain sets of objects, in which the objects may be different in physical or other properties, may have a common property: namely, they can be placed in object-to-object correspondence with each other. This property that the sets have in common—namely, their numerosity, their cardinality, their plurality, their manyness, their strength or power—we call the *number* of the set. As children study sets of different sizes, they learn to abstract the number property of the set and associate a fixed number name with all sets of the same size.

Although many children can say the number names in order by rote at this period of instruction, this activity is of little value in meaningful learning. The groups or collections of objects can be ordered according to their plurality or their manyness, and the number symbols associated with these collections can be written in corresponding order. The number symbols thus become in themselves a set, which, if used in the usual order, provide an excellent way of finding the number of any other set of elements. Instead of matching one set of objects with another, we match the set of numbers, beginning with 1, in order with any set of objects and the last matching name tells us the cardinal number of the set. Thus counting becomes man's way of finding how many. Right from the start we develop the concept of counting as a unary operation, which maps a set into the set of ordered numbers. We do not tell children to count, but to count some set of objects.

Each time we join another element to a set we get a new enlarged set, and we invent a new symbol or name for the number of the augmented set. Eventually these names become so many that we create some sort of repetitive system in naming the numbers. We are thus led to a system of numeration. Our system is a decimal, multiplicative, additive place system, and these latter three aspects form the foundation of all the computational work of our arithmetic. When these ideas are grasped, there is little trouble in learning the rest of arithmetic. How to gain meaningful knowledge of the decimal system of numeration is developed in Chapter 2. *Children who have learned to count rationally by the use of a decimal place system can use numbers intelligently in subsequent experience. When rote counting is primary, children have great difficulty in further learning.*

The structure is now extended to include the concept of addition. Physically, addition can be interpreted as the counterpart of combining or joining two sets into one single set. In arithmetic this is construed as finding the number of the combined set from the numbers of the separate sets. Thus addition can be *based* on counting. If children can count, they can add. But knowing what addition is does not suffice in our life affairs. We must be able to take a series of numbers, no matter how large, and find their sum efficiently.

This means that certain basic additions must be learned and committed to memory for future use. Since we operate in a decimal system, we need learn no basic additions beyond 9 + 9. With the explicit use of the decimal system of notation and the *intuitive* awareness of the commutative and associative laws, children can develop these fundamental addition facts for themselves and then practice the facts until they are remembered. At some point, children sense that the sum 3 + 5 equals the sum 5 + 3, and that both are 8. To explicitly call this a commutative property at this time of learning is ridiculous. When sums go beyond ten we use the associative law:

$$6 + 7 = 6 + (4 + 3) = (6 + 4) + 3 = 10 + 3 = 13.$$

Thus the operation of addition is related directly to the decimal system of notation. The extension to the addition of numbers of any size is then developed.

Physically, in set operations, subtraction has its counterpart in finding the complement of a given part of a set. In arithmetic, it is finding a *number* from two given numbers, one of which tells us the size of a given set and the other the size of a part to be removed. That this operation is related to addition is not recognized by children at the start, nor need it be. The basic subtractions needed are really those up to minuends of 10, but for effectiveness we learn the subtractions to 18 − 9, and practice them until they are quickly and easily recalled. The use of the decimal system permits us to extend these basic subtractions to subtracting a number of any size from the same or a larger number. Subtracting a larger number from a smaller number is impossible in the arithmetic of whole numbers, and thus subtraction is an operation that differs in its properties from addition. Finally, the operations on physical sets enable us to see how addition and subtraction of numbers are reversible numerical operations.

We now build on our structure to introduce a new operation called multiplication. This operation can be related to addition.

But there is also a new element in it, since the multiplier is not necessarily connected with a given set of objects, but acts as an operator in the following manner. Consider a collection of sets (we could say a set of sets) all having the same number, for example, 6. I shall select a certain number of these sets and combine them into a single set. The corresponding arithmetical operation is called multiplication; the number of sets which were selected is called the multiplier; the number of the combined set is called the product. Multiplication can also be defined by the Cartesian product of two sets, but this concept of multiplication has little validity in the elementary school program. It need not even be mentioned, except for enrichment.

Multiplication can also be looked on as explaining the result of replacing each element of a given set by other sets, each replacement set having the same number. A concrete illustration is replacing each orange in a half dozen by sets of 7 cents. The result is the product set of 42 cents. This, indeed, is the most common model of multiplication in our everyday life. Again, knowing what multiplication is and how to add, the child can develop his own basic multiplication facts, or so-called tables. However, knowing how to discover a product is not enough. The pupil must practice what he has discovered until he knows all the basic facts by quick recall. The informal use of the commutative law helps him, since, for example, $9 \times 7 = 7 \times 9 = 63$. Again, in extending multiplication to numbers of any size, the intuitive use of the associative law plays an important role also, since, for example, 20×8 is the same as

$$(10 \times 2) \times 8 \quad \text{or} \quad 10 \times (2 \times 8) \quad \text{or} \quad 10 \times 16 \quad \text{or} \quad 160.$$

Thus pupils can easily learn how to multiply by 30, 40, and so on, before tackling such problems as 26×234, in which the informal use of the distributive law plays a large role.

The last operation on whole numbers is division. There has been much verbiage about this operation in the past ten years, including such words as measurement, sharing, dealing out equally, partitive, etc., all of which confuse rather than aid learning. Division can be conceived of as expressing the reverse of multiplication. For example, consider a given set of objects and partition this set into a number of equivalent subsets. If the number *in* the subsets is known, we are asked to find the number of these subsets;

13

but if the number *of* desired subsets is known, we are asked to find the number in each subset. Under this definition, partitioning is not always possible. There are remainders, not enough elements to make another subset, or not enough to enlarge each subset by one more element. In the corresponding division of the numbers our answer does not come out exact. Of course, we treat these remainders intelligently, seeking the relation of the remainder to the dividend when we desire a total quotient, or later, when fractions have been taught, making further subdivision of some of the elements that were originally given, so as to provide an exact answer.

Children easily learn the fundamental division facts by relating them to corresponding multiplication facts. In more extensive computation they relate division to subtraction; this will be well explained in Chapter 6.

In summary, the structure of the arithmetic of whole numbers is based fundamentally on sets or collections of things. From these collections of things we obtain:

1. A set of elements called numbers arranged in order

2. A decimal-place system of numeration to represent these numbers

3. A closed operation called addition ($+$), bound by the laws

$$a + b = b + a, \quad \text{commutative,}$$

and

$$a + (b + c) = (a + b) + c, \quad \text{associative}$$

4. A closed operation called multiplication ($\times$) bound by the laws

$$a \times b = b \times a, \quad \text{commutative,}$$

and

$$a \times (b \times c) = (a \times b) \times c, \quad \text{associative}$$

5. A law combining these two operations, called distributive

$$a \times (b + c) = a \times b + a \times c \quad (\times \text{ is distributive over } +)$$

6. An inverse of an addition, called subtraction ($-$):

$$a - b = c \quad \text{if} \quad c + b = a.$$

This inverse does not always exist.

7. An inverse of a multiplication, called division ($\div$):

$$a \div b = c \qquad \text{if} \qquad c \times b = a.$$

This inverse does not always exist.

8. There are two numbers, 0 and 1, which play a unique role in addition and multiplication, respectively:

$$a + 0 = 0 + a = a; \qquad a \times 1 = 1 \times a = a.$$

They are called the *identity elements* of the respective operations.

This last summary has been very formal and illustrates an advanced endpoint in learning, good for the teacher to know, but far too sophisticated for the children.

The preceding pages have outlined the structure of the finite cardinal (or whole) numbers in a sequence of concepts, the understandings of which are requisite for the study of all the other number systems with which an elementary school child will deal. The understandings are also essential for the intelligent application of the number system to the solution of everyday practical problems. Hence the study of these concepts should occupy a major part of the primary instruction time given to mathematics.

Some hints have already been given on a theory of learning mathematics. We shall close this chapter with a more extended discussion of learning.

1–8 THE LEARNING OF MATHEMATICS

In the past, there were current two major ideas about the learning of mathematics. One was that the subject was to be learned as a tool and that the way to teach it was to *show* the child how to do it and then have him practice and make perfect the skill to be learned. This viewpoint has now been abandoned. It is still recognized that a skill, to be usable, needs practice and perfecting, but practice comes only after the theory underlying the performance is understood. The second viewpoint, quite prevalent in some educational movements today, is that the subject is to be learned by logical reasoning from a primitive set of accepted ideas about number. This point of view does not work for the majority of children from ages 5 to 10 years, and indeed can interfere with real learning.

Mathematical activity at this age does not consist in being able to deduce conclusions from long chains of reasoning.

Good mathematical instruction at the elementary school level consists in getting the pupils to construct the subject for themselves through scientific inquiry. In general, this method involves teaching children to do four main activities, namely: to observe, to select, to generalize by abstracting, and to conceptualize the result. At all stages of learning mathematics, these activities are demanded. (Of course, in formal mathematical instruction at a later age, other mental activities are also required.)

If a child must observe, select, generalize, abstract, conceptualize and "do" his mathematics, it will be necessary to furnish him with activities conducive toward these ends. Physical objects and other multisensory aids can be overemphasized and used in improper and incorrect ways, but generally they are too often neglected or despised by persons who devote their teaching to descriptions, involved symbolic representations, and deductions. The teacher who has made more or less use of the sensory world—the schoolroom environment—of strings, rubber bands, watches, shadows, alignment of objects, *grouping* of objects (chairs, desks, books, erasers, etc.) knows the richness of mathematical situations which they suggest. In fact there is no need to use any of the many so-called structured materials and special methods now on the market at high prices, for every type of school environment holds far superior models of mathematical concepts.

Besides this concrete material there is also abstract material. In the mind of every student who has had any previous mathematical experience there exists a reservoir of acquired mental concepts, which for the pupil are equivalent to concrete material. The teacher can dip into this reservoir of mathematical concepts and combine established concepts as needed in elaborating a new physical system so as to lead to the discovery of new concepts.

Any material we teach must be governed by the concepts and experiences which the pupil has acquired at a given time. It must also be adapted to the mental maturity of the pupil; we cannot proceed too fast or too abstractly, or too slowly or too obviously. On the other hand, there is a limited time in which we can give the necessary instruction in mathematics, so we need economy and efficiency in our teaching. We cannot satisfy the needs of mathematics by cramming into the program more mathematical material, nor by squeezing down into the lower grades material usually assigned to higher grades. Instead we will have to cast out useless and outmoded parts of the program, make broader and more general approaches, and use modern unifying concepts which are within the mental capabilities of the pupils.

Finally we must teach our mathematics in a way that will be pleasing and satisfying to the learner. We must attempt to make it have esthetic appeal so as to captivate the interest and attention— yes, even the spirit—of the children.

These demands for a sound pedagogical procedure in teaching mathematics are great, and a general psychological theory that will satisfy all the criteria is not in existence today. There are, however, two or three general principles on which we can establish learning procedures that have proved valid. The first of these is that structured learning is more meaningful and more conducive to long retention than is incidental learning. To this end, *school mathematics is to be reconstructed by making use of mathematical structures both as a means to learning and as a desirable end product.* Mathematics is not to be taught in terms of special principles, skills, and isolated facts—hundreds of them—but is to be organized around a number of general themes or threads that pervade all mathematical study. Recent experiments have indicated that when students are taught in this manner, they acquire not only an astonishing mastery, but also an intellectual drive which enables them to forge ahead more rapidly.

The verb "to learn" is both active and transitive. If a child is to acquire generalizations, concepts, and structures at a naïve level, the method of teaching must be based on the application of psychological structuring of knowledge. This method of teaching mathematics will make the learner participate and construct for himself all that is learned. The pupil must be educated to mathematize a given physical situation. This demands the search for and recognition of patterns, the assembling of data, an inquiry into the nature of these data, simple inductions and deductions, calculations, and interpretations. This method of learning makes as much use of imagination and intelligent guesswork as it does of verification and criticism. It develops ability to cope with unknown relations and confidence to use already acquired knowledge. It calls for the discovery of knowledge, followed by its organization into some form of scientific structure. This is the way mathematics is to be learned. The rest of the book is an exposition of the application of this philosophy.

In this book, at the end of each chapter, there is a set of exercises which require a critique or investigation of the exposition in the chapter. Each exercise should require not more than one-half hour for study and written exposition. After the exercises there is a brief bibliography which may be used as assigned or optional study to extend and deepen the material presented in the chapter.

EXERCISES

1. Looking at your own life experience, what mathematics do you consider essential in an elementary school program of instruction? Criticize this method of attempting to determine content for elementary school instruction.

2. What advantages accrue when one teaches mathematics as a unified subject rather than as separate branches of arithmetic and geometry?

3. Give further support to, or rebut, the purposes of mathematical education suggested in this chapter. Give additional purposes that you feel support greater emphasis on mathematics teaching.

4. The goals listed in this chapter are general. Select one of these goals and list under it at least five specific goals which you feel can be objectively tested for their realization.

5. Make an outline or chart of the overall presentation of whole numbers given in this chapter, indicating the structure of learning about whole numbers.

6. Give two distinct psychological theories of the learning of mathematics at the elementary school level. Select the one of these which you regard as having greater potential for learning, and state the reasons why you hold this opinion.

7. What outcomes of mathematical instruction other than computational skills are essential for basic education? Give support to each proposed outcome.

8. Tell what the term "modern mathematics" signifies to you. What "modern mathematics" is proposed as possible content for the elementary schools?

9. How is the mathematics curriculum for the elementary school constructed? That is, who decides the content (scope) and the grade placement (sequence) and by what means is the decision made?

10. List at least two large national-scale experiments in the teaching of school mathematics and indicate the nature of the programs developed in these experiments. Comment on: (1) their readability, (2) their provisions for development and practice of skills, (3) their teaching of problem-solving.

REFERENCES

NATIONAL COUNCIL OF TEACHERS OF MATHEMATICS, *Arithmetic in General Education*, Sixteenth Yearbook, 1941, Chapter 11, "Recent Trends in Learning Theory; Their Application to the Psychology of Arithmetic," pages 268–289

NATIONAL COUNCIL OF TEACHERS OF MATHEMATICS, *Instruction in Arithmetic.* Twenty-Fifth Yearbook, 1960, Chapter 3, "Structuring Arithmetic," pages 33–61; Chapter 4, "Guiding the Learner to Discover and Generalize," pages 62–93

NATIONAL COUNCIL OF TEACHERS OF MATHEMATICS, *The Learning of Mathematics; Its Theory and Practice.* Twenty-First Yearbook, 1953, Chapters 1 and 11

PHILLIPS, J. M., "'Basic Laws' for Young Children," *The Arithmetic Teacher* **12,** No. 7, November 1965, pages 525–532

WEAVER, J. F., "Basic Considerations in the Improvement of Elementary School Mathematics Programs," *The Arithmetic Teacher* **7,** No. 7, November 1960, pages 269–273

sets, number, counting, numeration

2-1 THE CONCEPT OF SET

A basis of all contemporary mathematics is the concept of *set* and operations on sets. The manner in which the word "set" is used in mathematics is similar to that of ordinary usage, when we speak of a set of dishes or a social set, but there is one very important difference. In mathematics, a set is always a collection of distinct, separate objects (beings or things) that are recognized as belonging to the *specific* collection we are calling a set. All other things, then, do not belong to this set. The word "set" in a mathematical context should always be used in such a way that there can be no doubt about which objects belong to the set and which do not.

It is important for teachers to know that a set is a mathematical entity; a set is precisely as abstract as a number. Neither a set nor a number can be described as red or green, straight or crooked, heavy or light, and so on. The *members* of a set may have a great variety of characteristics which are not characteristics of the set. Thus it makes no sense to say, "color one-half of this set blue," or "we are going to use straight sets today." It is not necessary to belabor the children with matters of this kind, but teachers should take care to keep the distinction between a set (a collection regarded as a single mathematical entity) and the members of the set (objects which may have all sorts of physical attributes) clear in their own minds, and to act accordingly.

In developing the concept of sets, we start with physical objects of a sort which are easy for children to handle. These objects can be moved and put into separate piles, collections, groups, bunches, and so on, each of which we shall call a set. A set whose members are physical objects is sometimes referred to as a *concrete situation*. We start by using precise descriptions so that no doubt remains in the mind of the child as to which objects belong to the set we are describing, and which do not. Then, to strengthen the concept we are building, we use vague phrases at times, so that it is impossible to be sure whether a given object is, or is not, a member of the set. Some sets in kindergarten and first-grade classrooms that help children develop recognition of sets are the following:

1. The set of boys (or girls) in the class. The members of these sets can be placed in separate sections of the room. A boy in another class does not belong to the set of boys in this class. The teacher? Is he (or she) a member of the class? No? Why not? The class has pupils only, the teacher is not a pupil. The pupils form her class, and since we have described the set of boys (or girls) *in* the class, the teacher is not a member of the set.

2. The set of books on a given shelf in the room. Ask what books belong and which do not belong to this set of books. Ask children to name or describe other sets of books in the room.

3. The set of pupil chairs in the room. Compare this set with the set of pupils in the room. Does each pupil have a chair? Are there more chairs than pupils or just enough, or too few chairs? How can you tell? (Matching should be suggested.)

4. The set of lights in the room, the set of windows, the set of doors, the set of walls, the set of tables, the set of clothes pegs (or hangers, or lockers), and so on. Have the children describe as many other sets of things as they possibly can.

For pedagogical reasons, in the first approach to sets, one should use only things that are alike in some way. This likeness should be maintained until children are able to make sharper distinctions to name a set. Thus the set {this dog, this horse, this man, this boy} as living things a child is looking at, is a fairly sophisticated concept of set and should be introduced at a much later stage. The set {the moon, the Taj Mahal, Mr. Alphonso Gordoni} meets the mathematical requirements for a set, but it is not likely to appear useful to first-graders.

2–2 COMPARING SETS

Basic to the concepts of *number* and *order* is the mapping (or matching) of sets. Only two kinds of mappings are considered at the first approach. One is the kind of mapping in which one set is mapped or matched into the other set, object for object, until one of the sets is exhausted and objects still remain in the other set. This is a matching of one set (the exhausted one) *into* the other set. We say that the second of these sets has *more* elements than the first or the first has *fewer* elements than the second. The other mapping is *onto*, that is, a mapping, one object to one object, and both sets are exhausted: neither one has more or fewer elements than the other.

One pupil can be asked to match his set of blocks with that of another pupil. He can do this by moving the blocks so that each block is touching the one it is paired with. Then the pupils can say that one has *more*, one has *fewer*, or one has the *same*, as the other. The word "same" leads to the question, "same what?" Certainly not the same blocks. We say the sets have the same *number* of blocks. At first no particular name of a number need be given, just the phrase "same number." In this way, number comes to be associated with the manyness of objects in a set. After a few illustrations, most children will be able to match sets (or make a mapping of one set into or onto the other) and tell which set has the *greater number* because there are *more things*, or the *same number* because the sets match exactly. The concepts of *less than* and *fewer than* are more difficult for children to acquire than the concepts of *greater than* and *more than*, probably because "fewer" involves using ghosts of objects which are not there. The teacher should be aware of this psychological phenomenon, and act accordingly.

When children are matching sets, it is very important that they make mappings in different arrangements of the objects. They should check to see that different arrangements do not change the manyness of the sets; that is, the larger set is always the larger, no matter how you compare the sets; or the sets match exactly, no matter how you arrange the elements of both sets and then pair them off.

The types of physical sets that can be paired are at hand in almost all classrooms: e.g., pupils with chairs; boys with girls; books with books; coat pegs or lockers with pupils; one pile of papers with another, and so on. A teacher should make a list of 25 to 50 such sets for ready reference.

After working with physical objects, the children can move on to pictures of members of sets of things. First, children will be asked to identify sets of objects in a picture: e.g., a set of children, a set of people, a set of cats, a set of dogs, a set of animals, a set of bananas, and so on. Then children can match the sets represented by two different pictures. A good way is to have two sets of things illustrated on a sheet of paper. Then children can match an object to an object by drawing curved arrows.

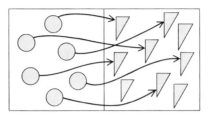

If some elements cannot be matched the child knows at once which picture has the larger set of objects (or pictures).

After a number of such assignments, the children can be given two separate cards which can be placed side by side, and the matching indicated by using pieces of string weighted at each end so that the ends will stay in place. Pieces of string may have little suction cups at each end for similar exercises on the chalkboard, or for matching objects pictured on the chalkboard with those placed on the chalk rail. Strings have an advantage over arrows in that the pictures are not changed at all when the strings are used, and the same pictures can be used to show several mappings of the same two sets of objects.

After many experiences of the above types, pupils are ready to make their first study of number and number names. Whether or not they already know these number names, either by rote or with a meaning already established, they should go through the experiences listed in the next section.

2–3 CARDINAL NUMBER

The *sine qua non* of mathematics is the concept of cardinal number, a number which answers the question "how many?". Young children must know, in their bones, so to speak, what numbers are. They need not be able to verbalize this knowledge specifically, but they must be able to perform correctly in appropriate situations.

Once a youngster really "feels" 5, for instance, he knows all sorts of "number facts" involving 5 regardless of whether he has ever seen one of these facts in print. A youngster who cannot tell when he has 5 counters on his desk should not be spending his time learning to write meaningless (to him) squiggles such as '3 + 2 = 5'. The teacher should realize that the understandings described in the next few sections are so fundamental to everything a child learns about numbers later that time spent on developing these understandings now will be time repaid tenfold later, and he should act accordingly.

The teacher can take an informal survey of each child's understanding of cardinal numbers. He may ask the child to bring him two books, or three jars of paint, or to choose five children to play a game, seizing whatever opportunities the general routine of the class may offer for such requests.

One of the best ways to get children to understand the nature of cardinal number is to make a study of several numbers, one at a time, not necessarily in any given order. Usually, the first number a child really understands is 2. The explanation probably lies in the bilateral symmetry of his body, and the fact that he has two parents. To some children, 'two' means "one for each hand." The concept of 1 comes later, after 4 and 3, and possibly after 5. Two, then, is a good number to start with.

The teacher may ask each child to place exactly 2 counters on his desk. If no child has difficulty in doing this, and if other evidence indicates that each pupil in the class has the concept of "twoness," the teacher may proceed to some other activities associated with the number 2. If some child does have difficulty, the teacher should pick up 2 of something and ask the child to put enough counters on his desk to match one-to-one with the objects the teacher is holding. A most convenient (and correct) terminology to use here is illustrated by saying, "We are going to call this set of counters a *two-set*. Any other set whose members can be matched with this so that each member has a partner is also a two-set." Then the teacher should ask the children to describe other two-sets, and after that, to pick out the two-sets from a batch of collections of pictures or objects, of which some are two-sets and some are not.

After the children understand the number property of a two-set, they can learn to recognize the symbol '2' and the word 'two'. These are learned the way any other written language is learned: by practice in association with appropriate objects, pictures, sounds, and actions. The teacher may hold up a card with '2' or 'two' printed on it and say, "Hold up this many fingers," or "Clap your hands this many times," or "Get the erasers from this chalk rail. Are there this many erasers?" The children may use similar cards as labels for the two-sets they can find.

The next step is learning to write the symbol '2', first written by the teacher and traced by the children, through various steps providing intermediate guidance, and finally written without guidance:

1. Trace this '2' written on the chalkboard, or on a worksheet, or in the sandbox. *Start at the top.*

2. Write this '2'. *Start at the top!* (There might be 25 or more of these on a worksheet, and the children should be encouraged to speed up a little bit as they proceed.)

3. Write '2' with no guidelines.

Just as it is proper for an art teacher to speak of drawing a tree (since "draw" implies "picture"), so it is proper for a mathematics teacher to speak of writing a number (since "write" implies "symbol"). Of course, the picture is not the tree and the symbol is not the number, but no great to-do should be made about that in a primary classroom. *A number is a mathematical entity; a numeral is a linguistic entity.* Most of the time, in mathematics lessons, we want our attention on mathematics, and *we should be working with numbers and speaking about numbers.*

Pictures of sets with the number 2 can be collected and put in a scrapbook with the label '2'. All the pictures should be such that the objects in one picture can be matched exactly with the objects in any other picture in the book. Any picture can then be used to represent a set for which the number is 2. A further extension is to have children make drawings of a set that numbers 2. For example,

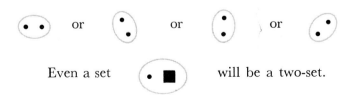

Note that braces are unnecessary, are difficult for children to draw, and do not in any way aid in the formation of the fundamental concept. Thus $n\{\bigcirc, \square\} = 2$ is not recommended as the way to teach the meaning of 2. This is oversymbolization and should be deferred until the teaching of mathematics in the middle grades or high school.

Thus the learning of two, or any other number, begins with the matching of physical objects, then the matching of elements in pictures, then the drawing of representations of objects in a set, and finally the writing of the symbol '2' which represents the entire idea we have developed, the manyness or cardinality of a set of objects. After the number two is studied, the pupils can proceed to study the number four, then the number three, then the number five. A deliberate avoidance of the rote order which so many children have already learned is advocated so that children really grasp the idea of cardinal number. Although we refer to these as whole numbers (an accident of historical development) it is the principle of cardinality, of manyness, that we desire to develop first.

To some children "number" and "manyness" signify more than a single element. Hence special care must be used to develop the number one as representing the manyness of a set, a singleton. To this end, before teaching the number one, have the pupils select a set with a single element. Some examples may be the set of clocks in the room, the set of teacher's desks in the room, the set of wash-bowls in the room, the set of fathers in a home, etc. These are sets, and we can get pictures of their members and make a scrap-book for the number 1.

The number zero has only recently been accepted as such in elementary school arithmetic. It does provide a little difficulty, and for this reason the study of zero can be delayed until the numbers from 6 to 10 have been developed. Equating zero with nothing is the source of most of the difficulty. However, the use of the idea of an empty set as the set containing no elements (but not a nonexistent set) aids in developing the idea of zero. By the time we come to the study of zero in the first grade, children have had a good deal of experience in describing sets. Now we describe sets that have real meaning, but no element is in the set. For example, we could describe, for several consecutive days, the set of pupils in the class who are absent. This set may have several members, or one member, or no members (on days when everyone is present). The set of pupils who are absent exists whether it has members or not. We tell the children that a set which has no members is an *empty* set.

Now other examples must be given of an empty set, and the pupils should produce some themselves. The set of mothers in the classroom is empty; the set of ships in a certain picture is empty; and so on. Then we say, "How many are in the set?" and we answer, "That many is zero." Zero is the number of the empty set. Then the children learn to write the symbol for zero. What would a scrapbook for 0 look like? A book of blank pages!

The numbers from 6 to 10 cannot be grasped at one glance at a set of objects except by people with extraordinary sight. To develop these numbers, we use the idea of enlarging a set by joining a new element to it. We also use grouping of elements, which aids in recognizing the manyness of a set. Thus a set

  is readily recognized as fewer than

We teach the numbers of these sets and the symbols for naming the numbers in the same manner as we did for the numbers from 2 to 5, but less time and fewer illustrations are needed if we have done our initial teaching correctly. Our principal task is to get a real understanding of the cardinality of sets with from zero to ten members, and recognition of the symbols for these numbers, coupled with a certain amount of skill in writing these number symbols.

2-4 ORDERING THE NUMBERS

If, in ordinary life, we always had to compare sets with some standard sets to know how many of a thing we had, we would be at a great disadvantage. The next step in structured learning is to use the *numbers* which we have abstracted from matching sets to help us in our problems of "how many?". To do this we use two new ideas which are important: the first is *order*; the second is *counting*. The concept of order is necessary if one is to acquire meaningful mathematical knowledge.

An order is an arrangement of things in a sequence by some rule or principle which we call an *order relation*. To develop this idea with children we resort to order relations which are familiar to them. Consider five children, picked out because they are of different heights. Ask them to line up from one side to the other so that for any one, the next one is "taller than he (or she) is." Thus the children arrange themselves

and the class sees that they are in the order of '*a*' is taller than '*b*' if '*a*' comes after '*b*'. (It will cause confusion at this stage to use "to the right of" or "to the left of.") Next we can line up the children by the relation "is smaller than" and get an arrangement

Now consider a family: mother, father, sister, brother, me, and our dog. We can make pictures by arranging these by "is taller than" and "is smaller than." Then we can try another arrangement, "is more important than," in which we may obtain: me, our dog, mother, etc. If we have a rule we can order things.

Now we can order the sets we have been studying by the phrase "has more elements than." This can be done with sets of pupils, sets of chairs, sets of blocks, and finally by sets of objects in pictures. (It is good to use large pictures, say $8\frac{1}{2} \times 11$ inches at least.) A productive way to start is to arrange such pictures in random order on the chalk rail and ask who would like to change the arrangement. Usually, with no further help from the teacher, the children will "line them up in order." If they do not, the teacher suggests comparisons that result in ordering the sets from smallest to largest. (In this context, it is important to note that all three-sets, for instance, are the same size regardless of whether their members happen to be fleas or elephants.) When we have the sets in order, we can write the number of each set above the picture. In this way we get a new set: an ordered set of numbers.

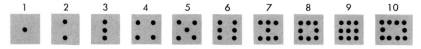

We now say the names of the numbers in order and make sure that each child knows to what kind of a set the number refers. We can then discard the pictures and physical sets and use the ordered numbers as a *new set* of things to learn about the manyness of any set.

Basic to the notion of counting numbers is a concept given far too little attention in most classrooms: the concept of *increase by one*, usually paraphrased for the children as *one more*. The counting numbers are not only ordered, they are well ordered: there is a first number (1), and each number has a unique immediate successor (next number). This second consideration implies that there is no last number, and young children can be led to sense this. There is *always* a number which is one more than whatever number we happen to be working with.

The teacher may have the children place in order cards suggesting the numbers 2, 5, 4, and 1, for example. Some child is sure to claim that there is a card missing. Which card is missing? How does he know? If we wanted to continue the sequence, which card would we use next? Which card comes after that? Why?

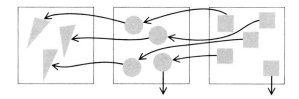

If strings are used to show matchings, the card for the successor of a given number will always have a string with a single loose end, as shown in the illustration above. Now, what should the next card look like? Could we keep on making "next cards" as long as we might wish? Would we ever reach a point at which, if we had enough time, we could not make a "next card" for the number that is one larger than the one we just used? The child does not need to know the names of large numbers in order to acquire this concept.

2–5 COUNTING

The first counting numbers for a child are the cardinals from 1 through 10. We can write these in the form

$$C = \{1, 2, 3, 4, 5, 6, 7, 8, 9, 10\}.$$

Later on, after we have developed a scheme for writing the numbers for sets of any "manyness," no matter how great, we shall enlarge the set of counting numbers beyond ten. We do not consider zero as a counting number (although it is a cardinal number) because any way of counting other than that described below (the usual way) involves an extra step and is therefore less efficient.

The reader, to orient himself to the basic concept of counting, should find the cardinal number of the set of elements pictured in the margin.

How did you find the number? With which star did you start? Could you have chosen a different star as a first star? With which number did you start? Could you have chosen a different number as a first number? How many times did you refer to each star? Does the order in which you use the stars affect the result? How many times did you refer to each number? Does the order in which you use the numbers affect the result? The answers to these questions can guide you to the method of teaching counting. What you did, if you counted correctly, was to establish a one-to-one correspondence or matching of the set of stars (in any order) and the subset of the counting numbers *in order* beginning with 1 and ending with the number you matched with the last star.

It is important to note that the matching can take place in any order of the set of objects being counted, but the numbers (number names) must always be used in the given order, 1, 2, 3, and so on. Even in counting a set of two objects, there are two possible orders, as shown. Note also that we match the objects to the number names in order; that is, we select an object and assign 1 to it, then another object and assign 2 to it. Could we reverse this order? Yes, but we would have to be careful to select our number names in the counting order.

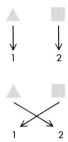

If there are three elements to be counted, the pairing could be made with the ordered numbers 1, 2, 3, in six different ways.

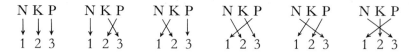

The number of possible pairings increases very rapidly with the number of elements to be counted. For example, for 4 elements it is 24 (4 × 3 × 2 × 1), and for 5 elements 120. Hence in counting it is best to select *an* order of the elements and match them with the ordered counting numbers.

In doing this, a child must be assured that *any* order of the objects to be counted will yield the same cardinal number for the set. This can be done, and should be done, in a number of variations until the child is assured. As examples consider the following.

1. The child lays out the objects he is counting, in any array or pile. He not only touches each object as he assigns a number name (in order) but he also moves it away from those not yet counted. So, when he says "one" he has one object under his hand; when he says "two" he has two objects aside (he has counted 2 objects so far); . . . , and when he says "seven" he has made a new pile of the objects and knows that the number of the set is seven. Then he should count the pile of objects again, starting with a different arrangement and thus not only verify his answer, but realize a set of seven is always seven, no matter how the elements are arranged.

2. A child may be given a number scale showing only the numbers from 1 through 10.

This may be on the wall or at his seat. Then he can connect his pile of objects one at a time to the numbers in order, using strings. Different assignments will be made by different children as they are asked to do this, but the last number assigned will always be the same.

3. A group of seated children can be asked to "count off" and to rise as they say *their* number. When the child who has said "four" rises, the class is asked to look at the set of standing children. Thus the last number given in counting is the number of the set. The children are asked to rearrange themselves and count off again. The last number spoken of is again the number of the set.

This last procedure can also be used to introduce the ordinal aspect of number. When the children count off, the one who says "five" may be asked "Are *you* five?" The child may say yes or no. If the child says yes, then the teacher may say, "You look like only one person." The child will admit he is only "one" but the group is "five." "Good, but you are the *fifth one* to count." Thus the ordered numbers can be used to put a set in order. In a set of five ducks as they are counted, they are put in an order and the fourth duck merely means that "all together so far there are four ducks."

By many such counting experiences and continual questioning by the teacher, the children will become aware of the following counting principles:

1. The cardinal number of a set of counting numbers which begins with 1 and proceeds in increase-by-one order is the last number of the set. Thus

$$1, 2, 3, 4, \quad \text{is a set of four numbers,}$$
$$1, 2, 3, 4, \ldots, n, \quad \text{is a set of } n \text{ numbers,}$$

where, for children, n may always be replaced by the numeral for any number they choose.

2. The way to find the cardinal number of a set is to match the objects of the set with the ordered set of counting numbers. The last number assigned is the number of the set.

3. When an assignment is made, the objects have been placed in an order. In this order there is a first object, a second object, and so on, until the last object is in the nth place, where n is the number of the set of objects and of the set of numbers that were used.

When a child has learned to count meaningfully (as exhibited in the illustrations above), *he has the basic structure on which to do all the rest of his study of arithmetic.* If he learns only by rote, he will have great difficulty as he proceeds in further study.

2-6 READINESS FOR LATER STUDY

Before building a system of numeration, and before establishing a formal study of the four rational operations of arithmetic, a child should have a host of experiences with relations of the numbers from 0 through 10. The more experiences he has, the more readily he will conquer the formal aspects of (a) reading and writing numbers with decimal numerals of several digits, (b) learning the fundamental facts for the four operations, and (c) constructing the mature algorisms for finding the results of the operations. He needs game. The activity provides readiness for learning the decimal system of notation.

Thus, as we give the children experience with joining and counting sets of individual elements, counting collections of elements (each collection having the same number of individual elements), and counting by collections of collections (each higher collection associated with the same number of elements as the previous collection), we prepare the way for addition, numeration, multiplication, and an understanding of a system of measurements.

2–7 THE DECIMAL SYSTEM OF NUMERATION (NOTATION)

The first step in counting beyond ten is to prepare a systematic way for saying or recording the number names. The system used universally by all people in all activities is the so-called Hindu-Arabic decimal-place system of notation. This system is not only decimal and place, but also multiplicative and additive. As the reader well knows, the numeral 263 refers to the number which is

$$2 \times 100 + 6 \times 10 + 3 \times 1.$$

The symbols '0', '1', '2', '3', '4', '5', '6', '7', '8', and '9' are of Hindu-Arabic origin and are called *digits*. A single digit by itself or *place* arrangement of two or more digits produces a *numeral*. The proper multiplication of each digit by its *place value* and the addition of these products yields the *number*. How do children learn all this?

A first thing for the teacher to recognize is the fact that if a child can count a number of objects to ten, then he can count any set of objects up to one hundred without learning any new words. (He learns some minor variations of old words.) He does this by counting groups of size ten, forming ten-sets. A common word for these groups today is *subset*, but this word is not necessary. We can start by counting the children in the room. The children start counting off. When a child says "ten," the teacher says "Stop. Will the members of that set of children go over to the side of the room?" Then the children seated start with one, counting off again to ten and a stop. This group is asked to go to the front of the room. Then the counting off starts all over with the children in the seats. The last child may say "six." Then the teacher asks,

"How many pupils in all?" The answers could be:

> ten and ten and six,
> two ten-sets and six one-sets,
> two groups, each ten, and six extra,
> two tens and six,
> two-tens six.

Of course the teacher helps abbreviate the response to two-tens six but the meaning is clear: there are two sets each with the number ten and six sets with the number one. That is what "two-tens six" means.

This process can be repeated by counting and grouping in sets of ten the chairs in a room, the books (in piles of ten), sheets of paper, every ten sheets clipped together, etc. At first all answers are given in terms of so many tens and so many individual items.

The next step is to create a way of writing the names of these numbers, using only the digits '0', '1', '2', '3', '4', '5', '6', '7', '8', '9'. There are ten of these symbols and so our writing is in a decimal (*deci* means ten) system, a base-ten system. For the purpose of learning to write these numbers, we make use of a pocket chart, in which we can place material objects as individual elements and as packages or sets of ten objects. Thus, using toothpicks, tongue depressors, pieces of cardboard, etc., we can count to ten, placing 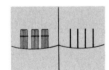 each object counted in the "ones" pocket. When we get ten objects, we bind them together as one ten-set and place them in the "tens" pocket. This process is repeated until the objects have all been counted. Then we place a digit under each column which tells the number of elements in each pocket, as shown in the figure. The child says "3 tens and 4 ones" or "3 tens, 4 ones," omitting the "and," but understanding that the two pockets must be considered together to give the total number of elements.

A follow-up device, used several weeks later because it is much more abstract, is to have children count off as one child tallies them on the board. When ten is reached the tallier shouts "halt."

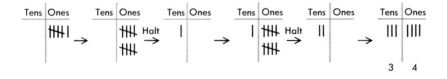

He then erases the ten strokes (two sets of five each) and places a single stroke in the tens column. This represents as much as the 10 ones. The tallied group goes to one part of the room and the count-off begins again, and again until the class of children has been counted. At the final tally, the tallier writes the number of tens and number of individual items below the columns, as shown in the figure.

Children can repeat this process at their seats, counting all conceivable objects. Thus they can learn to count and tell the number of any set in terms of tens and ones. It frequently happens that there are exact groups of ten, and here the number 0 takes on real significance. For if there are exactly 4 groups of ten each, and no individual elements left over, the set of individual elements is empty and the number of that column is zero. Of course we must write this '0' in recording the number of elements counted, for if the drawing or tallying were erased and only '4' remained to be read we would not know that it referred to the number of ten-sets. So 4 is always 4, but '40' refers to 4 sets of ten each and no individual items.

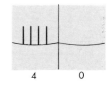

4   0

Two things must be clearly established: (1) In writing the number of tens and number of ones we always write the number of tens first, then the number of individual elements from left to right. So we practice with children on reading and telling the difference between 34 and 43, 62 and 26, and so on. (2) A number such as 20 signifies 2 ten-sets and no individual items.

A final stage to be reached is to obtain an efficient way to say these numbers so that we can recognize their order at once. Of course children recognize that we must get 1 ten-set before we can get 2 ten-sets, and 2 ten-sets before 3 ten-sets, because the numbers of ten-sets follow the same order as the numbers one to ten. So we count by tens and ones as follows, where "one-ten" means 1 ten-set:

one, two, . . . , nine,

one-ten, one-ten-one, one-ten-two, . . . , one-ten-nine,

two-tens, two-tens-one, two-tens-two, . . . , two-tens-nine,

three-tens, three-tens-one, . . . , three-tens-nine,

four-tens, four-tens-one, . . . , four-tens-nine,

five-tens, five-tens-one, . . . , five-tens-nine,

nine-tens, . . . , nine-tens-nine.

1	2	3	4	5	6	7	8	9	10
11	12	13	14	15	16	17	18	19	20
21	22	23	24	25	26	27	28	29	30
									40
									50
									60
									70
									80
									90
91	92							99	

A numbers board such as that shown is a good device to use, both to read and to write the number names to nine-tens-nine. This device is especially useful in this context, since each row except the last lists a set of 10 numbers. [If you follow the pattern for writing numbers in the last column, what should be the entry in the empty cell? (100) What might you call this number? (ten-tens).] Here a child will note that 41 is more than 39 because we never have more individual items than 9; if we get another item we combine these 10 one-sets into 1 ten-set and this gives us another ten. Hence any two-digit number in which the tens digit is larger than that in another must represent the larger set of things, and hence is the greater number. At this stage the symbols '>' and '<' for 'is greater than' and 'is less than' need not, and perhaps should not, be used; the words are more significant to children.

Next we abbreviate 'ten' to 'ty' (read tee) and say:

one, . . . , nine,

one-ty, one-ty one, one-ty two, . . . , one-ty nine,

two-ty, two-ty one, two-ty two, . . . , two-ty nine,

three-ty, three-ty one, . . . , three-ty nine, four-ty,

five-ty, . . . , six-ty, . . . , nine-ty, nine-ty one, . . . , nine-ty nine.

This is a sensible, meaningful, well-constructed system of naming numbers from 1 to 100. However, tradition has introduced other names, and for everyday communication the child must learn these. So, as a final step (certainly before the end of first grade) the child learns the words 'eleven' to 'nineteen', 'twenty' for 'two-ty', 'thirty' for 'three-ty', and 'fifty' for 'five-ty'. All the other words have already been learned properly.

When 99 has been reached, a new activity is needed. Of course another item would make 10 tens. How would this be written? Let the child first review why ten was given the symbol 10. Then 10 tens would be written 100 and we now have three digits in our numeral. This is the same as combining the 10 groups of ten into one new group and placing it in the next column to the left. We give a group of this size a new name and call it 'hundred'. Thus a hundred is 10 tens. In the second grade it is easy to take counting up to 999 and then introduce the word thousand for 10 hundreds. A good way to show the meaning of this is to use cubical blocks, 1 inch or 1 centimeter on a side. A row of 10 such blocks is called a ten. Ten tens then form a square of blocks called a hundred, and 10 hundreds form a cube of blocks called a thousand.

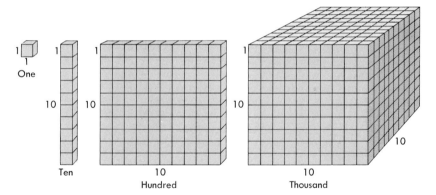

In teaching, once a thousand has been derived meaningfully, the extension to a million or more is made abstractly by a process analogous to that already used to go from 1 to 1 thousand. This is done in Grades 3, 4, and 5.

Since to the early arithmeticians there was no way to extend the cubical block, in the manner in which the single item was extended to a row, then a square, and finally a cube, the process of extension was started all over again. Thus 10 thousands made a new row called a ten-thousand. Ten of these rows made a new square called a hundred-thousand, and 10 of these squares made a new cube called a million. A million is 1000 thousands because it is derived from a thousand in the same way that a thousand was derived from one.

After the child has learned the meaning of the decimal system of notation, he must practice using it until he reaches mature efficiency. He must be able to tell the meaning of 14, or 63, or 237 in terms of hundred-sets, ten-sets, and one-sets. He must know that 60 refers to 6 ten-sets, but that each ten-set can be broken into one-sets, so that 60 can also refer to that many individual items. So 237 may refer to 2 hundreds, 3 tens, and 7 ones (where "ones" means individual objects), or it may mean 23 tens and 7 individual objects, or it may refer to 2 hundreds and 37 individual objects, or indeed to 237 individual objects. Thus a decimal system is merely an efficient way of telling the number of a set when the set has been partitioned into subsets 1, 10, 100, etc. The numeral always refers to the total number of individual objects, but it can also be interpreted in terms of various different combinations of subsets.

A good way to develop this notion is to use 2 bundles of ten and 7 individual objects for 27, and then to open the bundles of ten and have a single set of 27 objects. We can interpret '27' in two different ways. After children learn this, have them practice on 65, 138, etc. A very good activity is to get children to recognize that 64 can also be thought of as 50 and 14, that is, 5 groups of ten and 14 individual items. This can be extended to thinking of 264 as the number of the union of 1 hundred-set, 15 ten-sets, and 14 one-sets.

After the numbers have been learned to 100, another important activity is the use of a number scale from 0 to 100. Such a scale can be made from old calendar numerals and a roll of cash-register paper and would look as follows:

On this scale, the children can learn to count (always beginning with 1) by twos, by threes, by fives, and by tens. They can also show how a given number of objects, say 36, may be grouped into subsets of size 3 each, 4 each, 5 each (with a remainder), etc. They can learn to *count on* from a given number to find out, for instance, how many a 17-set joined to a 12-set would make. They can count backward along the scale to see how many are left when 15 are removed from a set of 28, etc. All such activities at this stage should be informal and practical experiences to familiarize the children with numbers up to 100.

Children who understand the numbers and their names from 0 through 10, who can count meaningfully from 1 through 10, and who are thoroughly familiar with the decimal system of notation will have little trouble, and a great deal of satisfaction in continuing their study of arithmetic.

2–8 HIERARCHY OF LEARNING

The above development of number was based on the psychological structuring of knowledge through experimental scientific inquiry that can be expected of children ages $4\frac{1}{2}$ to 7 years. It took cognizance of the fact that a concept, once acquired, can be used along with further experimentation to gain new knowledge. It involved a minimum of symbolization, but a great deal of experience, and a gradually developed facility for verbalization of the desired relations and ideas. At the kindergarten level all the learning was of an informal nature. The development proceeded from the use of physical objects to pictures, to mere representations, and finally to the use of number symbols when the concept was established and the symbol was to be used constantly for the concept. In general, the only ideas present were those of sets, number, and numeral, and the use of these ideas.

Once an idea has been introduced, it need never be discarded, only broadened and deepened. In general the sequence of learning may take the following order.

Sets

1. Recognizing a set, describing a set, seeing the uniqueness of each element in the set (using physical objects only)
2. Comparing sets by matching (assigning) an element of one set to an element of another. Ordering the sets (using both physical objects and drawings)

3. Finding equivalent sets (or sets that match exactly). Realizing that the number of a set is the same for all exactly matching sets. Developing the idea of cardinal number from concrete objects and drawings

4. Thinking about the empty set: what it means; why one cannot draw pictures of its members

5. Grouping (partitioning) a set into subsets having the same number; having different numbers (using both physical objects and drawings)

6. Grasping the idea of the set of numbers as the first abstract set {0, 1, 2, . . .}

7. Matching a set of objects into the set of ordered numbers

8. Partitioning a large set into subsets of size ten

9. Continued partitioning of sets by ten, to ten-tens, etc.

Number

1. Realizing that sets that match exactly have the same number

2. Becoming familiar with the number of a set with readily grasped manyness

3. Arranging the numbers and the number names in order

4. Learning the numbers from 1 through 10; through 100

5. Learning the number of the empty set

6. Seeing the relations among the numbers 0 through 10

Counting and Numeration

1. Becoming aware of the numbers in order as a set

2. Counting as a mapping of a set of things into the ordered set of numbers

3. Counting by twos, threes, fives, and tens

4. Representing sets with more than ten members by the number of tens and of individual items remaining

5. Learning the numerals through '100'

6. Understanding the various interpretations of a numeral: 24, 73, etc.

7. Being able to use a number scale (or number line) to illustrate relations among the numbers

EXERCISES

1. Give at least three activities in which children can be led to describe sets and elements belonging to a set so as to form a correct idea of a set. List twenty sets that children in a kindergarten or first grade might find in their classroom.

2. Explain the difference between a physical set and an abstract set. Why is the set of cardinals $\{0, 1, 2, \ldots\}$ an abstract set? Is a drawing depicting a set of four dogs a representation of a set or the actual set? What is the set in your answer to the preceding question?

3. Explain the difference between a mapping of the children in a class-room *into* the chairs in the classroom, and the usual use of the phrase one-to-one correspondence. What kind of matching do you use to order sets according to their size? How do you teach this ordering to 5- or 6-year-old children?

4. List a series of activities by which children gradually come to understand the concept of cardinal 4. Would you or would you not use the notation $n\{\bigcirc, \square, \triangle, \bigcirc\} = 4$? Defend your answer. Tell how to abstract the cardinals 0 and 1 from the study of sets.

5. It is customary to first develop the numbers from 1 through 5, then 6 through 10, and then zero. Why is this order proposed? Is there any justification for learning to say the number names in order merely by rote?

6. The general concept of order is "comes before" in a given sequence. Why is it essential for a child to learn the order relation for the cardinal numbers? Give at least three activities by which you could get children to understand order.

7. What is counting? What concepts must be known before counting can be learned? Is zero a counting number for children? How soon would you introduce counting into the school program?

8. Give a description of readiness as a mathematical activity for children. Does readiness depend more on the maturity of the child or on his being provided with appropriate experiences? Tell what you would do in a class as readiness for learning addition.

9. Why is the decimal system of notation so important for general education in mathematics? Explain the meaning of "Hindu-Arabic decimal-multiplicative-additive-place system of numeration." Why should a child be able to count to 100 or higher if he can count to 10?

10. Other systems of numeration are taught in some schools. In particular describe the Roman system, and a place system to the base five. When would you teach these systems, if at all, in the elementary school? How can a system to base five be taught?

REFERENCES

BROWNELL, W. A., "Arithmetic Abstractions: Progress Toward Maturity of Concepts under Differing Programs of Instruction," *The Arithmetic Teacher* **10,** October 1963, pages 322–329

FEHR, H. F., and T. J. HILL, *Contemporary Mathematics for Elementary Teachers,* Boston: D. C. Heath, 1966; Chapters 1, 2, and 5

PAGE, D. A., *Number Lines, Functions, and Fundamental Topics,* New York: Macmillan, 1964

PHILLIPS, J. M., "The Counting Process," filmstrip A in *Seeing the Use of Numbers, Set VII,* Eye Gate Productions, Jamaica, N.Y. (A filmstrip useful to teachers of primary and middle grades; not for use with children at those levels.)

SCHOOL MATHEMATICS STUDY GROUP, *Studies in Mathematics,* Volume 9, "A Brief Course in Mathematics for Elementary School Teachers," Pasadena, Cal.: A. C. Vroman, 1963

operations

in

arithmetic

When a child has learned how to count, he has available a skill
with which he can do all the arithmetic he needs for social,
financial, and scientific purposes. The truth of this statement is
evidenced by both the ancient abacus which is still widely used
today and by the electronic digital computer, which is essentially
a counting machine working at terrific speed. However, human
beings do not have this speed in counting, nor do they usually
have an abacus, a digital computer, or an electric calculator at
their command. Yet every day every human being is confronted
with a multitude of situations in which he must compute a numerical answer to solve a genuine problem. Hence it is necessary for
him to have a procedure by which he can compute the answer
correctly and in a reasonably short time with unhurried calm.
For this purpose it is necessary to invent ways to compute other
than counting. The so-called fundamental operations of arithmetic (addition, subtraction, multiplication, and division) have
been aptly described as "shortcuts to counting" (forward or
backward), and to carry out the operations special procedures
called *algorisms** are necessary.

---

* See footnote on page 77.

First the child must understand the nature of an operation, and the fundamental facts stated in the decimal system of numeration. How does he learn these ideas? By abstracting them from analogous operations on sets, preferably sets of physical objects. Learning in general proceeds in the following order:

a) Learning the concept involved

b) Learning the nature and use of the language involved

c) Learning, by discovery or construction, the fundamental facts

d) Practicing with the facts until automatic recall is established

e) Applying the facts to learning efficient computational algorisms

The word 'algorism' is used to refer to a special method or procedure for finding the number which is the result of an operation. In this chapter we consider the learning of the basic concepts, language, and facts of the addition and subtraction operations. In the following chapter we shall study the development of the algorisms.

3–1 OPERATIONS IN GENERAL

Although we refer to addition, subtraction, multiplication, and division as the four basic operations on number, we seldom say what we mean by *operation*. Frequently the word is erroneously related to the algorism, or to a *rule* for "carrying out" the operation. It is necessary for a teacher to have a clear mathematical understanding of a binary operation.

In any binary operation, the first thing to be recognized is an *ordered pair* of numbers; the order is important. These numbers are in order: (operand, operator); that is, a number to be *operated on*, and a number that *operates* on it. To designate an operation, we use a symbol such as '$+$', '$-$', '$\div$', or '$\times$', or in general '$\circ$' which is read "is operated on by." Thus

$$a \circ b$$

may be read

operand a is operated on by operator b.

The number that this operation associates with the given ordered pair is called the *result*. We can thus write in symbolic form

$$
\underbrace{(a,\ b)}_{\text{terms}} \longrightarrow \underbrace{c}_{\text{result}}
$$
$$
\underbrace{a \circ b = c}
$$

A binary operation

As an illustration, given $(5, 3)$ and using addition, we may write:

$$(5, 3) \rightarrow 8$$

and say, "The result of applying this binary operation to the pair $(5, 3)$ is the number 8." Or we may write

$$5 + 3 = 8$$

and say "3 *added to* 5 yields the sum 8" or "5 *plus* 3 is 8." Note that in this example, 3 is the operator; it operates on 5. If we write $3 + 5 = 8$, then 5 is the operator and it is added to 3. Since $3 + 5$ yields the same number as $5 + 3$ we say the operation is *commutative*. Not all operations are commutative; e.g., the result of $8 - 3$ is not the same number as the result of $3 - 8$.

Note also that '$a \circ b \circ c$' or '$3 + 4 + 5$' do not refer to a binary operation, since they involve more than two numbers and more than one operation sign. Such writings, if they can be given meaning, are *expressions* that must be defined. Generally, when they can be defined, they are defined as a sequence of operations from left to right. Thus

$$\cdot \ 3 + 4 + 5 \qquad \text{means} \qquad (3 + 4) + 5$$

and

$$8 - 3 - 2 \qquad \text{means} \qquad (8 - 3) - 2.$$

In the addition example, 5 is added to the sum of 3 plus 4. If we had placed the parentheses around the expression involving the last two numbers, as

$$3 + (4 + 5),$$

we would have been adding the sum of 4 plus 5 to 3. Either way we do it, the final sum is 12; and since this holds for all additions of the type $a + b + c$, we say the operation is *associative*. Children should be made aware of commutativity and associativity without using these formal words. Note that subtraction is not associative, for $(8 - 4) - 3 = 4 - 3$ or 1, while $8 - (4 - 3) = 8 - 1$ or 7.

In particular operations, the operand, operator, and result are given particular names. These names are not necessary to the first teaching of the operation, but eventually should be introduced. Thus we have

$$\left\{ \begin{array}{ccccc} 3 & + & 2 & = & 5 \\ \text{Summand plus addend equals sum} \end{array} \right\},$$

$$\left\{ \begin{array}{ccccc} 8 & - & 2 & = & 6 \\ \text{Minuend minus subtrahend equals difference} \end{array} \right\},$$

$$\left\{ \begin{array}{ccccc} 8 & \times & 3 & = & 24 \\ \text{Multiplicand multiplied by multiplier equals product} \end{array} \right\},$$

$$\left\{ \begin{array}{ccccc} 36 & \div & 9 & = & 4 \\ \text{Dividend divided by divisor equals quotient} \end{array} \right\}.$$

In mathematics we also *operate* on sets or collections, and while there is an analogy between certain set operations and arithmetic operations, it is necessary to note that they are distinct and have a different terminology. Consider a set of oranges and a set of pears. We think of a set whose members are these oranges and these pears together. We write:

Set A   joined to   set B   is   union of sets A and B

It is essential that teachers recognize this as an operation on sets, not numbers; the language we use with set operations is not the same as the language we use with number operations. The set of boys in a class and the set of girls in the class can be joined and this *union* is the class. If there are 13 girls and 11 boys we do not join 13 and 11. However, if we add 13 to 11, the sum 24 tells us the number in the class or in the union.

In ordinary language, people speak of adding the oranges to the salad, or adding the flour to the batter, but this is a vernacular, not a mathematical, use of the word. In arithmetic we shall always use 'addition' to refer to a binary operation on numbers. In mathematics, sets and operations on sets are abstractions with no physical actions implied. With young children, we use *physical models of sets* and maneuvers on the objects which belong to the sets in these models to suggest the abstractions we seek.

3-2 TEACHING THE CONCEPT OF ADDITION

All operations should be abstracted from a study of many physical situations. It is in this way that a pupil comes to recognize how to apply the arithmetic he learns to a new situation, or to a problem he needs to solve. Thus he learns to think of addition as being related to the union of disjoint sets, sets that have no element in common. At a later stage, a numerical problem involving the joining together of sets will suggest to the child the operation of adding the numbers of the sets.

In an initial lesson, a teacher asks a child to display a 4-set (a set of objects whose number is 4). Then the child is asked to show a 3-set.

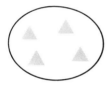 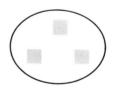 

Then the teacher asks him to join the second set to the first to form a new set, and to find the number of this new set.

The set language is:

If a set with 4 elements is joined to a set with 3 elements, the result is a set having 7 elements.

The corresponding arithmetic language is:

If 3 is added to 4 the sum is 7, or

$$4 + 3 = 7$$

or four plus three is seven.

Note that the arithmetic symbolic language at first is always written in a line the way we have taught the children to read, from left to right. Note also that we record *correctly* what we have done: We selected a set of four objects first, so the '4' comes first. Then we *joined to it* a set of three objects, so '+3' or 'add 3' comes next.

Finally we have the union of these two sets, which is a 7-set, where the 7 can be discovered by counting. The first number 4 is an *operand*, the number 3 is an *operator*, the *sum* is 7. This same activity should be repeated by all the pupils, using sets of various sizes, but keeping the number of the union of the sets less than, or at most equal to, ten.

A nice device for demonstration is a wire line with movable markers and sufficient space to separate the markers into two or three distinct groups. A ready-made device is a wire coat hanger with plastic pinch clothespins. On this device children can indicate sets of various sizes, join them together, and find the size (number) of the union. In this way children learn to say mathematical sentences in correct language. There are a number of ways of stating the correct operation. That is, we can say:

$$\text{Two plus three}\begin{cases} \text{is} \\ \text{equals} \\ \text{yields} \end{cases}\text{five.}$$

If three is added to two the sum is five.
The sum of 2 plus 3 is 5.
$2 + 3 = 5$.

Activities involving a number line should be used to reinforce the concept of addition. At first it is a good idea to use masking tape on the floor, or use a ladder, or some other device which allows for large-muscle activity on the part of the children.

Choose a place to start. Mark this as the starting point (not 0 at this stage), then number the steps in what is to be the forward direction. Now have a child make two successive moves forward and record both the moves and the net result. "Four steps forward, then three steps forward lands you seven steps forward," a child might say. He can write this in shorthand: $(4, 3) \rightarrow 7$. As soon as he sees that this is like adding (has an additive structure), he should write: $4 + 3 = 7$. Each child should have experience in moving forward on the number line using a variety of ordered pairs of numbers and keeping a record of what he has done. He should

note what happens if the order of the numbers in the pair is reversed. He should observe other children participating in the
activity and keep records for them. At first he will always start
at the starting point. As soon as he himself sees that he can start
at the point labeled with the first number of the pair and count on
from there, he should be encouraged to do that. Eventually the
teacher can give problems or exercises involving addition facts
which may be new or old to the child, and the child should be
able to use either models of sets or a number line to find the answers.

It is not enough for children to know what addition is, and
to be able to find sums by using models of the union of sets or by
counting forward on a number line. If they are to become efficient
in mathematical application, children need to know all the fundamental sums up to $9 + 9$ so well that, at any given time, recall of
the associated number, the sum, is (almost) automatic. To attain
this facility, children need to discover the facts by their own mental
construction, organize them into some form (usually a table), and
then practice them until they have automatic recall. If children
are allowed to discover their own facts, and see relations between
these facts, the practice time needed to attain automatic recall is
much less than the time needed to attain it by means of rote learning.

Every time a child learns a fact, that is, a true sentence of the
form

$$3 + 4 = 7,$$

he should sense, or be made aware, that he also has another fact,
namely

$$4 + 3 = 7.$$

Since the order in which one joins two sets does not change the
number of the union, it is clear that *either order* in which one adds
two numbers gives the same sum. In formal mathematics, we
would refer to this as the commutative property of addition, but
this phrase need not be used at all in the primary school. The
swinging around of the marker frame, as shown in the picture,
illustrates the property sufficiently.

Next the children are urged to remember a fact that they have
discovered by the process of counting. It is perfectly all right to
use fingers and count on the fingers to discover a sum. If, however,

the children are still doing this to an appreciable extent at the end of the first year of study, the desired educational goal has not been accomplished. By this time, recall of most of the facts should be automatic.

The process of learning follows a sequence of (a) discovery of the fact, (b) correct communication in language, (c) correct writing in symbolic form, (d) practice for recall. All these steps should involve numbers first to sums of 5, then to sums of 10, and finally to sums of 18. Once a child has discovered that, when he adds, any order of the two numbers gives the same sum, we can also write the result in vertical form, as shown, in which the interpretation depends on whether you read the expression upward or downward, and at this stage of learning no distinction need be made. So, for example, the expression on the left is read "four plus three is seven" if we read up, and "three plus four is seven," if we read down. Again, so far as the result is concerned, it is not necessary for the child to think or remember that in writing $3 + 4$, 4 is the operator which is added to 3, while in $4 + 3$, 3 is the operator. The important thing for him to know is that, in either order, the sum is 7.

$$\begin{array}{r} 3 \\ +4 \\ \hline 7 \end{array} \qquad \begin{array}{r} 4 \\ +3 \\ \hline 7 \end{array}$$

Children proceed in various ways to learn the sum of two numbers. Some children prefer to learn doubles first, $1 + 1$, $2 + 2$, etc. Knowing this, some children use their readiness activities to find sums such as $2 + 3$, $3 + 4$, etc., as *one more than* $2 + 2$, $3 + 3$, etc. The "one more," of course, refers to adding 1 to the sum of $2 + 2$ to get the sum of $2 + 3$. Slower children may always use the union of two sets and count the members (1, 2, 3, 4, 5 for $2 + 3$). More quick-minded children count on, saying 2, and then 3, 4, 5, for $2 + 3$. All ways should be encouraged, as the more relations a child sees, the easier the recall will be.

After all the sums to 10 have been discovered, including the addition of 0 to any number (or any number to 0), the numbers may be arranged in a table, where all the relations can again be studied. The addition table would look like Table 3–1.

Pupils can see that in the lower left to upper right diagonals all cells have the same sum, that the main diagonal (upper left to lower right) has only even numbers, that the column and row numbers increase by one, that the numbers in the diagonal parallel to the main diagonal always increase by two, and so on. They should read addition sentences from the table. The empty cells in the incomplete table should provoke much discussion.

TABLE 3–1

Operated on by	Second number										
+	0	1	2	3	4	5	6	7	8	9	10
0	0	1	2	3	4	5	6	7	8	9	10
1	1	2	3	4	5	6	7	8	9	10	
2	2	3	4	5	6	7	8	9	10		
3	3	4	5	6	7	8	9	10			
4	4	5	6	7	8	9	10				
5	5	6	7	8	9	10					
6	6	7	8	9	10						
7	7	8	9	10							
8	8	9	10								
9	9	10									
10	10										

First number

Eventually the facts must be committed to automatic recall by practice. This practice should take a variety of forms, and it should be given frequently for relatively short periods of time. (Note that advertisers have found that six 30-second commercials produce better results than one 3-minute commercial.) The alert teacher will think of many activities which are particularly suitable for his class, and will find a wealth of suggestions in books and magazines. Quite often teacher-made, or pupil-made, materials are better than those made commercially because the former may be tailored specifically to the purpose at hand. Here are a few suggestions:

1. There should be simple worksheets so that the children can reinforce their visual images of the way the facts are written, vertically and horizontally, and also get practice in writing them.

2. The teacher should give, and have the children make up, problems in which addition is used to find the answer.

3. Old-fashioned flash cards may be used occasionally in the old-fashioned way, but the children enjoy them more, and learn more from their use, when the teacher incorporates them into some sort of game. A bingo-type game is easy to make for any desired level of difficulty. Each child should have a "bingo" card and a supply of markers with which he can cover up the appropriate squares. The caller has a supply of flash cards. If the caller holds up a card bearing '3 + 4', for instance, children who have a '7' on their cards cover that square.

| 3 + 4 | 7 |
| Front | Back |

4. A card game which is played like "Old Maid" can be made from some unlined 3 × 5 filing cards. The deck always contains an odd number of cards all but one of which can be paired with one or more other cards. Regardless of what is on this odd card, the children usually call it the old maid. For the cards which can be paired, '3 + 2' could be written on one card and '5' on another, for example. When the children get a little more proficient with the addition facts, a pairing of '3 + 2' with '1 + 4', and so on, might be allowed. When three or four children play this game, at least one of them should be sufficiently sure of the facts to check on the rest.

5. Addition dominoes may be made from cardboard, or wood, or plastic. Each domino has an indicated sum on one part of its face and a simple numeral on the other. At first the rules for playing might be that a domino with a '3' on it must be played to the left of the one shown here, and a domino bearing any combination with a sum of 6 must be played to its right. Later, the children themselves may decide to change the rules, to allow '6 + 1' to be played against '5 + 2' or '3 + 4', for instance.

| 1+2 | 6 |

6. An imaginary addition machine may be made of wood or cardboard, or drawn on posterboard or the chalkboard.

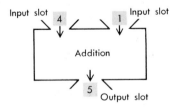

A supply of cards is needed for the input and output numbers. The machine shows graphically that addition is a binary operation, since there are two input slots. It serves as an excellent vehicle for developing the idea that addition is commutative: the children readily see that if they reverse the order of the two input numbers the same output number still applies. An activity which foreshadows one aspect of subtraction takes place when the children see that, given any two of the occurrences of number, they can tell what the third should be. The children see also that if they are given just the output number, they cannot be sure of the input numbers; the addition machine is not reversible. Each child may make his own supply of cards for the machine, this in itself being another worth-while activity. A complete set would consist of two cards for each of the numbers within the range the teacher decides upon. The teacher needs a similar set of cards. The simplest way to use the machine is for the teacher to show a number for each of the input slots and have each child think of the output number, find the appropriate card in his set, and hold it up for the teacher to see. Usually, the children will suggest ways to vary this activity.

7. The teacher may find commercially made films, filmstrips, charts, projecturals, or games which may be used for practice or for summarizing specific learnings his pupils have acquired.

In all addition situations the children should be taught to differentiate between the *sets* and the *numbers* involved, yet at the same time always to look for the number property of a set and recognize that the union of two sets is related to the addition of the numbers of the sets.

3-3 TEACHING THE CONCEPT OF SUBTRACTION

It is not a good practice to *introduce* addition and subtraction at the same time. They are, at first, two distinct and different operations. After the addition concept has been thoroughly developed, we can develop a new concept called subtraction. When the latter concept is well understood, then we can relate the two operations, giving added reinforcement to the structure we are developing. As children study subtraction, many of them will discover a relation of an addition of a number to the subtraction of that number and then is the time to clarify and deepen the relation, not before.

The first activity is to get children to describe and to recognize the idea of a part of, or subset of, a given set. Thus the girls are a part of the class; the books on this table are a part of all the books in the room; the dolls Mary brought to class are a part of all her dolls. Then the children learn the meaning of taking a subset away from the set. Ten balls are on the table; four are rolled off the table. The set of balls left on the table is called the *remainder set*.

It is wise to start very soon to use the word 'subset' along with the word 'part', gradually placing more and more emphasis on the former word. We wish to speak eventually of removing the entire set or the empty set (to treat numerical analogs such as 4 − 4 and 4 − 0) and, while each set is a subset of itself and the empty set is a subset of every set, a child may find it peculiar to think of either of these as a part of the set.

The symbol used in set theory for removing a subset is '\' which is called 'slash' or '*take away*' or 'remove'. Thus

$$\{a, b, c, d, e\} \backslash \{a, b\} = \{c, d, e\}.$$

"Taking away elements" is an operation on models of sets of things, not on numbers. Children should illustrate and practice taking away a subset from a given set, with no reference to numbers. Thus when, from a set {Mary, Jane, Susan, Edith, Margy} we send away the subset {Susan, Jane}, we have the remainder set {Mary, Edith, Margy}. Similar activities may be performed with a set of books, a set of sheets of writing paper, a set of chairs, a set of tongue depressors, etc.

Next we relate the numbers of the given set, the subset removed, and the remainder set. The problem we give to the children is, "If we know the number of a set, and the number of the subset to be removed, can we find the number of the remaining set?" Of course we can.

8 − 3 = 5

Cover or remove

The remaining set can be illustrated by using pegs or counters on a table, pins on a clothes hanger, by taking chairs out of a row, etc. Counting always gives us the answer.

The set language is:

If from a set of 8 objects a 3-membered subset is removed, the remainder set has 5 members.

The corresponding arithmetic language is:

If 3 is subtracted from 8, the difference is 5. We write

$$8 - 3 = 5.$$

Eight minus three equals five.

As children discover a number of these facts, they write the arithmetical operation in the horizontal form we usually read. In a short while we also write it in the vertical form, where it is read either "8 minus 3 is 5" or "3 subtracted from 8 is 5." There is no question here as to which is the operand (minuend), which the operator (subtrahend), and which the result (difference).

$$\begin{array}{r} 8 \\ -3 \\ \hline 5 \end{array}$$

Minuend minus *subtrahend* equals *difference*.

The words 'minuend' and 'subtrahend', although they are mathematically significant in later study, are not important at the initial stages of learning the meaning of subtraction and probably should not be used. However, the word *difference*, in the sense of "the result in subtraction," can and should be used from the start. Note that the word for the result in subtraction is 'difference', not 'remainder'. Note also that we cannot *take* 4 from 8, for these are numbers; we *subtract* 4 from 8.

When children have developed the concept of subtraction as finding the number of a remainder set, we encourage them to find all the subtraction facts—and write them—up to minuends of 10. Thus with no more than 10 counters, they select sets of various sizes (numbers). They remove a part of the selected set, and count the number of objects in the remainder set. Then they write the whole process as a mathematical statement; for example, $6 - 2 = 4$, $8 - 7 = 1$, etc. To lessen the learning load we help them discover that for each fact they write they can write another.

If $8 - 3 = 5$,   it follows that $8 - 5 = 3$,

because the removed set and the remainder set may be interchanged; therefore so may the subtrahend and the difference in a subtraction. To help them recall the discovered facts, we use a variety of drill techniques similar to those suggested for addition until automatic recall is established.

Maneuvers on a number line, counting backward this time and keeping an appropriate record, help to reinforce the concept of subtraction and the subtraction facts. For example, whether a subtraction problem is given as '(8, 3) → ?' or '8 − 3 = ?', the child should start at the point labeled with the first number, count back the number of spaces indicated by the second number, and find and record the required third number.

A subtraction table helps to give further understanding to the operation. If this table is prepared on the chalkboard or on a large cardboard, children will notice that there are limitations to subtraction that did not exist for addition. The subtraction of

TABLE 3–2

Operated on by	Second number (subtrahend)										
−	0	1	2	3	4	5	6	7	8	9	10
0	0										
1	1	0									
2	2	1	0								
3	3	2	1	0							
4	4	3	2	1	0						
5	5	4	3	2	1	0					
6	6	5	4	3	2	1	0				
7	7	6	5	4	3	2	1	0			
8	8	7	6	5	4	3	2	1	0		
9	9	8	7	6	5	4	3	2	1	0	
10	10	9	8	7	6	5	4	3	2	1	0
11			9	8	7	6	5	4	3	2	
12				9	8	7	6	5	4	3	

First number (minuend)

zero is easy, since this corresponds to the removal of the empty set, and thus for any number, $a - 0 = a$. Again, if we remove the entire set, the empty set is the remainder and so, for each number, $a - a = 0$. The subtraction table would look like Table 3–2.

In this table children can explain why the number 0 appears in the main diagonal, why the other diagonals always have the same number [$a - b = c$ implies that $(a + n) - (b + n) = c$ also], and why the diagonals in the opposite direction (lower left to upper right) always decrease by 2 from one cell to the next. It is important to discuss the cells which are blank; *within the set of whole numbers*, it is not possible to subtract a larger number from a smaller number. Note that a blank cell implies something far different from a cell containing a '0'.

3–4 RELATING ADDITION AND SUBTRACTION

When children have acquired the concepts of addition and subtraction, we reinforce the learning by showing how *adding a number* has an inverse operation, *subtracting the same number*. Of course we do not use this language with children; we speak rather of a family of facts, or of related facts, or of fact teams.

First, by the use of models of sets, we can show how forming a union can be undone by slashing away one of the sets in the union. The boys and girls form a union called the class. Taking away the boys from the union leaves the girls, but taking away the girls leaves the boys. This can be illustrated also with sets of pegs, blocks, clothespins, and the like.

In the first illustration, the two sets may be commuted (reversed in order) and the union is the same. In the second illustration, the set removed may be interchanged with the remainder set and the result is true. Each of these operations on sets has an analogous arithmetical sentence.

$$4 + 3 = 7 \quad \text{is related to} \quad 7 - 3 = 4,$$
$$3 + 4 = 7 \quad \text{is related to} \quad 7 - 4 = 3,$$

or:

adding 3 to 4 to obtain 7 is related to
subtracting 3 from 7 to obtain 4, and vice versa;
adding 4 to 3 to obtain 7 is related to
subtracting 4 from 7 to obtain 3, and vice versa.

It is in this way that a single fact, such as $4 + 3 = 7$, gives rise to three other facts, all four of which constitute a family. Similarly, $5 + 4 = 9$ has an inverse, $9 - 4 = 5$. It also has a commutative fact, $4 + 5 = 9$, which has the inverse $9 - 5 = 4$. Now children, given two numbers, can create, *by recall*, a family of facts in two ways. Given the numbers 5 and 3, a child may write:

$$5 + 3 = 8, \quad 8 - 3 = 5, \quad 3 + 5 = 8, \quad 8 - 5 = 3,$$

or

$$5 - 3 = 2, \quad 2 + 3 = 5, \quad 5 - 2 = 3, \quad 3 + 2 = 5.$$

With the knowledge of a family of facts the child can further reinforce the relation of the two operations by using a mathematical sentence with a frame in which a numeral must be placed to give a statement. Such sentences are called *open sentences*. Open sentences are neither true nor false. When the frame is replaced (or filled in) by a numeral, the statement is true or false, depending on the choice made. Usually, especially at first, we ask the child to produce a true statement. For this purpose it is not only necessary for the child to know the answer, but to tell how he has found the answer from the numbers given in the sentence. The following are examples of the use of sentences with frames in addition or subtraction.

a) $6 + 3 = \square$ We *add* to find the answer.
b) $\square + 6 = 9$ The answer is 3.

A pupil may recall that $3 + 6$ is 9, but from the known numbers he finds $9 - 6$. Thus, finding the number to which 6 must be added to yield 9 is equivalent to (or "amounts to the same thing as") subtracting 6 from 9. This means that

$\square + 6 = 9$ and $9 - 6 = \square$ are related (inverses).

c) $9 - \square = 6$ The answer is 3.

A pupil may recall this as a subtraction fact, $9 - 3 = 6$, or as $9 - 6$ from the given numbers, or as

$9 - \square = 6$ is related to $9 = 6 + \square$,

and recall that $6 + 3$ is 9.

d) $\square - 6 = 3$ The answer is 9.

A pupil may recall this as a subtraction fact. He may also note that

$\square - 6 = 3$ is related to $\square = 3 + 6$,

and hence obtain the answer from addition of the given numbers.

e) $6 + \square = 9$ The answer is 3.

But the sentence is different from (b) above, because $\square$ is the operator. A child may recall the addition fact. He may also know that

$6 + \square = 9$ is related to $6 = 9 - \square$

and recall the subtraction fact. From the given numbers it is evident that he must subtract.

f) $9 - 6 = \square$ The answer is found by subtraction.

Although certain pairs of open sentences, such as (b) and (c) above, may be regarded by an adult as equivalent, and therefore interchangeable, sentences (b) and (d) are more difficult than the rest for a child to contend with. In (b) and (d) the frame (the hole in the sentence) comes first. The child has, figuratively speaking, no place to put his feet at the start. The teacher must keep this psychological consideration in mind when preparing exercises for the child to do.

The frames may be of any shape, but at this stage of learning only one frame should occur in a sentence. The same value can also accrue if one uses a '__' above which a numeral is to be placed.

In textbooks, sometimes the frames are screened to discourage writing in the book, but generally children should be encouraged to copy all problems from the book onto a piece of work paper.

Frames, or equivalently, different kinds of underlinings (blanks), are variables.

$$5 + \square = 12, \quad 5 + \underline{} = 12, \quad \text{and} \quad 5 + y = 12$$

are three ways of writing the same open sentence. A variable does not ask a question; it does not hold a place for a specific numeral or other symbol; it does mark a place which is open to substitution. If a teacher wishes to ask, "Five plus what number equals twelve?" he should write '$5 + ? = 12$'. Here the '?' is not a variable, but an abbreviation for 'what number'. There is a large place for questions like this, as well as for open sentences, in any mathematics program.

The important ideas for the teacher to keep in mind are:

$a + b = c$ implies $c - b = a$. These are inverse statements.
$b + a = c$ implies $c - a = b$. These are inverse statements.

These four statements form a family of facts.

After the children understand this relationship, the teacher may bring in new addition and subtraction facts at the same time.

3-5 LEARNING THE SUMS TO 18

When we are learning the addition facts to sums of 18, we make use of everything we have learned in previous study. This means the decimal system of notation, the addition facts to sums of 10, and the subtraction facts to minuends of 10. We also use another principle which must be established for the pupils. This principle deals with additions involving three numbers; it is called *associativity*. (This word need not be used with children; they need merely the intuitive sense of the idea.)

First we present the children with models of three sets which are to be joined into one set. How do we do it?

Up to this level of learning, the pupils have been combining two sets of objects, or removing a subset from a given set of objects. We now confront the pupils with three sets that are to be joined into one, but we always combine *two sets at a time*, no more. Union

of sets and addition of numbers are binary operations. Given three
sets,

A B C

in the order shown, we can join B to A to form one set, and then
join C to the new set. This we represent by

$(A \cup B) \cup C$ or

We might also join C to B, and then join the union to set A, represented by

$A \cup (B \cup C)$ or

The final set is the same set either way. Thus whether we join
B to A first, or join C to B first, the result of combining three sets
into one remains the same. The parentheses merely indicate which
sets were joined first.

Not all children realize that the number of elements is pre-
served when they associate the middle set with one flanking set and
also, in another experiment, with the other flanking set. Once
this notion of conservation is established they can generalize that
when three sets arranged in a given order are to be joined, the
middle set may be associated with either of the other two sets first,
and then the result joined to the third set. The joining of sets is
associative.

When we have a numeral, or a combination of numerals and
operation signs that is meaningful, we call the numeral or the
combination a *numerical expression*. Thus '3', '3 + 5', '5 + 3', and
'6 − 4' are numerical expressions, but '4 − 6', '3 + + 5', and
'3 − − + 5' are not meaningful in whole-number arithmetic,
so they are not expressions in this context. But what are
'2 + 3 + 5' and '8 − 4 − 1'? If we can give these writings a
meaning we shall call them expressions. To do this we agree that
'2 + 3 + 5' means "add 3 to 2 and add 5 to the sum":

2 + 3 + 5   means   (2 + 3) + 5,   which is 5 + 5,   which is 10.

We now ask the question: is the result for '2 + (3 + 5)' the same? It is. It is 2 + 8, which is 10. Will it always be true that, for any three numbers connected by two '+' signs,

$$a + b + c = (a + b) + c = a + (b + c)?$$

A number of examples, such as 1 + 2 + 3, 1 + 3 + 4, 4 + 2 + 3, and so on, convinces children that if two additions are indicated, the middle number may be associated with either of the two other numbers as the first addition, and that this sum is added to the other number. Children need the intuitive feeling that it is possible to add the first two numbers, or the last two numbers, and then add this sum to the other number. We shall use this idea to learn new sums.

There is no need to learn sums of 11, then sums of 12, and so on. We can learn to create all the sums from 11 through 18 in any order. We select a few examples first and then permit children on their own to complete all the other sums. Suppose we are asked to find 6 + 7. The first tendency of children is to exhibit a 6-set and a 7-set, join the sets and count. This is correct, but it makes little use of previous learning. In this situation we ask what must be added to 6 to give 10. This requires either the recall of an addition fact, 6 + 4 gives 10, or the use of subtraction: 10 − 6 = 4. The 4-set must be a subset of a 7-set which we now separate into a 4-set and a 3-set. The 4-set is now joined with the given 6-set to form a 10-set.

a) 6 + 7

b) 6 + (4 + 3)

c) (6 + 4) + 3
   10 + 3 = 13

```
||||||      |||||||
||||||  (||||  |||)
(|||||| ||||)  |||
    10 + 3 = 13
```

This and the remainder 3-set are joined to form the union. The set maneuvers and number arrangements are shown in the diagram. Thus a regrouping of two sets of objects into three groups, so that the union of the first and second set give a 10-set, shows how we can write a sum of two numbers as a double sum of three numbers, for which the sum of the first two is 10. It is easy to find the sum of 10 and a number less than 10 by the way we constructed our numeration system; for example, 10 + 6 is 16, 10 + 8 is 18, and so on.

Using the regrouping of objects and at the same time rewriting the sum of two numbers as an expression of two sums, and also employing the associative property, enables the children to discover all sums up to $9 + 9 = 18$. After a little practice with the use of sets of objects, the children should be encouraged to a more advanced type of mental activity, namely *thinking* the entire procedure without the use of objects or writing. Thus they can be led, by proper questioning, to do $8 + 7$ in their minds as follows: 8 is 2 less than 10; 7 is $2 + 5$, then $8 + 7$ is $8 + 2 + 5$, which is $10 + 5$, or 15. This is a series of mental recalls of previously learned facts applied to the creation of a new fact. It is this type of mental activity that will be used time after time in further learning of mathematics.

Once a new fact has been discovered, it should be stored in the mind as a fact, for future use. Thus, as soon as the child knows $8 + 7$ is 15, he should write $8 + 7 = 15$ and say "eight plus seven is fifteen," and all intermediate steps in the discovery of the fact should be relegated out of recall. The commutative principle, already learned in the sums to 10, may be used to establish recall. Thus $8 + 7 = 15$ immediately implies $7 + 8 = 15$. The use of flash cards, written practice, and other devices suggested earlier help to achieve automatic recall. The completion of the addition table (see page 53) also helps to develop recall. Practical and real problems given by the teacher or created by the pupils aid not only in recall but also in understanding and applying the operation.

Many children, when they discover the facts to sums of 18, invent ways of their own. Some children will learn the doubles, that is, $6 + 6$, $7 + 7$, etc., first. Then they argue that $7 + 8$ must be 15 since 8 is "one more than" (but better expressed as "one greater than") 7. This type of thinking should be encouraged, but the "one more than" should be rationalized for the children. What the discoverer is really saying is $8 = 7 + 1$, hence $7 + 8$ is $7 + (7 + 1)$. Since he knows $7 + 7$, he writes or thinks of the associated expression $(7 + 7) + 1$ or $14 + 1$, which is 15. This is further experience with the associative principle of addition.

This philosophy of learning by using various (correct) methods of discovering new relations is based on the assumption that (1) children should always use any previously learned knowledge to gain new knowledge and (2) there should be a *gradual* departure from the use of physical objects or sets of objects, to thinking in

terms of the abstractions (numbers) and the relation of these
numbers through the operations on them. This latter activity lays
the foundation for continuing mathematical study at a later stage
and for a higher level of cognitive intellectual activity.

Children can now explore what used to be called upper-decade
facts, including those which bridge the tens (but no such expressions
are required in meaningful teaching). To add $25 + 7$ the child
uses the idea of $5 + \square = 10$. Thus he thinks

$$25 + (5 + 2) = 30 + 2 = 32.$$

After a little practice with this type of problem, as well as $25 + 3$
which is $(20 + 5) + 3$, he will soon distinguish situations in which
the sum of the units digits exceeds 10 (and hence we have a sum
in the next-higher decade) and those in which it does not. The
goal of this activity is learning the principle of adding a single-digit
number to a two-digit number.

A number line is an excellent device for showing how adding
a single-digit number to a two-digit number is related to the simple
addition facts.

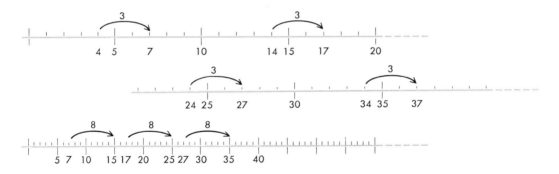

In each illustration above, the left-hand part shows a simple
addition fact (or a subtraction fact, if you reverse the arrow) and
the other parts, which could be repeated again and again, show
how the same relation is just moved 10 units higher on the scale
each time. A child who intuitively grasps the idea just stated here
can tell at once what the sum of $64 + 3$ is, and what the sum of
$87 + 8$ is. (Obviously a similar device may be used to show the
subtraction of a single-digit number from a two-digit number.)

When using a number line, one must take care that a number is assigned to each unit step forward. Some children start at the point named '0' and say "one"; they arrive at '6' when they say "seven." Starting at 0, we make a step forward and say "one" (the name associated with the point at which we arrive). In this way the number names agree with the number of moves we make. Next we begin at any number, say 7, and start counting again. Hence we say "one" as we move one space (to 8) then "two" as we move another space (to 9) and so on, saying "eight" as we arrive at the name 15. Hence, starting with 7 and adding 8 to it yields 15.

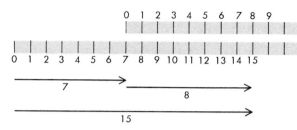

Since this procedure depends only on counting, and counting motions, it is wise to use it as a final and not an initial procedure in developing the concept of addition. Note also that this procedure lacks the quality of reinforcing the earlier learning of addition and subtraction facts and the use of the decimal system of notation. An addition slide rule, i.e., two like-sized number scales that slide along each other, as illustrated, may also be used as a final device to aid in finding sums.

A final goal of teaching addition as a special binary operation is the recognition that addition is the operation that assigns to two numbers, given in order, another number called their sum. To indicate this special operation we use the symbol '+', read "plus." To indicate the assignment of a number we use the symbol '=', read "equals" or "is" (singular). Since for any two selected numbers a and b, the order (a, b) or (b, a) gives the same sum, the operation is commutative. That is, $a + b$, where b is added to a, and $b + a$, where a is added to b, are the same sum. This is a mathematical distinction of importance in later study, but one that is not to be stressed as such. Most elementary school children will never sense its mathematical importance, but they will recognize its usefulness in learning and applying the facts.

3-6 SUBTRACTION TO MINUENDS OF 18

Using the fact that 16 is $10 + 6$, 14 is $10 + 4$, etc., children can easily subtract a single-digit number from a teens number if the units digit of the teens number is equal to or greater than the single-digit subtrahend. Thus $16 - 6$ is thought of as $10 + (6 - 6) = 10$; $15 - 3$ is $10 + (5 - 3) = 10 + 2 = 12$. These subtractions are not considered as facts to be learned, because the difference is immediately found.

However, when the subtrahend is larger than the units digit in the teens number, for example, $15 - 8$, where $8 > 5$, the subtraction fact must be learned for automatic recall for use in the subtraction algorism to be learned later. These facts can be discovered in many ways, and a variety of ways is desirable. The choice of which way to stress depends on the kind of subtraction algorism that is to be taught in subsequent study.

Suppose that we wish to stress the relation of subtraction to *taking away* a subset from a set, and to reinforce the facts previously learned. One method of doing this is to have children expand the minuend, then subtract the subtrahend from 10 and add the difference to the units of the minuend. To illustrate: $14 - 8$ is thought of as $(10 + 4) - 8$ or $(4 + 10) - 8$. We subtract the 8 from 10, thinking that $(4 + 10) - 8$ is the same as $4 + (10 - 8)$, and hence find that the difference is $4 + 2$, or 6. We immediately write and say "$14 - 8 = 6$; fourteen minus eight is six." Now we can write and say another fact, namely $14 - 6 = 8$. After a little practice—all verbal with occasional writing of the steps—the children can discover all the subtraction facts from $11 - 2, \ldots,$ $11 - 9$, through $18 - 9$. The child should say (and in the discovery think) "$16 - 9$ is $(10 - 9)$—that is, 1—plus 6, which is 7. Therefore $16 - 9 = 7$ and $16 - 7 = 9$."

Another way is to rewrite the subtrahend. Thus $13 - 9$ can be thought of as $(10 + 3) - (3 + 6)$. The 3 is subtracted from 3 and the 6 from 10 to give the difference, 4. Similarly, in $14 - 6$ the child subtracts 4 from 4 and the other 2 from 10 to obtain 8. He immediately writes '$14 - 6 = 8$' and '$14 - 8 = 6$'. In doing this operation a child must be made aware that the subtrahend is changed to a sum and that each addend is subtracted. For example, to say that $12 - 6$ is $12 - (8 - 2) = (12 - 8) - 2$ is not correct. *Subtraction is not associative.*

A third way to discover the subtraction facts is by the use of the inverse of an addition fact. Thus, since $8 + 7 = 15$, we know that $15 - 7 = 8$. At the same time we know that $7 + 8 = 15$ and $15 - 8 = 7$. This is a more general and broader concept on which to build subtraction facts, and one which should be emphasized. Thus every sum in the addition table yields a family of facts. For example:

$$\boxed{\begin{aligned} 9 + 7 &= 16, & 16 - 7 &= 9 \\ 7 + 9 &= 16, & 16 - 9 &= 7 \end{aligned}} \qquad \boxed{\begin{aligned} 8 + 8 &= 16 \\ 16 - 8 &= 8 \end{aligned}}$$

Often the children themselves are a most productive source of techniques for discovering, or reinforcing, facts. When a child has a correct procedure of his own, he should be commended and encouraged to seek others. For instance, a child who finds $8 + 5$ by saying "8 is $3 + 5$, and $3 + 5 + 5$ is $3 + 10$, or 13" is using a correct method and an insightful one.

Once the facts have been discovered, they must be practiced until recall is automatic. Here again practice with flash cards, with written examples, and with a subtraction table, as well as an addition table, will soon help to establish all the facts in the mind of the child. The use of frames, as given on page 61, is a very fruitful way of relating the new addition and subtraction facts. The addition slide rule used in reverse and counting backward (right to left) along the number line are other devices. When we count backward, we must take care that, when we begin at a number, we make a move before we count 1.

$$17 - 8 = 9$$

Thus, in the figure, starting at 17 we move to 16 saying "one," then to 15 saying "two," and so on, until, when we move to 9, we say "eight." Hence $17 - 8 = 9$.

The complete addition and subtraction tables should be listed and compared. All the necessary facts and only the necessary facts for all subsequent work in addition and subtraction are listed. The children should finally see how one table (it does not matter which one) can suffice for both operations. Thus in the addition table the

TABLE 3-3   ADDITION

b

+	0	1	2	3	4	5	6	7	8	9
0	0	1	2	3	4	5	6	7	8	9
1	1	2	3	4	5	6	7	8	9	10
2	2	3	4	5	6	7	8	9	10	11
3	3	4	5	6	7	8	9	10	11	12
4	4	5	6	7	8	9	10	11	12	13
5	5	6	7	8	9	10	11	12	13	14
6	6	7	8	9	10	11	12	13	14	15
7	7	8	9	10	11	12	13	14	15	16
8	8	9	10	11	12	13	14	15	16	17
9	9	10	11	12	13	14	15	16	17	18

a is the left column label.

$$a + b = \boxed{c}$$

cell *under* 7 which contains 15 is *opposite* 8. This means that $8 + 7 = 15$ or $15 - 7 = 8$. What does the cell under 8 which contains 15 signify? It is opposite 7 and signifies either $7 + 8 = 15$ or $15 - 8 = 7$. Similarly, in the subtraction table, the cell *under* 7 that contains 8 is *opposite* 15. This signifies that $15 - 7 = 8$ or $8 + 7 = 15$.

Such work with tables is an activity which will prove useful to the child not only in his later study of mathematics, but in his reading of all sorts of tables in newspapers, magazines, and in social and physical science textbooks.

3-7 GENERALIZATIONS

The more children know about relations among numbers and operations on numbers, the easier it will be for them to gain insight into new relations. Thus, at appropriate times, the teacher should

TABLE 3–4   SUBTRACTION

b

−	0	1	2	3	4	5	6	7	8	9
0	0									
1	1	0				O				
2	2	1	0				P			
3	3	2	1	0				E		
4	4	3	2	1	0				N	
5	5	4	3	2	1	0				
6	6	5	4	3	2	1	0			
7	7	6	5	4	3	2	1	0		
8	8	7	6	5	4	3	2	1	0	
9	9	8	7	6	5	4	3	2	1	0
10		9	8	7	6	5	4	3	2	1
11			9	8	7	6	5	4	3	2
12				9	8	7	6	5	4	3
13					9	8	7	6	5	4
14	Closed but					9	8	7	6	5
15	not listed						9	8	7	6
16								9	8	7
17									9	8
18										9

a (left label column)

$$a - b = \square$$

ask questions which require the children to generalize the concepts they have acquired. These questions can be formulated by the alert teacher. The following questions and answers are merely indicative of the type that may be asked.

Can you add like things? No, you add numbers, not things. What can you do with sets of things? Join them, form their union, or take away part of a set from a set. Is zero a number? Yes; it is the number property of the empty set. Is the set of wheels on a car the number four? No, a set is not a number. What is a number? The manyness of a set of objects. All these questions are aimed at distinguishing sets and operations on sets from numbers and operations on numbers.

When you are adding, must one addend be different from the other? No, you can add a number to the same number. Is the sum always greater than either addend? No, not when one of the addends is zero. Can you add 25 to 8? Yes, the sum is 33. Can you add 2 tens (or 20) to 7? Yes, the sum is 27. Can you add the number of tens in 38 to the number of ones in 26? You can, but the sum $3 + 6 = 9$ does not mean anything, it does not tell how many tens altogether, or how many units. Can you add any number to any other number? Yes, always.

In subtraction, is the difference always less than the minuend? No, not if the subtrahend is zero. Which is larger, the subtrahend or the difference? Either, or they could be the same, $16 - 8 = 8$, $16 - 7 = 9$ and $16 - 9 = 7$. As the subtrahend grows larger and the minuend is the same, how does the difference change? It grows smaller. Explain this with a set of objects by taking away larger and larger parts.

If you put 1 with 2 what do you get? It depends; if you put a numeral '1' with a numeral '2' you get '12' or '21'. If you put a 1-set with a 2-set you get a 3-set. You cannot *put* a number with a number. You add or subtract numbers. Can you find the difference of any two unequal numbers? Only if the minuend is the greater number. That is, $9 - 6 = 3$ but $6 - 9$ cannot yield a difference within the set of whole numbers. When the questions are put to the children, the answers, whether correct or incorrect, should be studied until all children understand the implications of the questions and have verified correct responses.

3–8 GRADE PLACEMENT

There was a time when, for each school year, a designated body of mathematical study was assigned to each grade for all pupils in that grade. This practice is all too prevalent today and most textbooks carry a number indicating the grade level at which a given book should be studied. However, for almost a century we have become well aware of the differences that exist in the ability of pupils to learn. Some children learn very fast, others exceedingly slowly. Some children know a good deal of arithmetic on entering first grade, others do not know the numbers to 5.

Children should always start with fundamental ideas (about which some may know something but can always learn more and clarify their initial ideas). They should proceed at a rate of learning adapted to their ability through some designated sequence of structured learning. All the content suggested in this chapter can be learned by a large segment of children before they are seven years old, or by the end of Grade 1. In addition to this learning they will also have acquired knowledge of simple measures of time, money, weight, and liquids, recognition of simple geometrical figures, and the use of such fractions as one-half, one-third, and one-fourth.

There can be different sequences, all of which yield the same end product of learning. The following is merely indicative of how the learning of addition and subtraction may proceed in kindergarten and Grade 1, assuming the sequence on sets, numbers, and counting as given in Chapter 2.

1. Combining of sets (union)
2. Learning addition as the corresponding operation on the numbers; learning how to use a number line
3. Learning the language and discovering addition facts to sums of 10
4. Practicing addition facts and constructing a table of these facts
5. Taking away a subset of a set, leaving a remainder set
6. Learning subtraction as the corresponding operation on numbers
7. Discovering and learning the language of subtraction facts to minuends of 10; learning the use of a number line
8. Practicing and recalling of addition and subtraction facts; learning families of facts; counting and operations
9. Constructing a subtraction table
10. Learning the addition facts to sums of 18

11. Learning the subtraction facts to minuends of 18

12. Practicing for recall; solving problems involving both operations

13. Attaining readiness for the algorisms of addition and subtraction

EXERCISES

1. Explain the meaning of 'a binary operation over a set of numbers'. Use *av* as a symbol for an operation which is defined as follows:

$$n_1 \; av \; n_2 = \frac{n_1 + n_2}{2}.$$

   Show that for the set of whole numbers and fractions with denominator 2 the operation always exists, and that it is commutative, but not associative. Explain the need for an *ordered* pair of numbers in defining a binary operation.

2. List a sequence of learnings, from the combining of two disjoint sets to assigning the number 9 to (5, 4), which will develop the concept of addition. Explain the rational, practical, and/or psychological structure of the sequence.

3. List at least 5 different types of physical materials that can be used in first grade to develop the concepts of addition and subtraction. Choose one of these types and show how you would use it to develop each concept.

4. Explain how you would introduce, construct, and use a number line to develop the learning of addition facts. What other activities would you use to supplement the use of the number line?

5. Consult references on the nature and use of an abacus in carrying out addition and subtraction. Select one type of abacus and show how to use it to develop the addition facts for sums of 10 through 18.

6. What is "frame" arithmetic? Describe in detail how you would use frames to relate addition and subtraction; to solve problems.

7. Is $\square + 6 = 9$ an addition or subtraction exercise? Defend your answer and explain how you would use this sentence, as well as $6 + \square = 9$, to relate addition and subtraction.

8. Explain how you would teach children the distinction between the operation $8 + 5$ and the expression '$8 + 3 + 2$'. How and to what extent would you develop the ideas of commutativity and

associativity? To what extent would you differentiate between the operand and operator in a binary operation?

9. One means of comparing the relative sizes of two groups of objects is to find the difference of their numbers. Explain how you would relate this procedure to that of taking away a subset from a given set. How would you relate it to two points on a number line?

10. "Using what you know to learn something new is the best practice of what you know." Explain how this principle was exemplified in the development of the basic sums and differences.

11. At what point would you begin teaching new addition and subtraction facts together? Give reasons for your answer.

12. How could you use a number line made of masking tape attached to the chalkrail and a toy frog (or other animal) to facilitate discovery or recall of addition facts? of subtraction facts? When would you start using number lines on worksheets? Why?

REFERENCES

ASHLOCK, R. B., "The Number Line in the Primary Grades," *The Arithmetic Teacher* **8,** 2, February 1961, pages 75–76

BOTTS, T., "Linear Measurement and Imagination," *The Arithmetic Teacher* **9,** 7, November 1962, pages 376–382

FOLSOM, MARY, "Frames, Frames, and More Frames," *The Arithmetic Teacher* **10,** 8, December 1963, pages 484–485

HOLLISTER, G. E., and A. G. GUNDERSON, *Teaching Arithmetic in the Primary Grades*, Boston: D. C. Heath, 1964

KING, ELIZABETH B., "Greater Flexibility in Abstract Thinking Through Frame Arithmetic," *The Arithmetic Teacher* **10,** 4, April 1963, pages 183–187

NATIONAL COUNCIL OF TEACHERS OF MATHEMATICS, *Topics in Mathematics for Elementary School Teachers.* Twenty-Ninth Yearbook (Washington, D.C., National Council of Teachers of Mathematics, 1964), pages 20–23, 51–58, 65–70, 80–83, 88–89, 134–166

PAGE, D. A., *Number Lines, Functions, and Fundamental Topics*, New York: Macmillan, 1964

PHILLIPS, J. M., "Putting the Tic in Arithme," *School Science and Mathematics* **66,** 3, March 1966, pages 259–268

PHILLIPS, J. M., *Seeing the Use of Numbers, Sets I and II* (filmstrips), Eye Gate Productions, Jamaica, N.Y.

Operations in arithmetic

PHILLIPS, J. M., "We've Been Framed," *The Instructor*, January 1967, pages 103–139

UICSM PROJECT STAFF, "Arithmetic with Frames," *The Arithmetic Teacher* **4,** 3, April 1957, pages 119–124

WIRTZ, BOTEL, BEBERMAN, and SAWYER, *Games and Enrichment Activities, Math Workshop*, Chicago: Encyclopedia Britannica, 1964

algorisms
for addition
and subtraction

It is not sufficient for an adult to know the meaning of 'the sum of two numbers', or the meaning of an expression such as '341 + 638 + 594'. He must know how to find the simple name for the single number which is the result. How this can be accomplished is discussed in this chapter.

4-1 ALGORISMS

Although the word *algorism** (alternate spelling *algorithm*) has been in the mathematical literature for a long time, its usage in the teaching of elementary school mathematics is fairly recent. Generally the word refers to a step-by-step procedure for finding the result of an operation. For instance, there is a Euclidean algorism for finding the square root of a given number.

At the top of the following page, there are three different algorisms (procedures) for finding the product of two numbers (236, 78). Each of these procedures is an algorism, and each one is correct. Do you know the reason why each of these algorisms is a correct way of finding any product?

---

* The word *algorism* is of Arabic origin, referring to the early mathematician al-Khuwarizmi. The Greek spelling *algorithm* is also used.

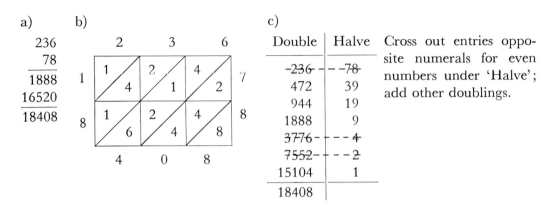

a)
```
  236
   78
 1888
16520
18408
```

Do you know why each algorism you use in solving mathematical problems is a correct way of getting the answer? It is quite usual to find many people who can perform an algorism but have no idea why it works.

In general, when an algorism is developed, there is a period of discussion on ways of getting the result. The ways discussed are refined until we get an *efficient*, easily applied algorism that is completely understood. The algorism developed in this manner becomes a part of the permanent, quickly recalled knowledge of a person throughout his life.

It must be recognized that the standard algorisms for the various operations are standard not because they are the most efficient procedure for working any particular example, but because each of them is effective for all examples in the given category. The pupil who understands the rationale of a standard algorism is not a prisoner of that algorism; he can invent "neat tricks" for special cases.

4–2 THE ADDITION ALGORISM(S)

The child has learned the sums to 18, and he can recall how he learned these sums. He has also learned how to find the value of expressions such as '2 + 4 + 3', '3 + 4 + 7 + 10', and so on. He must now learn how to use what he already knows to find the sum of any two numbers, for example, 26 + 93 or 258 + 367, and sums named by expressions such as '28 + 49 + 63'. The pupils must be guided to discover an effective way.

It is essential that the teacher analyze the subsidiary under-standings and skills the pupils need before they can be successful in an enterprise of this kind. They need a reasonable command of the basic addition facts; they need a lot of experience in adding 10 to a number and seeing the effect of this addition on the numerals; they need an operating knowledge of place value; they need to know that they can think of (rename) a number in all sorts of ways and they need practice in doing this, with particular attention paid to examples such as $36 = 30 + 6 = 20 + 16$ and $40 + 13 = 50 + 3 = 53$. An abacus, a number line, sticks or tickets which can be grouped by tens, pocket charts, and other comparable learning aids should be used extensively in establishing these subsidiary understandings.

A pocket chart can be made in a few seconds from a manila folder, the kind used for filing. The other necessary materials are a stapler, a pair of scissors, and a marking pen. Cut the leftover pieces into strips to use for tallies.

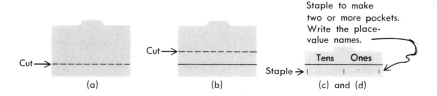

Learning the addition algorism should start with a period of discussion. We ask the child to find the single number (sum) which is equal to $36 + 47$, for example. If the children are permitted to do this on their own, various ways will be suggested. Among these may be:

a) Add 4 to 36 to get 40, then subtract 4 from 47 to get 43. Now add 43 and 40. The two 40's are 80, and the 3 to be added yields 83. This method should be examined to find the reasons why it works.

b) Another suggestion: 36 and 40 is 76. Now 7 is left from the 47 to be added to the 76. $76 + 7 = 76 + 4 + 3 = 80 + 3 = 83$. Again the solution should be examined step by step.

c) We can also say that 6 plus 7 is 13 and 30 plus 40 is 70. Then 70 plus 13 is 80 plus 3, or 83. Since there is much in this solution that leads to an ultimate desired algorism, it should be

36
47
―――
13
70
―――
83

analyzed thoroughly. If we record this as shown in the margin, we have a display which leads easily into the form we wish to arrive at.

d) Still another way is to say that 30 plus 40 is 70, 6 plus 7 is 13, and 70 plus 13 is 83. This solution is particularly productive when an estimate is desired.

Of all these methods, the one which will best lead to the standard algorism with paper and pencil is the one which begins by adding the number of units, then the number of tens, and combining these two sums. We examine this method more carefully. It is wise to start this learning with an example that calls for the exchange of 1 ten-set for 10 one-sets. (We use 'tens' as an abbreviation for 'ten-sets' and 'ones' as an abbreviation for 'one-sets'.) The steps in teaching may be as follows:

a)

	Tens	Ones			
$36 \Rightarrow$	3	6	or	$30 + 6$	This makes use
$+ \ 47$	4	7		$40 + 7$	of expanded dec-
	7	13		$70 + 13$	imal notation.

b) When we exchange 10 of the ones for 1 ten and combine it with the 7 tens, we obtain 8 tens, 3 ones, or $80 + 3$, or 83.

c) If we add the ones first and find 10 or more, we can always use 10 of the ones as 1 ten and add this extra ten to the rest of the tens before writing the answer. Thus we say $6 + 7 = 13$, or 10 and 3. This is 1 ten and 3 ones. The number of units in the sum is 3. Then the number of tens is $1 + 3 + 4$, and 8 tens is 80. The sum is 83.

The final algorism may be illustrated as follows, where the line through numerals merely indicates that the operation has been completed.

$$
\begin{array}{c}
36 \\
47 \\
\hline
\end{array}
\Rightarrow
\begin{array}{c}
\overset{1}{} \\
3\cancel{6} \\
4\cancel{7} \\
\hline
3
\end{array}
\Rightarrow
\begin{array}{c}
\overset{1}{} \\
\cancel{3}6 \\
\cancel{4}7 \\
\hline
83
\end{array}
$$

Placing the numeral 1 above the tens column is referred to as a *crutch*. At the start this procedure is useful and should be encouraged. It shows exactly how the algorism works.

d) Deeper understanding is fostered by the use of sets of objects.

1. Let us represent 36 by 3 bundles of ten sticks and 6 individual sticks. We represent 47 by 4 bundles of ten sticks and 7 individual sticks.

2. We wish to find the numbers in all, so we put together the objects we are using. (This suggests the union
of sets.)

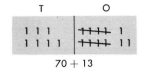

$$70 + 13$$

3. We bundle 10 of the ones and transfer this bundle to
the place where we have the other tens.

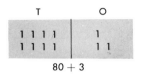

$$80 + 3$$

4. By counting, or adding the numbers of the sets involved, we
find that there are $(3 + 4 + 1)$ tens and 3 ones; the number is 83.

Once the children have grasped the concept and practiced
making the exchange, we then confront them with a problem in
which no exchange is necessary, for example, $33 + 44$. The
child who understood the exchange he made in adding 36 and 47
will find this too easy for words. The child who did not understand
needs more work with models of sets and pocket charts. After this
type of study and explanation, all children should be able to tell
when an exchange of 10 ones for 1 ten occurs in the addition
process and when it does not. Repeated practice in which both
types of examples occur is the best way to establish the algorism
in the child's mind.

Children who learn addition without understanding the need
for exchanging (sometimes called "carrying") are prone to do the
following: Add the units and place the sum below the units place.
Then add the tens and place the sum below the tens place. Frequently, children who are taught by this "how-you-do-it" method
write

$$
\begin{array}{r}
27 \\
18 \\
\hline
315 \ \text{(False)}
\end{array}
$$

as the sum, because that is how you do it. When questioned by a
teacher, one child who did this said: "Well, when you think it
out it is 45, but when you write it out it is 315!" By discussion,
stressing when an exchange is necessary and when it is not, and
practicing all types of additions of two-digit numbers, a child
builds the knowledge which is basic to all the extensions that
follow.

4–3 EXTENSION OF THE ALGORISM

684
369
237
+ 594
———

The algorism must be extended to finding the sum of any two numbers as well as finding the sum of three or more numbers; that is, to examples of the type 2684 + 563 and to examples of so-called column addition (which is merely another way of writing the expression

$$684 + 369 + 237 + 594$$

if you read down the column, or in reverse order if you read up the column). The first and easier extension (since less mental retention is required) is to finding the sum of two three-digit numbers.

If it is necessary to use sensory aids in this extension, at least one bit of abstraction should be learned previously, namely that instead of using a bundle of 10 things to represent 1 ten, we may use a single thing (of a different size or color, at first) to represent the bundle of 10 things. We do this when we use 1 dime for 10 pennies, or when, on an abacus, we use 1 bead in the next row to the left to represent the value of 10 beads in a given row. Once the child grasps this representation, the numbers-pocket idea can be used to demonstrate the analogous process in arithmetic. The same idea can be developed by tallying in the ones place (or column) as the child counts to 10 and then erasing a tally 'ⅧⅢ ⅧⅢ' in the ones place and replacing the erasure by a single tally '|' in the tens column. Thus the new tally represents 10, or 1 ten, which is equal to 10 ones. Similarly, when we tally 'ⅧⅢ ⅧⅢ' in the tens column, we erase it and replace it by '|' in the hundreds column. Thus the child learns how to extend the reading and writing of numbers from 100 to 1000, and then to 10,000. The extension of numeration to higher powers of 10 can be delayed until later. The process of adding 268 to 537 then becomes:

$$\frac{268}{537} = \frac{26\cancel{8}}{53\cancel{7}} = \frac{2\cancel{6}\cancel{8}}{53\cancel{7}} = \frac{\cancel{2}\cancel{6}\cancel{8}}{\cancel{5}\cancel{3}\cancel{7}}$$
$$5 \qquad 05 \qquad 805$$

where the lines through numerals merely indicate that the partial operation has been carried out. The so-called crutch will soon be abandoned by the more apt pupils who can make the exchange (or carry) mentally. Average pupils can eventually be encouraged to do the algorism mentally, writing only the sum and avoiding writing the carrying number. For slower pupils it is not necessary to remove the crutch. It is better for them to know what they are doing, and get a correct sum, with unhurried calm, than to be concerned with speed or elegance in computation.

The extension to four-digit numbers is merely an extension to a longer attention span, and not to any new ideas. By the end of the third grade, children should be able to add any two six-place numbers. However, there is something new to be learned when we come to finding the sum of three or more addends, the algorism for which is usually written in columnar form. Children must be made continuously aware of the fact that addition involves exactly two numbers at a time. Thus $3 + 4 + 8$ is not *an* addition, but *two* additions, either

first

$(3 + 4) + 8,$ that is, $3 + 4 = 7, \quad 7 + 8 = 15$

second

or

first

$3 + (4 + 8),$ that is, $4 + 8 = 12, \quad 3 + 12 = 15.$

second

Thus so-called column addition is merely finding the value of a numerical expression involving addition.

$$\begin{array}{r} 36 \\ 48 \\ + \ 63 \end{array}$$ means $36 + 48 + 63,$ which is
$(36 + 48) + 63$ or $36 + (48 + 63).$

However, the algorism that is developed will find the sum in a way quite different from that suggested by the statement of the meaning. We shall add the numbers represented by the units digit of each of the numbers, then by the tens digits, and as in the case of two numbers, make exchanges when necessary. To prepare for this type of addition, children first practice column addition of one-digit numbers. It is wise to encourage children to do the additions in order, either upward or downward, and *not* to encourage them to look for special combinations.

Adding downward   Adding upward

By adding in order, the children reinforce the facts they have learned, they are unlikely to miss an addend, and they gain confidence and reasonable speed in the computational process.

The diagrams show that

$$8 + 6 + 4 + 3$$

means

$$\{8 + [6 + (4 + 3)]\}$$

third second

first

for adding up and

$$\{[(8 + 6) + 4] + 3\}$$

first

second third

for adding down. Either way is a good check on doing the sums the other way. Once the children have learned this columnar process, we study the problem in steps as follows:

$$
\begin{array}{c}
36 \\
48 \\
+\ 63 \\
\end{array}
\left(
\begin{array}{c}
\text{Think} \\
6 \\
8 \\
3 \\
\hline
17 \\
\end{array}
\right)
\Rightarrow
\begin{array}{c}
1 \\
36 \\
48 \\
63 \\
\hline
7 \\
\end{array}
\Rightarrow
\begin{array}{c}
1 \\
36 \\
48 \\
63 \\
\hline
147 \\
\end{array}
\quad \text{or finally} \quad
\begin{array}{c}
1 \\
36 \\
48 \\
63 \\
\hline
147 \\
\end{array}
$$

where the strokes indicate that the operation has been completed. Some teachers may prefer expanded notation:

$$
\begin{array}{c}
36 \\
48 \\
63 \\
\end{array}
\Rightarrow
\begin{array}{c}
30 + 6 \\
40 + 8 \\
60 + 3 \\
\hline
130 + 17 \Rightarrow 140 + 7 \Rightarrow 147.
\end{array}
$$

This is a good way to explain what is done, but it must eventually be reduced to the foregoing method if children are to achieve a mature, efficient algorism.

The extension to more complex expressions, that is, to a series of additions involving four, five, or even ten numbers, of three, four, five, or six digits each is merely one of a more complex mental activity, but certainly no new ideas or procedures are required. These extensions should take place in the third and fourth school years. Pupils should attain adult-level performance by the end of the fifth school year.

A suggested order of steps for teaching the addition algorism, with approximate grade placement, is as follows:

$$\begin{array}{r} 14 \\ + \ 3 \\ \hline \end{array} \qquad \begin{array}{r} 36 \\ + \ 7 \\ \hline \end{array}$$

Grade 1. Adding a two-digit and a single-digit number

Grade 2. Adding two-digit numbers, both with and without exchange; adding three-digit numbers both with and without exchange; introducing the continued addition of three single-digit numbers

Grade 3. Adding four single-digit numbers; adding three two-digit numbers; adding two and three three-digit numbers, including sums involving money; adding four- and five-digit numbers

Grade 4. Achieving adult-level performance; being able to add a column of five four- or five-digit numbers

Grades 5–6. Gradually extending the child's facility, until he can add decimal fractions, including ten to twelve numbers of the type $3.62, $21.56, etc.

In all grades, problems involving addition should be solved, and also constructed, by the pupils.

4–4 THE SUBTRACTION ALGORISM

There are two common algorisms used in subtraction, one usually referred to as the *subtractive-decomposition* method and the other either as the *Austrian* or the *additive* method. The additive method has certain properties that commend it as a more mathematically oriented method. However, the subtractive-decomposition method is easier for most children to comprehend because it is easier to demonstrate with models of sets, and it does not change the example to an equivalent one, as the Austrian method does. First we shall develop the subtractive-decomposition method, and then show several other algorisms which are possible but not particularly recommended at the elementary school level.

Before children can understand the subtractive method, they must learn how to think about and write a two-digit number in ways other than the standard way. Thus 23 is also $10 + 13$, 64 is $50 + 14$, and so on. An illustration of a way to test such thinking is to pose the problem to the class: There are 2 dimes and 3 pennies—that is, 23 cents—here on the table. Eight cents of it belongs to me. How can I take my 8 cents, *if there is no other money in the room?* After a few tries, the children give the answer: it is not possible. Next place a pile of pennies on the other side of the table and ask them whether it can be done now. Some children may suggest that you take 3 pennies and borrow 5 pennies from the pile. But then you object to any borrowing—you can take only what belongs to you. This finally leads to an exchange of 1 dime for 10 of the pennies in the pile, resulting in 1 dime and 13 pennies to make the 23 cents. Then you can *take* your 8 pennies from the 13 pennies, leaving 1 dime and 5 pennies, 15 cents. The children are told to recognize that 23 can be thought of as 10 + 13, or as 1 ten and 13 ones. After several similar examples, using other sets of objects, the children are ready to discuss the subtraction process.

We start with an example requiring regrouping. The children may discuss the problem

$$\begin{array}{r} 43 \\ -\ 17 \end{array}.$$

There are many ways this can be done. For example,

$$43 - 10 = 33,$$

then

$$33 - 7 = (33 - 3) - 4 = 30 - 4 = 26.$$

Or we could say that $43 - 3 = 40$, then subtract 4 more and $40 - 4 = 36$, then subtract 10 and the difference is 26. After we have examined all these suggested ways, we direct the discussion to using what we have already learned, namely the subtraction facts, and rethinking the minuend. This leads to the following sequence:

$$\begin{array}{r} 43 \\ -\ 17 \end{array} \Rightarrow \begin{array}{r} 30 + 13 \\ 10 + 7 \end{array} \Rightarrow 20 + 6 \quad \text{or} \quad 26$$

or

	Tens	Units		Tens	Units		Tens	Units	
43	4	3		3	13		3	13	
− 17 $\Rightarrow$	− 1	7	$\Rightarrow$	4	3	$\Rightarrow$	− 1	7	$\Rightarrow 26.$
				− 1	7				

Ultimately we want to get the children to change the minuend mentally and to think of forty-three as thirty-thirteen.

If the pupils have difficulty in understanding the explanation, then the teacher can resort to sets and number pockets. Here 4 bundles of tens and 3 individual sticks or blocks are placed in the pockets. The child can remove (or take away) 1 ten, but to take away 7 individual sticks it becomes necessary to (open or) exchange 1 bundle of ten for 10 individual objects. Only then can he take away 7 ones. This operation should at all times be related to the arithmetic; for example,

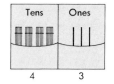

Tens	Ones
4	3

$$43 - 17 = 33 - 7 = (20 + 13) - 7 = 20 + (13 - 7) = 26.$$

Of course you can subtract the number of tens first, but if you place the result in the answer row it will be necessary in this case to change one of the tens back to the minuend so you can subtract 7. This would appear as follows:

Tens	Units		Tens	Units	
4̸	3	⇒	4̸	13	⇒ 26.
1̸	7		1̸	7	
3			3̸	6	
			2		

Obviously, it is not nearly so efficient as using the exchange of a ten first; that is, not so efficient as beginning by subtracting the units.

After the procedure of exchanging is well understood, we study problems where no regrouping, or rethinking of the number, is necessary; for example

$$\begin{array}{r} 47 \\ - \ 23 \ . \\ \hline \end{array}$$

If a pupil starts by making an exchange and using $17 - 3$, ask him to explain why he did this. Was it necessary? When is it necessary and when is it not necessary to rethink the minuend? What is the difference of $17 - 3$? How will you record the result of this subtraction? The bright child who may be listening will see that this could be the start of a correct procedure, but it surely is more trouble than it is worth.

Another argument in favor of introducing subtraction with an exchange problem is to foment thinking and avoid blind rote. A teacher who begins with $47 - 23$ and says "subtract the ones,

53
38
—
25 (False)

and place the answer in the ones column, then subtract the tens and place the answer in the tens column" will find many children following the incorrect procedure shown in the margin, because $8 - 3 = 5$ and $5 - 3 = 2$. After children have fully comprehended the algorism, they must practice with exercises which randomly demand exchange or no exchange in the minuend, until the children can compute correctly with confidence and reasonable speed.

4–5 EXTENDING THE ALGORISM

The first extension is to the subtraction of 2 three-place numbers, where the same process of exchange is immediately possible. Thus in problems of the types:

a) 863
  − 415
   ———

we think

(800 + 50 + 13)
− (400 + 10 + 5)

and obtain 448

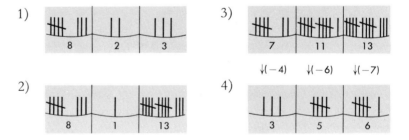

b) 823
  − 467
   ———

where a line through a numeral shows that the process has been completed and the last representation shows the ultimate desired mental action. For slower children, or for those who need concrete situations to make the abstraction, the process can be exhibited by using a pocket chart.

1)
| 8 | 2 | 3 |

3)
| 7 | 11 | 13 |

↓(−4)   ↓(−6)   ↓(−7)

2)
| 8 | 1 | 13 |

4)
| 3 | 5 | 6 |

The necessity of making two exchanges—tens to ones and hundreds to tens—demands eventually that the child store in his mind the fact that a digit in a place to the left has, or has not, been reduced by 1, and this demands both memory and concentration. However, all children must develop this memory and concentration on the process if they are successfully to pursue later work in division. Thus we practice for mastery, not speed.

One of the difficulties that arises in subtraction is the so-called exchange through a zero, that is, making a regrouping (exchange or rethinking) of the minuend when the digit in the place to the left, or in each of several places to the left, of a given column is zero. This necessitates going to the first place to the left that is not zero and then making the necessary exchanges in the columns to the right. Thus in

$$804$$
$$-\ 347$$

there is no ten available to exchange for 10 ones. Hence we exchange one of the 8 hundreds for 10 tens, and one of these tens for 10 ones, which means that we have changed the minuend to read

$$700 + 90 + 14.$$

To prepare pupils for this type of thinking we practice renaming a number so as to have "no empty column" or no zero. Thus 60 becomes $50 + 10$; 207 becomes $100 + 100 + 7$ or perhaps $100 + 90 + 17$; 300 becomes $200 + 90 + 10$, etc. After such practice, the method of rethinking the number (or number name) can be taught in the following manner:

$$
\begin{array}{r}
804 \\
-\ 347 \\
\hline
\end{array}
\Rightarrow
\begin{array}{r}
700 + 90 + 14 \\
-\ 300 + 40 + \ 7 \\
\hline
400 + 50 + \ 7
\end{array}
$$

or

H	T	U
7	10	4
3	4	7

$$
\begin{array}{r}
804 \\
-\ 347 \\
\hline
\end{array}
\Rightarrow
$$

Similarly

500 − 276 becomes

H	T	U
4	9	10
2	7	6
2	2	4

or we can think 400, 90, 10, for 500.

The extension to numbers of four or more digits requires no new knowledge. All that is required is a greater span of attention and memory. Thus a problem 40,003 − 7489 is thought of as

ten thousands	thousands	hundreds	tens	units
3	9	9	9	13
	7	4	8	9

where ultimately the thinking is from the right to the left; that is, 13 − 9, 9 − 8, 9 − 4, 9 − 7, 3.

A suggested order of procedure and grade placement for teaching the subtraction algorism is as follows:

Grade 1. Subtracting a single-digit number from a two-digit number, with no exchange; for example,

$$
\begin{array}{r} 17 \\ -\ 4 \\ \hline \end{array}
\qquad
\begin{array}{r} 36 \\ -\ 5 \\ \hline \end{array}
$$

Grade 2. Subtracting a single- or two-digit number from a two-digit number, first with a regrouping of the minuend, then without regrouping; for example,

$$
\begin{array}{r} 37 \\ -\ 8 \\ \hline \end{array}
\qquad
\begin{array}{r} 43 \\ -\ 27 \\ \hline \end{array}
\qquad
\begin{array}{r} 48 \\ -\ 22 \\ \hline \end{array}
\qquad
\begin{array}{r} 40 \\ -\ 2 \\ \hline \end{array}
$$

Grade 3. Extending this to three- and four-digit numbers with exchange or regrouping through a place-value zero:

$$
\begin{array}{r} 368 \\ -\ 239 \\ \hline \end{array}
\qquad
\begin{array}{r} 322 \\ -\ 197 \\ \hline \end{array}
\qquad
\begin{array}{r} 504 \\ -\ 219 \\ \hline \end{array}
\qquad
\begin{array}{r} 8407 \\ -\ 3949 \\ \hline \end{array}
$$

Grade 4 on: Achieving adult-level performance with six- or seven-place numbers. In all grades problems involving subtraction should be constructed and solved by pupils. Beginning in Grade 2, problems involving both addition and/or subtraction (two-step problems) should be given. Note that in the entire process described above, at no time was the word "borrow" used. This word is not needed, nor does it contribute to understanding of the algorism.

4–6 OTHER SUBTRACTION ALGORISMS

The Austrian method of subtraction depends on the arithmetic property that, for any two given numbers a and b, where a is greater than or equal to b, and for any third number k, then

$$a - b = (a + k) - (b + k).$$

That is, if the minuend and subtrahend are both increased by the same number k, then the difference of the new numbers is the same as that of the given numbers. (This is easily demonstrated on a number line.)

Consider the example $67 - 39$. Since $7 - 9$ is impossible, we increase 67 by 10 and write $60 + 17$. To keep the difference the same, we increase 39 by 10 and write $40 + 9$. In the minuend we add 10 ones to the units place and in the subtrahend we add 1 ten to the tens place. Thus the problem is solved in the following steps:

$$
\begin{array}{c}
67 \\
- \ 39 \\
\hline
\end{array}
\Rightarrow
\begin{array}{c}
60 + 7 \\
- \ 30 + 9 \\
\hline
\end{array}
\Rightarrow
\begin{array}{c}
60 + 17 \\
- \ 40 + \ 9 \\
\hline
20 + \ 8 \\
\end{array}
\Rightarrow
\begin{array}{c}
\text{(Think 17)} \\
6 \quad 7 \\
- \ 3 \quad 9 \\
\hline
2 \quad 8 \\
\text{(Think 4)}
\end{array}
$$

At no time should we use any such language as "borrow 10 and give it to the 7. Pay it back to the 3 to make 4." There was no borrowing nor paying back, merely the same addition to each number.

For children of average and above-average aptitudes, this method can be made meaningful. However, many children find it difficult to understand why the difference $a - b$ is the same as $(a + k) - (b + k)$. However, if a child has been taught this Austrian method and understands it, he should be encouraged to use it and not learn the algorism previously explained in this chapter.

For any future work in mathematics it is necessary that the child has only one satisfactory algorism for an operation, not several of them.

If children have been taught the additive aspect of subtraction, that is, if when they are given $\Box + 6 = 9$, they can answer

$3 + 6 = 9$, then either of the above algorisms is carried out in the same way, only using different language. Consider the example

$$86 \\ -\ 49 .$$

Under the first algorism this is

$$16 - 9 = \square, \qquad 7 - 4 = \triangle.$$

Under the Austrian method it is

$$9 + \square = 16, \qquad 5 + \triangle = 8.$$

Other methods may be found in the references at the end of the chapter.

In column addition the pupil can check his first attempt by adding in the opposite direction. This gives rise to using combinations (facts) different from those used in the first addition. In subtraction, we can check by doing the process over again, but this may tend to repeat errors made in the first attempt. A better check is to use the fact that if $M - S = D$, then $M = D + S$ or

$$
\begin{array}{c}
M \\
-\ S \\
\hline
D
\end{array}
\ \Rightarrow\
\begin{array}{c}
D \\
+\ S \\
\hline
M
\end{array}
$$

Some persons prefer to write the check as a separate addition problem. However, this practice is of doubtful value, since more work is required in the check than in the actual subtraction. It would appear that children who desire to check their work (and such a desire should be encouraged) can do it in the worked example by adding the difference to the subtrahend, obtaining a sum that should equal the minuend, as indicated in the diagram.

$$
\text{Subtract}\
\begin{array}{ccc}
8 & 3 & 2 \\
-\ 4 & 7 & 9 \\
\hline
3 & 5 & 3
\end{array}
\ +\ \text{Check by adding}
$$

Children who have no desire to check usually do not. They merely write the addition by placing the numbers in a new order.

4–7 APPROXIMATION; MENTAL ADDITION AND SUBTRACTION

In contemporary books on mathematics for the elementary schools the symbols ' >' and ' <' are appearing. These are read:

$$>\qquad \text{and} \qquad <$$
$$\text{is greater than} \qquad\qquad \text{is less than.}$$

Thus '3 > 1' and '5 < 6' are true statements.

These symbols denote the idea of *order*, a concept very important for children to understand. Before introducing the symbols, the teacher should give much practice in using the verbal phrases 'is less than' and 'is greater than', and synonyms for these phrases, in practical situations: the number of pupils *is less than* the number of seats; the amount of money *is more than* we need; and so on. When, and if, the symbols are introduced they should be used frequently thereafter through the school years, so that the symbols take on real mathematical significance. The danger lies in introducing symbols which are seldom if ever needed for the next few years of study. The symbols ' <' and ' >' can play an important role in mathematical learning only if they provide an efficient way of communicating a concept that is in continual use after it has been learned. It should be noted that the idea conveyed by 'is more than' is easier for young children to understand than the idea conveyed by 'is less than', the reason probably being that an excess is visible whereas a deficit is not. The teacher should bear this in mind, and should act accordingly.

An application of the inequality (order) relations arises in rounding a number to the nearest number of tens (hundreds, thousands, etc.). This is usually spoken of as "rounding to the nearest ten," and so on. "Rounding to the nearest ten" is a unary operation, for it assigns to any given number the multiple of ten nearest to this number. To teach the process, we use a number scale (or line).

$$\begin{array}{ccccccccccc}
20 & 21 & 22 & 23 & 24 & 25 & 26 & 27 & 28 & 29 & 30
\end{array}$$

On such a scale it is easy to visualize by distances that 26 is closer to 30 than it is to 20. But we also know this fact because 26 − 20 is 6, while 30 − 26 = 4. Thus the difference (larger number −

smaller number) is least with the number 30. We then say: "To the nearest number of tens, 26 is closer to 30. Rounding off 26 to the nearest number of tens gives 30." Then children are asked to repeat the same process for 28, 21, 24, and finally 25, which raises a new question.

Since 25 is just as much greater than 20 as it is less than 30, it is not nearer to 30 than it is to 20. We could round it off to either 20 or 30 and be correct. It is desirable, however, to have a rule so that only one of these numbers is selected. Although several rules exist, we shall use the one in general use in elementary school, namely:

If a numeral has a '5' in the units place, we round the number off to the next higher ten.

Hence 25 is rounded off to 30, 55 to 60, and so on.

In the first half of the twentieth century, mental arithmetic was usually conceived of as the ability to make calculations rapidly without the use of pencil and paper. Today we do not emphasize speed. We think of mental arithmetic as the ability to mentally arrive at an approximate or an exact result through the use of the properties of number and the decimal system of numeration. We shall discover that a mental algorism is frequently different from a written algorism.

Finding an approximate sum or difference mentally (i.e., *estimating answers*) occurs in everyday life, in industry, in science, and in business, far more frequently than finding such sums or differences by written processes. Thus all children should begin early (in the first grade) and continue throughout their life to practice and use mental approximations. *About* how much should the answer be? Is it more than 10? Is it less than 20? Is it *between* 10 and 20? Is it as much as 100? And so forth. In the early grades, a child's approximation to a result can serve as a partial check on his written work in mathematics. After a child has learned to round off, he is ready to do mental approximations in a structured manner.

As a first approach consider the sum 33 + 44. The pupil is asked to round off each number mentally. He says 30 + 40. About how much is 33 and 44? About 70. More or less? More. Why? Because 33 is greater than 30 and 44 is greater than 40;

therefore $33 + 44$ is greater than $30 + 40$. In symbols we may write

$$30 < 33$$
$$40 < 44$$
$$\overline{30 + 40 < 33 + 44}$$

We do not attempt to build a theory of inequalities, only an intuitive idea that when the lesser numbers are added, the sum is less than the sum of the greater numbers.

After a little practice on this type of problem, we pose one of the type $33 + 48$. Here $30 < 33$ and $50 > 48$. Again the sum is approximately 80. Greater or less? We cannot tell until we consider the units which we rounded off. Well, what did we do? Since 33 is 3 greater than 30, and 48 is 2 less than 50, we have 1 greater than 80, or 81. Good, then 80 is the approximate sum, and 81 is the exact sum. We practice a number of these examples.

Now the pupils are prepared to do exact mental addition. In this algorism they add the numbers of tens first, then the ones, and then combine the two partial sums, a process quite different from the written algorism. Consider $36 + 47$. The child thinks: $30 + 40$ is 70 (hold this in my mind) $6 + 7$ is 13. 70 (recalled) plus 13 is 83. If a child attempts to imagine in his mind's eye

$$\frac{36}{47}$$

and then to mentally place a 3 under the ones column, he should be stopped, for such imagery will impede, rather than aid, mental calculations.

This process of approximation and exact mental calculation can be extended to three-digit numbers. A first approximation is to round off to hundreds, then a second approximation to tens. Thus, $260 + 490$ is approximately $300 + 500$ or 800. (Less than 800. Why?) Similarly, $320 + 570$ is approximately $300 + 600$ or 900. Less or more? We consider 20 more and 30 less, and we get 10 less than 900, or exactly 890. This leads finally to finding the sum of $463 + 379$ exactly as follows: $400 + 300$ is 700 (remember), $60 + 70$ is 130 (recall 700); we now have 830 (remember, it is 830), and $3 + 9$ is 12. The sum is 842. At the end of the fourth grade most children should be able to determine mentally that $4.63 and $3.79 is $8.42.

A similar procedure should be developed for subtraction. First let us consider 83 — 31. Rounding off, this becomes 80 — 30, or 50. Further practice on this type may be followed by 78 — 22, which becomes 80 — 20 or 60. After a number of problems of this type we turn to exact results. Again we do not develop a theory of inequalities but merely an explanation by using the decimal system of notation and rounding off. Thus 83 — 31 is about 50. More or less? We must consider the units. Since 83 is 3 more than 80 and 31 is 1 more than 30, we have 2 more units; hence 83 — 31 is 52. Consider 78 — 41. Approximately it is 80 — 40 or 40. But 78 is 2 less than 80 and 41 is 1 more than 40; thus the difference is 3 less than 40, or 37. This gives further practice in realizing that if a minuend decreases and the subtrahend increases, the difference will decrease.

In going to larger numbers, such as 2350 + 5268, there is little value in demanding exact results. To round off to the nearest thousand, for example,

$$2000 + 5000 = 7000,$$

or at most the nearest hundred, such as

$$2400 + 5300 = 7700,$$

is sufficient. Similarly, 6246 — 5981 should be rounded off to 6200 — 6000 = 200. If exact answers are required, paper-and-pencil procedures are practically as fast as mental calculations.

At points determined by the course of study he is following, a child should be able to make statements analogous to those which follow (for both addition and subtraction), and at a somewhat later time, he should be able to write them in mathematical symbols.

a) Thirty-eight plus forty-three is approximately (about) eighty.

$$38 + 43 \approx 80$$

b) Fifty-three plus twenty-two is greater than seventy.

$$53 + 22 > 70$$

c) Twenty-nine plus sixty-eight is less than one hundred.

$$29 + 68 < 100$$

d) Forty-five plus twelve is greater than fifty. It is less than sixty. It is between fifty and sixty.

$$45 + 12 > 50, \qquad 45 + 12 < 60, \qquad 50 < 45 + 12 < 60$$

The value of mental arithmetic lies both in the satisfaction it gives the pupils and in the establishment in their minds of interrelations of numbers expressed in the decimal system of notation. If we are careful not to stress *speed*, but to stress unhurried calm, recall and storage (memory), procedures for computing, and deliberateness in arriving at results, then we shall be developing the characteristics for successful study of all the mathematics to come in the years ahead of the child.

EXERCISES

1. What is an algorism? Must it be written? State at least three different algorisms for subtraction, giving a mathematical explanation for each algorism; state what final adult-level performance is expected.

2. The addition algorism can be developed by using sets with or without a pocket chart, by using the extended form of notation, and by reasoning from the properties of number and addition. Describe each of these methods and tell how you would use any or all of them in teaching addition.

3. What is the difference between an expression of an addition, and an expression involving only the operation of addition? How do you interpret '63 + 24 + 38'? How do you interpret

$$
\begin{array}{r}
63 \\
24 \quad ? \\
+\ 38 \\
\hline
\end{array}
$$

4. What is the meaning of a "crutch" in an algorism? Should the use of "crutches" be encouraged or discouraged? Consider the result of combining by addition a set of twenty numbers of the type $2.68, $21.54, etc. Would you use a "crutch" in finding this sum? Why or why not?

5. The subtraction algorism can be developed by using sets with or without a pocket chart, by using extended notation and rewriting the minuend, and by rationalization of the properties of the system of

numeration and the subtraction operation. Describe how you would use any (or all) of these methods in teaching subtraction.

6. In the margin is an algorism for subtraction:

$$\begin{array}{r} 882 \\ -\ 457 \\ \hline 425 \end{array}$$

   a) What must I add to 7 to obtain 10? Answer: 3

   b) Add 3 to 2 and place 5 in the units column.

   c) What must I add to 6 to obtain 10? Answer: 4

   d) Add 4 to 8, which is 12; place 2 in the tens column

   e) What must I add to 5 to obtain 10? Answer: 5

   f) Add 5 to 9, which is 14; place 4 in the hundreds column.

   From this description find how much was really added to each number (the minuend and the subtrahend) and explain how and why the method works. Would you teach this method in elementary school?

7. What is expanded notation? Which of the following is (are) expanded notation?

$$874 = 800 + 70 + 4,$$
$$874 = 8 \times 10^2 + 7 \times 10 + 4,$$
$$874 = 8 \text{ hundreds, 7 tens, 4 ones,}$$

$$874 = \begin{array}{c|c|c} H & T & U \\ \hline 8 & 7 & 4 \end{array},$$

$$874 = 700 + 160 + 14.$$

   In your answer tell how you conceive of a "hundred"; that is, as a set, or as a number of a set.

8. What does *readiness* signify to you as a psychological aspect of learning? List a number of readiness activities which you would engage in as preparatory to learning the algorisms of addition and subtraction.

9. Discuss the relative merits of using the symbols '>' and '<' in mathematical statements as compared with using only the words "is greater than" and "is less than." Explain why for addition '$a < b$ and $c < d$' implies that '$a + c < b + d$', while for subtraction '$a < b$ and $c < d$' does not imply that '$a - c < b - d$'. Describe the difficulties that arise in teaching when one uses these inequality symbols combined with the operational symbols.

10. What is mental arithmetic? Illustrate what is meant by rounding off a number. Outline and discuss a possible program in mental arithmetic for the second grade.

11. Discuss the importance of estimating answers to numerical problems and exercises. Choose one instructional level and give examples of the estimating you would expect pupils at that level to do.

REFERENCES

BELL, C., C. HAMMOND, and R. HERRERA, *Fundamentals of Arithmetic for Teachers*, New York: John Wiley, 1962, pages 38–56, 78–90

NATIONAL COUNCIL OF TEACHERS OF MATHEMATICS, *Topics in Mathematics for Elementary School Teachers*. Twenty-Ninth Yearbook, 1964, pages 133–153

NEUREITER, P., "The 'Ultimate' Form of the Subtraction Algorism," *The Arithmetic Teacher* **12,** 4, April 1965, pages 277–281

SAUSJORD, G., "What Is the Complementary Method of Subtraction?" *The Arithmetic Teacher* **10,** 5, May 1963, pages 262–267

multiplication
of
cardinal numbers

Of the four common operations on whole numbers, addition and multiplication are considered the two fundamental ones. The principal reason for this is that these two operations are always possible within the set of whole numbers. That is, for each ordered pair of whole numbers, there exists a whole-number sum and a whole-number product. This is not true for subtraction and division; no whole-number difference or whole-number quotient can be found for $3 - 7$ or $3 \div 7$, for example. In extended number systems which include the rational numbers, both positive and negative, all four operations exist on any ordered pair of numbers except for division by zero. Since every subtraction example can be changed to an equivalent addition example and every division example can be changed to an equivalent multiplication example, addition and multiplication are usually regarded as the fundamental operations. It must be emphasized, right at the start, that multiplication is completely different from addition, and in fact could be taught without any reference to addition. For (5, 3) the sum is 8, and for (5, 3) the product is 15, so surely something entirely different from finding a sum dictates how we find a product.

5–1 THE CONCEPT AND LANGUAGE OF MULTIPLICATION

The mathematical meaning of multiplication is derived from analogous operations on sets. The simplest model is that of an

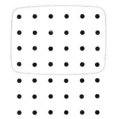

array of rows and columns of objects (chairs, people, checkerboard squares, and so on). In the diagram each row of dots has the same number, 6. Suppose that we wish to find the product 6 × 4: We operate on the number of dots in this row by a number 4, which tells us to form the union of four sets, each a 6-set. The union is indicated by enclosing the rows in a closed curve. By counting, we find that the number of the union of four 6-sets is 24. The corresponding operation in arithmetic is to abstract the numbers from the set operation and say "6 multiplied by 4 is 24." Here 6 is the operand, called a *multiplicand*, 4 is the operator, called a *multiplier*, and 24 is the result, called a *product*. Both the multiplier and the multiplicand are *factors* of the product. Summarizing, we say:

> The number of the union of *n* sets each having *m* members is the product of *m* by *n* (*m* × *n*).

Note that when we say "6 multiplied by 4," we mean that 6 is the operand and 4 is the multiplier.

The symbol generally used to signify the operation of multiplication is '×'. The usual verbalization of this word in elementary school is "times." When this interpretation is given to the symbol, that is, when we say

6 times 4   (operator × operand),

then 6 is the operator and 4 is the operand; we have an entirely different interpretation from

6 multiplied by 4   (operand × operator).

The word 'times' causes confusion at the start, since many children interpret '2 times 5' to mean that 2 is the size of each set and that there are 5 of them, and that "2 has been timesed by 5." However, the accepted meaning for '2 times 5' is that 2 operates on 5, and that 2 sets, each of size 5, form a union of size 10.

It might be well if the "times" language were never introduced, since it makes the symbols for a multiplication the only ones the children have to "read backward." Some of the new textbooks are not using it for this reason. However, it does have certain advantages, and it is widely used. When teachers use the language 'times' and 'multiplied by', they should know which numeral refers to the operator and which to the operand and express the operation accordingly in any work they do with a class. Since multiplication is commutative, it is not a serious matter if a child gets an occasional example "turned around."

One can form a similar concept of multiplication by studying the replacement of each element of a given set by equivalent sets. The union of the equivalent sets is the product set and the number of the replacement set has been multiplied by the number of elements in the given set. The diagram shows a set of 3 buns. Each bun has been replaced by its price, a set of 12 pennies. The set thus obtained is a product set of 36 pennies. We say

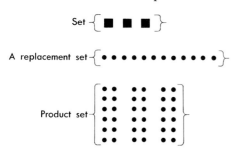

12 multiplied by 3 is 36

or

3 times 12 is 36.

These two statements express the same situation. This replacement concept of multiplication is used very widely in business, science, and everyday life.

The two concepts mentioned above are sufficient for all ordinary purposes of elementary school teaching. Another concept—useful in graphing and probability theory—will be discussed in Chapter 15, under the heading of enrichment study. The essential thing for the teacher to remember is that ultimately we move away from sets to pure arithmetic. In multiplication we are given two numbers, an operand and an operator; which comes first depends on whether the teacher reads '×' as "times" (operator first) or as "multiplied by" (operand first); the product is a number which can be obtained from a model by counting, or by addition.

5–2 DEVELOPING THE CONCEPT WITH CHILDREN

Children have already counted by twos, or by fives, and can tell that counting 5 twos yields 10. They know that if there are 4 teams with 5 members on each team, then there are 4 groups of 5 players and this is 20 players. The job of the teacher is to transform all this acquired knowledge, along with new situations, into the concept and language of multiplication.

While 'times' is an acceptable word in elementary arithmetic, it must be used correctly if it is used at all. Since children tend to imitate the teacher's language, they may be doing multiplication with extraordinary notions about it, unless the teacher's language expresses a correct concept of multiplication. Some poor language occurring in textbooks and used by teachers is shown in the following illustrations:

a) Multiplication is repeating a number so many times, so 5 times 4 is 4 repeated 5 times! What does this mean? How is 4 repeated? Is it written '44444'? Here the digit '4' is repeated 5 times. How does one repeat a number? This language is ambiguous and nonmathematical.

b) Multiplication shows how many times you take a number. Then 5 times 4 is 4 taken 5 times! Where is 4 taken? How do you take it? What do you do with 4 after you take it? This is really nonmathematical terminology.

c) Multiplication shows how many times a number is used. How is the number used? If it is used, what is left? This manner of speaking is certainly no explanation.

d) Multiplication shows how many times a number is added to itself. Thus 5×4 is 4 added to itself 5 times. What does this mean? Does it mean $4 + 4, 4 + 4, 4 + 4, 4 + 4, 4 + 4$? Of course not! Does it mean $4 + 4 + 4 + 4 + 4 + 4$, where there are 5 additions? No, it does not. Multiplication should not be *defined* in terms of addition.

When we try to get the word "times" in the proper place we discuss its meaning with the children. Thus if an apple costs 4 pennies, we ask how much 3 apples would cost.

$$\bigcirc \text{ is a cent}$$
$$n\{\bigcirc \ \bigcirc \ \bigcirc \ \bigcirc\} = \text{cost of 1.}$$

$$\begin{matrix}\text{Union of} \\ \text{three} \\ \text{sets}\end{matrix} \quad n\left\{\begin{matrix}\bigcirc \ \bigcirc \ \bigcirc \ \bigcirc \\ \bigcirc \ \bigcirc \ \bigcirc \ \bigcirc \\ \bigcirc \ \bigcirc \ \bigcirc \ \bigcirc\end{matrix}\right\} = \text{cost of 3.}$$

The answer "3 times as much" leads to the question, "as much as what?" "As much as one apple costs" leads to "3 times 4 (cents)." Thus the children can sense that 3 is an operator or multiplier which operates on 4, so as to produce 12 (cents). In this way, 4 is the operand; it tells the number which is multiplied. This is illustrated by the union of 3 sets each containing 4 cents.

A few varied examples of this type will enable children to discover the multiplication facts for themselves. If the "times" language is used to introduce multiplication, then the use of "multiplied by" should be delayed until a firm concept of multiplication has been achieved. It will then be a simple matter to recognize that "6 multiplied by 4" is another way of saying "4 times 6," so of course the result in both cases is 24.

In discovering the facts, children make use of the commutative principle intuitively without using the word or an explicit rule. The use of an array of dots or crosses on a board, chairs in a room, or children lined up for marching exhibit the principle. Children are shown an array and asked what they see. Some may say they see 5 three-sets, while others may say they see 3 five-sets. In each case, the product is 15. By induction from an appropriate number of examples, children agree that the order in which two numbers are multiplied does not affect the product. Hence, when they discover one multiplication fact involving two (different) numbers, they also have another fact at hand.

At first children discover the facts, and write them as

$$5 \times 3 = 15 \quad \text{or} \quad \begin{array}{r} 3 \\ \times\ 5 \\ \hline 15 \end{array} \quad \text{and also} \quad 3 \times 5 = 15 \quad \text{or} \quad \begin{array}{r} 5 \\ \times\ 3 \\ \hline 15 \end{array}.$$

They should read both the '=' and the bar in the vertical example as "is." They should be encouraged to remember the facts they discover for future use the rest of their lives. They should find illustrations of how mother and father use these facts every day. To aid the retention, we systematize the facts into a table. *The children should construct the table* and not have it given to them. The table is filled in in the right-hand column, first taking the tens table; that is, 1×10, 2×10, 3×10, or 10×1, 10×2, . . . , depending on how the '$\times$' is read. Here the multiplicand is the name of the table. Children already know these as 10, 20, 30, etc. But now they also know the commutative facts ($10 \times 2 = 2 \times 10 = 20$, etc.) and therefore they can fill in another row, the bottom one.

Now they can fill the ones table (left column) and the commutative facts (top row). The ones table and its commutative table should be stressed as a multiplication in which 1 behaves in the manner that 0 does for addition, namely $a \times 1 = a$ and $a + 0 = a$, where 'a' can be replaced by any numeral. Since most children learn to count by fives, the next-easiest table to fill in is the fives table.

TABLE 5–1 $a \times b$

Multiplicand, b

×	1	2	3	4	5	6	7	8	9	10
1	1	2	3	4	5	6	7	8	9	10
2	2	4			10				18	20
3	3		9		15				27	30
4	4			16	20					40
5	5	10	15	20	25	30	35	40	45	50
6	6				30					60
7	7				35					70
8	8				40					80
9	9				45					90
10	10	20	30	40	50	60	70	80	90	100

Multiplier, a

When this is done, the table appears as Table 5–1, and children will sense that there is not too much more to learn. As a rule, the next tables are those for two, three, and four, with their commutative facts. When this is accomplished, there is no reason not to go ahead and learn (fill in) the remaining 16 facts which are missing in the lower right-hand open square of the table.

Children can reinforce their grasp on facts they have already discovered and can figure out new facts by using facts they know and applying the associative or distributive principles, as well as the commutative principle. For example, if a child knows that $4 \times 6 = 24$ and that $2 \times 4 = 8$, he should be able to reason that 8×6 should be twice as much as 4×6. That is,

$$8 \times 6 = (2 \times 4) \times 6 = 2 \times (4 \times 6),$$

so that $8 \times 6 = 2 \times 24 = 48$. (Doubling is easy. He is not consciously contending with a two-digit factor.) This is an application of the associative principle, but the child does not need to have heard of a principle in order to use it informally any more than he needs to have heard of gravity in order to be able to fall down. After he has filled in '48' for 8×6 he can write another '48' for 6×8. Similarly, if he knows that $9 \times 5 = 45$ and $9 \times 2 = 18$, he can draw arrays of dots, if necessary, to see that

$$9 \times 5 + 9 \times 2 = 9 \times (5 + 2) = 9 \times 7,$$

so that $9 \times 7 = 45 + 18 = 63$. This is an application of the distributive principle, but no mention of the principle need be made at this time. Since $9 \times 7 = 7 \times 9$, he can write 63 in two places in the table. Other new facts may be discovered, or old facts may be reinforced, in the same ways or in other ways the child may invent. This last possibility should be strongly encouraged. Its results are totally unpredictable, and the teacher must be able to judge whether a procedure invented by a child is correct. The child should not be obliged to justify it in any formal way; he should have some sort of "commonsense" explanation.

Once the table is complete, we drill or practice all the facts, by written exercises, by using games devised for the purpose, or orally until recall is almost automatic. If the more able children have learned all the facts, they can study the table to discover relations in the table. For instance, the main diagonal numbers are square numbers. Why? Each entry in the nines column has digits whose sum is 9. Why? The table is symmetric about the main diagonal. Why? But all these activities are merely enrichment, to be taken up after the facts have been learned.

5–3 PREPARING FOR THE ALGORISM

To do any subsequent computation, children need learn the multiplication facts only to 9×9. However, for convenience, it is easy to learn the facts to 10×10. Further, children must eventually know how to multiply any number, no matter how many digits in its numerals, by 10, 20, . . . , 90, 100, 200, . . . , 900,

1000, 2000, . . . and so on. The first step is to learn how to multiply by 10. This can be done by (a) reference to numeration, (b) simple reasoning, (c) reference to sets, (d) actual manipulation of members of sets.

By the middle of the third grade, children have learned numeration to 1000, or to 10,000. Now we make a study of the numerals in which the units place has a zero. The numbers we treat first are 10, 20, . . . , 90, and each can be expressed by '1 × 10' or '10 × 1', '2 × 10' or '10 × 2', . . . , '9 × 10' or '10 × 9'. The next number is 100, which is expressed by '10 × 10'. Then '110' becomes '11 × 10', '120' becomes '12 × 10', '230' becomes '23 × 10', and '970' becomes '97 × 10'. By comparing the numeral for the first factor with that for the product, the child can discover the pattern for the shortcut for multiplying by 10.

Children, and frequently teachers, have stated this rule as "put a zero after the number," or "add a zero to the number." Of course they mean 'numeral' instead of 'number', but even with this evident meaning both statements are bad, the first because "put" is not an operation, and the second because it is incorrect. The important concept is: When we multiply a number by 10, we obtain the numeral for the product by moving each digit in the numeral for the number one place to the left and writing a '0' in the units place. Although this principle is learned by induction, some practice in reading numerals in terms of the number of tens is frequently helpful. Thus '234' is '23 tens and 4' (230 + 4). It could also be read as '2 hundreds and 34' (200 + 34). This type of interpretation of a numeral increases the understanding of the decimal system of notation.

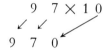

Another approach to multiplication by 10 can be made by reference to sets or by the actual use of sets, the latter only if needed. A number such as 23 may refer to 2 ten-sets and 3 one-sets. Now if we multiply the number by 10, each element of each set is replaced by 10 new elements. This is shown in the second picture of the diagram in the margin. Now, following past procedures, we can replace a set of 10 elements in any column by 1 element in the column to the left. This exchange gives us the 2 hundred-sets and 3 ten-sets. The units column is now empty. This state is indicated by the numeral '230' at the bottom. When they compare this result with the first picture, pupils will then be able to frame a rule for the position which the numerals will occupy in the product.

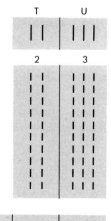

By pure reasoning we can say that multiplying a number by 10 gives a product in which each *one*, each *ten*, each *hundred*, ..., of the given number has been increased to 10 ones for each one, 10 tens for each ten, 10 hundreds for each hundred, and so on. Thus, for 23, the 2 tens become 2 hundreds and the 3 ones become 3 tens and $10 \times 23 = 230$.

This reasoning can be further justified by the distributive law, which will be introduced shortly. The next step after multiplying by 10 is to be able to multiply by 20, 30, ..., 90. To accomplish this we must develop the associative principle for multiplication. In this connection, it is useful to speak of a numerical expression.

> A numerical expression is a numeral, or a combination of numerals and operation signs, which is meaningful.

Thus '3', '5', '142', are numerical expressions. So are '3 + 5', '8 − 2', and '5 × 3', for they are meaningful combinations of numerals and operation signs. By this time the child knows that '3 + 2 + 5' is a numerical expression, for it means (3 + 2) + 5 or 3 + (2 + 5). Recall that the parentheses indicate the first addition, and this sum is to be combined with the remaining number by addition.

We now try to *decide on* a meaning for numerical expressions of the type '2 × 3 × 4'. Of course, such an expression has no meaning until we give it one. It could mean "find 2 × 3, then find 2 × 4, and then add or multiply the results," but it is not given this meaning. Taking the cue from addition, already learned, the children are encouraged to accept the definition:

'2 × 3 × 4'   means   (2 × 3) × 4,   which is   6 × 4   or   24.

(The parentheses tell us to find a product and use it with the remaining number to find another product.)

After children have worked a number of these examples, they should be asked to explore the relation between (2 × 3) × 4 and 2 × (3 × 4) and a number of similar examples. This leads to the general rule (not proved, but accepted intuitively) that in an expression involving two multiplications, you can begin by multiplying either the first two numbers, or the second and third numbers, and then perform the second multiplication. The value of the expression is the same either way you do it. Pretty soon the children also discover the generalized "any-order" principle, that you can start by multiplying any two of the numbers, and multiply that product by the remaining number. (With more than three factors, the "any-order" principle justifies multiplying in any order you please, so long as you use each indicated factor exactly one time.)

It is now easy to multiply any number by 20, 30, and so on. How can we find 8×20? Change the problem to multiplication by 10. How? 20 is 2×10; hence

$$8 \times 20 = 8 \times (2 \times 10) = (8 \times 2) \times 10 = 16 \times 10 = 160.$$

Again,

$$7 \times 90 = 7 \times (9 \times 10) = (7 \times 9) \times 10 = 63 \times 10 = 630.$$

Then 6×80 becomes 6×8 multiplied by 10, or 480. A little practice, and now all but one principle has been mastered: the *distributive principle*.

The distributive principle is one of the most important in all subsequent mathematics and its first informal and intuitive presentation should be correct and impressive.

Consider an array of chairs, pupils, or soldiers lined up as shown in the diagram. How can we find how many there are altogether? There are a number of ways to do this. Let us investigate this problem with the pupils' help. First we note that, in a row, there are $4 + 5$ items. But there are 6 rows. How can we find the total number? $6 \times (4 + 5)$ is 6×9, which is 54. But how many are in the squad to the left? 6×4. And to the right? 6×5. Then, from these two products, how can we find how many? Add $6 \times 4 + 6 \times 5$. Thus we see that

$$6 \times (4 + 5) \qquad \text{is the same as} \qquad 6 \times 4 + 6 \times 5.$$

We say that a number which multiplies a sum may be used as a multiplier of each of the addends, and each of these products is called a *partial product*. The product is the sum of the partial products. The above description is based on the assumption that '×' means 'times'. If we made '×' mean 'multiplied by', then we would write

$$(4 + 5) \times 6 = 4 \times 6 + 5 \times 6.$$

Generally at this stage we need make no distinction between the two meanings of the symbol '×', for commutativity has already been accepted.

Children should practice examples of the above type, and give set illustrations until the principle is an inherent part of computational procedures. Care must be taken to avoid the erroneous idea that $6 \times (4 + 5)$ is $6 \times 4 + 5$. The practice should be extended to $4 \times (10 + 4)$, $6 \times (30 + 7)$, and so on, so as to make use of all previous knowledge.

5–4 THE ALGORISM OF MULTIPLICATION

The first formal algorism to be taught is of the form

$$
\begin{array}{r}
37 \\
\times\ \ 8 \,. \\
\hline
\end{array}
$$

That is, we want to find the product of a two-digit number multiplied by a single-digit number. If children are permitted to study the way to do this, they can relate this problem to all their previous activities in multiplication. Various suggestions may come forth. For example, this problem means

a) $8 \times (30 + 7)$, which is $8 \times 30 + 8 \times 7 = 240 + 56$, which is 296.

b) $8 \times (7 + 30)$, which is $8 \times 7 + 8 \times 30 = 56 + 240$, which is 296.

c) 37 is to be multiplied by 8.

This last suggestion means that there are 8 groups of things, with 37 in each group. The group can be thought of as 30 things joined to 7 things. Then altogether there are $8 \times 30 + 8 \times 7$, which is $240 + 56$ things.

Suggestion (b) leads most directly into the algorism we wish to teach the children to master, so we work with it temporarily as follows:

$$\begin{array}{r} 37 \\ \times \quad 8 \\ \hline 56 \\ +\ 240 \\ \hline 296 \end{array} \rightarrow \begin{array}{r} 7 \\ \times \quad 8 \\ \hline 56 \end{array} + \begin{array}{r} 30 \\ \times \quad 8 \\ \hline 240 \end{array} \Rightarrow 56 + 240 \Rightarrow 296.$$

The two products, 56 and 240, are called partial products, and their *sum* is the product. After children understand the explanation, they can practice for a day or two on the form at the left. Slow pupils might work on it for a longer time. However, this is not the most efficient form of developing a more extended algorism. The next step is to do some mental work to shorten the written part of the algorism.

For this purpose we again resort to the meaning of a decimal numeral. Children know that '56' is '5 × 10 + 6 × 1'. They also know that '8 × 30' is '(8 × 3) × 10' and they can agree to speak of '*n* × 10' as '*n* tens'. So we learn to write the answer (product) in one line, by doing the addition of the partial products mentally. This requires a complex operation of storing a number in the memory compartment of the brain, then doing a second multiplication, recalling the number stored in the brain, doing a mental addition, and writing the rest of the numeral that tells what the product is.

Given much practice with the relatively immature algorism just described, and perhaps a little prodding, some children will discover a shortcut. Others will not. In any case, we usually do not wish to spend several months working with this particular algorism, so we develop the shortcut with the class. We use a place-value chart, resorting, if necessary, to a pocket chart with physical objects for tallies.

When children work with "long multiplication," they have a built-in place-value chart for every example if they do their work on lined paper held sideways. Since proper vertical alignment of the figures in the partial products is almost essential in computing the correct product, it is wise to use this simple device for a long time when children are just learning the algorisms for multiplying multidigit factors.

Before we proceed to the development of the mature algorism, (shortcut), it is well to review how a number expressed as "so many tens" or "so many hundreds" would appear in a place-value chart. As an example, 23 tens and 41 hundreds would appear as shown below. Do several such examples.

Th	H	T	0
	2	3	0
4	1	0	0

Then write the example you plan to use twice on the chalkboard. Draw vertical lines and label the columns for place value. Do the example the old way, and show, step by step, how the new way is a procedure for streamlining the old.

H	T	0
	3	7
	×	8
	5	6
2	4	0
2	9	6

For 8 × 37, the first step is: 7 × 8 = 56. Write '6' in the ones place of the product and store the 5 in the mind (remember that it refers to 5 × 10 and write '5' above the '3' in the tens column so that we can see it while we discuss this). The next step is to say that 8 × 30 is 24 × 10. Recall the 5 × 10 and then you have 29 × 10. Write this as '29' (tens) to the left of the '6' in the product. Why can we add the 5 to 24 to get 29 here? Because by the distributive principle,

$$5 \times 10 + 24 \times 10 = (5 + 24) \times 10 = 29 \times 10, \text{ which is } 290.$$

H	T	0
	⑤	
	3	7
	×	8
		6

And 290 + 6 = 296, so that when we write '29' beside the '6' we already have, the result is the numeral for 296. Be sure to emphasize, by comparing the two algorisms or by other explanations, that the 5 is not to be multiplied by 8, but that 5 tens are to be added to (8 × 3) tens. After the process is understood, the child finally drops thinking about 30 or 3 tens and, when he sees

$$\begin{array}{r} 37 \\ \times \quad 8 \\ \hline 296 \end{array}$$

he ultimately says: 8 × 7 is 56. Place '6' and remember '5'; 8 × 3 is 24; 24 plus 5 is 29; write '29' to the left of '6'. Answer: 296.

To remember the '5' is difficult for many children at first, so they should be allowed to write this "crutch" at the side, and

	3	7
×		8
2	9	6

scratch the '5' out after 5 has been added to 24; or they may write
the '5' above the '3' in '37', as suggested previously.

$$\begin{array}{r} 37 \;\; \cancel{5} \\ \times \;\; 8 \\ \hline 6 \end{array}$$

Treat seriously this development of the algorism for multiplying a two-digit number by a single-digit number because, once the
child thoroughly understands this algorism, the tail follows the
dog, so to speak, in algorisms for multiplying larger numbers.

The extension to multiplying a three-, four-, or five-digit
number by a single-digit number is now a relatively easy process.
First we establish a method of multiplying by 100, 200, 300, . . . ,
900, then by 1000, 2000, and so on. From what we know, it follows
that 8 × 100 is 800 and so is 100 × 8. We can also say that

$$8 \times 100 = 8 \times (10 \times 10) = 80 \times 10 = 800$$

by the multiplication-by-10 principle. Similarly,

$$200 \times 7 = 7 \times (20 \times 10) = (7 \times 20) \times 10 = 140 \times 10, \text{ or } 1400.$$

We can also use the rule for multiplying by 100 (learned just
previously) and write (or say)

$$200 \times 7 \quad \text{is} \quad (100 \times 2) \times 7 = 100 \times (2 \times 7) = 100 \times 14.$$

Using several ways to discover the rule gives better understanding.
The principle is that multiplication by 100 places each digit in the
numeral for the multiplicand two places to the left. A discussion
of what happens, for example, in the case of 201 × 400 will help
to generalize the process.

When we multiply 236 × 7 we first ask how we can find the
product. By this time, through imitation, recall, and understanding the decimal system of numeration, we expect to get the meaning

236 × 7 means $(200 + 30 + 6) \times 7$ or $200 \times 7 + 30 \times 7 + 6 \times 7.$

$$\begin{array}{r} 236 \\ 7 \\ \hline 42 \;\; \leftarrow 6 \times 7 \\ 210 \;\; \leftarrow 30 \times 7 \\ 1400 \;\; \leftarrow 200 \times 7 \\ \hline 1652 \end{array}$$

We write this at first in the form displayed above, but after a few examples it should be shortened to the form

$$236 \quad 6 \,④ \quad 3 \,② \qquad\qquad 2$$
$$\underline{7} \quad \underline{7} \quad \underline{7} \qquad\qquad \underline{7}$$
$$1652 \quad 42 \quad 21 + 4 = 25 \quad 14 + 2 = 16$$

and finally to: $7 \times 6 = 42$, write '2', retain '4'; $7 \times 3 = 21$, plus 4 is 25, write '5', retain '2'; 7×2 is 14, plus 2 is 16, write '16'; until the process is automatic. The extension to a product 2469×6 is merely a matter of a greater attention span.

A final activity in this multiplication is one of mental estimation, which demands the use of inequality relations. Again the symbols '$<$', read "less than," and '$>$', read "greater than," may be used, but it is doubtful that they add to the meaning of the situation; they merely serve as a more concise way of writing what we wish to say. Thus children readily agree that if 8 is less than 10, then 5×8 is less than 5×10, or $8 < 10 \Rightarrow 5 \times 8 < 5 \times 10$, where the symbol '$\Rightarrow$' may be read "implies." [Also '$\Rightarrow$' may be read "if . . . (the part which precedes the symbol), then . . . (the part which follows it)."] Similarly,

$$28 < 30 \Rightarrow 7 \times 28 < 7 \times 30.$$

Since 7×30 is a simple mental calculation it is easy to find an approximate answer to 7×28. The child's response is at first, "Since 28 is near to 30, 7×28 is near to 7×30, or 210." Similarly, since 23 is near to 20, 7×23 is near to 7×20, or 140.

The next step is to consider the order relation, that is, to consider whether the approximate product is more or less than the exact product, and to tell why. Thus 7×30 is more than 7×28, but 7×20 is less than 7×23; $210 > 7 \times 28$ but $140 < 7 \times 23$. After a number of these mental approximations, pupils who do well and like mental arithmetic can be encouraged to find the exact product mentally. Thus 7×28 is less than 7×30 or 210. How much less? Since 28 is two less than 30, and 7×2 is 14, 7×28 is 14 less than 210, so 7×28 is 196. Similarly, since 23 is 3 greater than 20, 7×23 is 7×3 or 21 greater than 140, so 7×23 is 161.

Of course, there are other possible ways to make such mental calculations. For example, 23 is 2 less than 25, hence 7×23 is 14 less than 175. However, rationalizations made on the decimal construction of the numeral are the procedures that give greatest mathematical insight. The extension to 8×243 includes first rounding to the nearest hundred and then thinking:

8×243 is approximately 8×200 or 1600 (but quite a bit more.)

Next we can round to the nearest ten and $8 \times 243 > 8 \times 240$. The latter is $1600 + 8 \times 40$, that is, $1600 + 320$ or 1920. Hence $8 \times 243 > 1920$, but pretty close to it. How close? 8×3 or 24. Hence, mentally, 8×243 is $8 \times 200 + 8 \times 40 + 8 \times 3$, or 1944. Note that in this mental multiplication the operations are usually performed in an order—highest place value to units place value—which is opposite to that of the written algorism.

When we are learning any computational algorism, drill or practice is essential. It used to be the custom, when algorisms were being taught, to lay much stress on *doing* the work. Today we stress equally the rationale, or mathematical reasons, underlying the procedure; we explain *why* and we *do*. Each of these two elements is essential. Some experimental programs and mathematicians are calling for a minimum stress on computation and more stress on the concepts involved. However, most people of today, and even of tomorrow, will need to be comfortably efficient in performing ordinary computations throughout every day of their lives. There is no evidence that they will carry machines with them to do these necessary computations, nor that they will learn concepts any better if their teachers do not stress computational skill. It is a necessary part of everyday usage for every citizen to be able, with unhurried calm, to carry out fundamental operational algorisms on whole numbers and fractions.

5–5 EXTENSION TO ADULT-LEVEL PERFORMANCE

The most important step in learning a multiplication algorism well enough to achieve an adult level of performance is to understand completely how one obtains the product of 2 two-digit numbers. When we follow the philosophy of using what we have already learned to learn more, a possible sequence of activities is the following:

a) Children are challenged to find the product of multiples of 10, for example, 30×50. Various methods may be suggested, but previous experience should indicate that

$$30 \times 50 = (10 \times 3) \times (10 \times 5),$$

which by the general principle of association of factors becomes

$$30 \times 50 = (3 \times 5) \times (10 \times 10),$$

which, in turn, is easily recognized as 1500. Similarly, 40×70 is $(4 \times 7) \times (10 \times 10)$, or 2800. This can be written in vertical form:

$$
\begin{array}{r}
30 \\
\times \quad 50 \\
\hline
1500
\end{array}
\qquad
\begin{array}{r}
40 \\
\times \quad 70 \\
\hline
2800
\end{array}
\qquad
\begin{array}{r}
70 \\
\times \quad 90 \\
\hline
6300
\end{array}
$$

b) Next we consider the product of any two-place number and a multiple of 10, for example, 27×30. By the same principle of association of factors, we analyze this as

$$27 \times (3 \times 10) = (27 \times 3) \times 10$$

and both indicated multiplications have already been learned. So we have

$$
\begin{array}{r}
27 \\
\times \quad 3 \\
\hline
81
\end{array}
\qquad
\begin{array}{r}
81 \\
\times \quad 10 \\
\hline
810
\end{array}
\qquad
\text{or, putting both op-}\atop\text{erations in one form,}
\qquad
\begin{array}{r}
27 \\
\times \quad 30 \\
\hline
810
\end{array}
$$

where the '0' in the units column of the product indicates multiplication by 10 and the '81' has been moved one place to the left. Thus pupils think "27×30 is 27×3, and the product multiplied by 10," but they place a '0' in the units column and then multiply 27 by 3. After practice on the two types above, pupils can proceed to the general product of any 2 two-digit numbers.

c) Consider

$$
\begin{array}{r}
26 \\
\times \quad 37 \\
\hline
\end{array}
\qquad \text{which we now write as} \qquad
\begin{array}{r}
\{20 + 6\} \\
\times \quad \{30 + 7\} \\
\end{array}
.
$$

We interpret the problem as 26 objects in a row with 37 rows, and the picture of the problem appears as shown. The partial products can easily be identified:

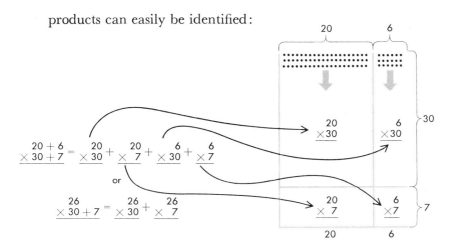

No matter which way we conceive of the problem—as four partial products or as two partial products—we already know how to find the product. For less-able students, perhaps the four partial products should be stressed first and then reduced to two. For the majority of students the method of two partial products is the most reasonable approach. Thus

$$\begin{array}{r} 26 \\ \times \quad 37 \\ \hline 182 \quad \leftarrow \quad 7 \times 26 \\ 780 \quad \leftarrow \quad 30 \times 26 \\ \hline 962 \quad \leftarrow \quad 37 \times 26 \end{array}$$

As a first lesson, some teachers prefer to write

$$\begin{array}{r} 26 \\ \times \quad 7 \\ \hline 182 \end{array} \qquad \begin{array}{r} 26 \\ \times \quad 30 \\ \hline 780 \end{array}$$

at the side and then place the partial products as shown. No matter which way is used, it is essential that the second partial product be represented by the complete numeral '780', not '78'.

If one uses a large card marked with equally spaced large dots in rows and columns, one can easily display the partial products by using long thin rods placed vertically and horizontally to indicate the partial products. Of course, the size of sets that can be illustrated this way is limited, and once pupils have recognized the partial products in the product, they practice to achieve skill, using an abbreviated procedure. Thus they say mentally: 8 times 6 is 48; write '8' (remember '4'); 8 × 3 is 24, plus 4 is 28, write '28'. Write '0' below the '8'; 6 × 6 is 36; write '6' (remember '3'); 6 × 3 is 18, plus 3 is 21. Write '21'. Now add. Product: 2448.

$$\begin{array}{r} 36 \\ \times \quad 68 \\ \hline 288 \\ 2160 \\ \hline 2448 \end{array}$$

At all times, however, pupils should be able to tell the reason behind each step of their work.

A very few teachers prefer to approach this multiplication through the formal use of the distributive law. Thus they first consider

26×37 as the number $(20 + 6)$ multiplied by $(30 + 7)$

and write

$$26 \times 37 = (20 + 6) \times (30 + 7).$$

Now considering $20 + 6$ as one number, by the distributive law, they obtain the expression

$$(20 + 6) \times 30 + (20 + 6) \times 7.$$

Again applying the distributive law to each of these terms, they obtain

$$20 \times 30 + 6 \times 30 + 20 \times 7 + 6 \times 7,$$

which gives the four partial products.

If a teacher desires only two partial products, he would write

$$26 \times (30 + 7) = 26 \times 30 + 26 \times 7,$$

and each of the latter products has a known algorism. The formal use of the distributive principle as a first approach is of questionable value to the child, either as an aid to understanding the operation or to gaining skill in computation. Whatever approach is used, the distributive principle is applied whether it is mentioned or not.

The extension to products of larger numbers is merely one of developing greater attention and retention, for no new principles are involved. The real educational value comes not from telling, but allowing pupils to suggest, to create, to discover, and to tell themselves how and why the algorism works. Thus, for example,

$$
\begin{array}{r}
268 \\
\times\ 47 \\
\hline
\end{array}
\Rightarrow
\begin{array}{r}
200 + 60 + 8 \\
\times\qquad 40 + 7 \\
\hline
\end{array}
\Rightarrow
$$

200	60	8	
200×40	60×40	8×40	40
200×7	60×7	8×7	7

Then 268 is multiplied by 7 (already learned) and 268 is multiplied

118

by 40, or (268 × 4) × 10, which is already learned. Thus

$$
\begin{array}{r}
268 \\
\times\quad 47 \\
\hline
1876 \leftarrow\ \ 7 \times 268 \\
10720 \leftarrow\ 40 \times 268 \\
\hline
12596 \leftarrow\ 47 \times 268 \\
\end{array}
$$

This type of multiplication is as complex as that most frequently encountered in social and business activities, but for mature performance the algorism is generally extended to include the following hierarchy:

a)   367   b)   346   c)   407   d)   46,832   Adult-level
  × 458   × 407   × 346   ×   569   performance

Type (b), in which a '0' occurs in the tens (or higher) place of the multiplier, sometimes presents a problem when the pupil is writing the partial products. In the case of 407 we may think of this number as 400 + 7, and then there are only two partial products. This appears to be the simpler approach. Then the process is as indicated in algorism (1).

(1)   Preferred   (2)   Not preferred

$$
\begin{array}{r}
346 \\
\times\quad 407 \\
\hline
2422 \leftarrow\ \ 7 \times 346 \\
138400 \leftarrow 400 \times 346 \\
\hline
140822 \leftarrow 407 \times 346 \\
\end{array}
\qquad\qquad
\begin{array}{r}
346 \\
\times\quad 407 \\
\hline
2422 \\
00000 \\
138400 \\
\hline
140822 \\
\end{array}
$$

If, however, we think of 407 as $4 \times 10^2 + 0 \times 10 + 7 \times 1$, there will be three partial products, of which one is

$$(0 \times 10) \times 346 = 0 \times (10 \times 346) = 0.$$

Some teachers insist on showing this partial product by writing a string of '0's. There is no need for this; it stems from an outmoded rote system of teaching the algorism. The important fact in this use of expanded notation of the numeral '407' is that the product of any number and zero is zero, and zero is the identity element of

119

addition (that is, $a + 0 + b$ is the same as $a + b$). The use of expanded notation, if used, should ultimately lead to the algorism form (1) shown here.

5–6 HIERARCHY OF LEARNING

There is a long series of activities, mental and sensory, that lead from the initial ideas of multiplication to a mature concept and an efficient algorism. Since the learning involves discovering and retaining new facts, recalling all previous learning, having a greater attention span, and being able to handle a more complex operation involving storage and recall of numbers during the operation, the work should be spread over a period of years. While a grade placement of these activities is suggested here, it must be recalled that bright children can do the learning at a faster pace, while the less-able children may need a more deliberate and slower approach to the learning.

In Grades 1 and 2, through the use of *skip counting, addition,* and *grouping* of objects, pupils may engage in many readiness activities. The following are examples of these activities.

1. Forming small groups or teams of children, with the same number in each group, and finding the total number of children in 2, 3, or 4 of these teams.

2. Counting the chairs in a row, and the number of rows, and then counting all the chairs: 3 rows of 5 chairs yields 15 chairs.

3. Counting by twos, threes, fives, and tens. Thus 2, 4, 6 is a way to find the number of the union of three sets of 2 members each. Six sets of 10 each have a total of 60 elements and 10, 20, 30, 40, 50, 60 counts them by tens. The teacher can supply many similar activities.

In Grade 3, the concepts developed in this chapter are introduced, the fundamental facts from 1×1 to 10×10 are learned, multiplication by zero is stressed as a separate principle, and the year can terminate with the multiplication of a two-digit number by a single-digit number.

In Grade 4, the work of Grade 3 is reviewed and the main emphasis placed on multiplying 2 two-digit numbers. The teacher may terminate the year by extending the algorism to the product of a three-digit number and a two-digit number.

Finally, in Grade 5, the multiplication is extended to adult-level performance of the algorism. At all times the algorism is related to practical situations. Problems involving addition, subtraction, and multiplication are introduced to encourage children to see a mathematical model of a physical situation.

Beginning in Grade 3 and continuing on through high school, the inequality order relation should be used. The symbols ' $<$ ' and ' $>$ ' should be introduced no later than Grade 4, and pupils should be encouraged to use these symbols in expressing the methods they use in rounding off numbers, making estimations or approximations, and in correcting an estimation to get an exact answer. This mental activity is one that should be continued throughout the life of each child.

By the end of Grade 6, every child should have developed an intuitive, useful, and well-understood concept of each of the following:

a) Commutativity. Any order of multiplying two numbers gives the same product.

b) Associativity. In a continued multiplication expression, involving 3 numbers, the association of the first two or the last two as the first product to be performed yields the same final product.

c) Rearrangement of factors. In an indicated multiplication of more than two numbers, no matter in what order the factors are associated, the final product is the same.

d) Identity element. Multiplying any number by 1 yields that number as a product. One is the identity element for multiplication.

e) Zero-product law. The product of any number and 0 is 0.

f) Distributivity of multiplication over addition. If a sum is multiplied by a number, the product is the same as the sum of the products of each addend and the number. This distribution of multiplication over addition can be extended to more than two addends.

g) The use of all the above principles with the rules of the decimal system of numeration permits us to formulate a procedure (algorism) by which we can find the product of any two given numbers.

Thus, for example, it is possible to have an algorism as shown in part (a). First we multiply by 20, then by 4, then add the partial products. Why can we do this? Because $268 \times (20 + 4) = 268 \times (20) + 268 \times (4)$, that is, multiplication is distributed over addition.

(a) 268 × 24

$$5360 \leftarrow 268 \times 20$$
$$1072 \leftarrow 268 \times 4$$
$$6432 \leftarrow 268 \times 24$$

(b)

Another method is shown in part (b). Tell why it works by showing how each diagonal column from the lower right to the upper left represents units, tens, hundreds, and so on, respectively. Then show why the digits are placed in each section of each square.

EXERCISES

1. Describe three operations on sets which can be used to develop the concept of multiplication as a binary operation. Which of these set operations would you use to introduce multiplication in the third grade?

2. Discuss the vocabulary and language of multiplication, giving explicit illustrations of each word, phrase, or sentence, and describe how you would introduce this language in teaching multiplication.

3. What is a multiplication table? Must a table include the so-called zero facts? In a decimal system of numeration what is the largest product that need be memorized for use in the standard algorism? How would you construct and use a multiplication table in Grade 3 or 4?

4. Describe in detail how you would teach multiplication by 10, by 70, by 100, by 300, with particular reference to the language you would use. Would you differentiate between number and numeral in this teaching? Differentiate between '20 × 30' as '(2 × 10) × (3 × 10)' and the same product as '2 tens multiplied by 3 tens'. In the latter expression how do you conceive of 'tens'?

5. Why is 3 × 4 × 5 not a binary operation? What is '3 × 4 × 5', and what meaning is given to it? Why does '3 × 4 × 5' have the same value as '5 × 3 × 4'? How would you teach this to children?

6. Using an array of dots, 14 in a row with 17 rows, tell how you would illustrate

   a) Commutativity: $14 \times 17 = 17 \times 14$,

   b) Associativity: $(2 \times 7) \times 17 = 2 \times (7 \times 17)$,

   c) Distributivity: $(10 + 4) \times 17 = 10 \times 17 + 4 \times 17$ and
   $(10 + 4) \times (10 + 7) = 10 \times 10 + 10 \times 7 + 4 \times 10 + 4 \times 7$.

7. Outline the steps, in order, from which you would proceed from the multiplication table to the mastery of multiplying any 2 two-digit numbers. Justify or criticize adversely the use of expanded notation in teaching 463×407.

8. If pupils know the sevens table, they can easily use an order relation to build the eights table, as follows:

$$8 = 7 + 1 \qquad \therefore \qquad x \cdot 8 = x(7 + 1) \quad \text{or} \quad x \cdot 8 = x \cdot 7 + x.$$

That is, $\qquad 4 \cdot 8 = (4 \cdot 7) + 4, \quad \text{or} \quad 28 + 4,$

which is 32. Explain how this relation could be used to gain greater insight into multiplication.

9. Discuss the role of both meaning and drill in the teaching of multiplication from the point of view of (a) structural learning, (b) permanency of learning, (c) retention, (d) post-elementary-school use and satisfaction.

10. Analyze the amount and degree of abstraction of earlier learning needed to develop knowledge of multiplication. What sensory aids would you use along with this earlier knowledge? What new concepts would be developed? What sorts of practice materials would you use?

11. State four distinct useful algorisms for multiplication of whole numbers, and explain why each algorism is mathematically correct.

REFERENCES

ADKINS, B. E., "A Rationale for Duplation-Mediation Multiplying," *The Arithmetic Teacher* **11**, April 1964, pages 251–253

BROWNELL, W. A., "When Is Arithmetic Meaningful?" *Journal of Educational Research* **35**, September 1944, 321–337

HAINES, MARGARET, "Concepts to Enhance the Study of Multiplication," *The Arithmetic Teacher* **10**, February 1963, pages 95–97

teaching division
of
cardinal numbers

When the child learned each of the operations addition, subtraction, and multiplication, he first manipulated collections of objects in a manner that enabled him to abstract the arithmetical operations corresponding to the object manipulations. Thus, in joining two discrete sets of objects,

$$A \cup B = C,$$

the child learned the corresponding addition,

$$n(A) + n(B) = n(C).$$

Similarly, in the operation of removing a subset from a set, the child learned that

$$A \setminus B = C \qquad (B \subset A)$$

corresponds to the subtraction

$$n(A) - n(B) = n(C); \; n(B) \leq n(A).$$

After he learned both these operations, their meaning was deepened and strengthened (reinforced) by relating the corresponding addition and subtraction facts. For example,

$$6 - 2 = 4 \text{ is related to } 6 = 4 + 2,$$
$$6 - 4 = 2 \text{ is related to } 6 = 2 + 4.$$

Since division can, in fact, be related to multiplication in a similar manner, there are persons today who advocate that in teaching division we bypass manipulations with sets of physical objects and relate the arithmetic of division directly to the arithmetic of multiplication. There are at least two strong reasons for not accepting this abstract and more formal approach. One is that it limits division to exact quotients and thus the operation is not always possible. (Some mathematicians would go further and say that division of cardinals is really not an operation.) Under this treatment, $17 \div 3$ does not have an answer, since there is no corresponding cardinal number n for which $3 \times n = 17$.

The other reason, more important both pedagogically and socially, is that the child is better able to grasp the meaning of the division operation after he has done a considerable amount of mental and physical partitioning of sets of elements into equivalent subsets. It is in this practical, problematic situation of partitioning which occurs many times daily in the life of most persons that division of cardinal numbers gives a useful solution. We shall first discuss the mathematical concept of division and then show how children can learn the concept, basic facts, and an algorism to obtain the result of dividing one number by another.

6-1 THE CONCEPT OF DIVISION

Situations in which it is necessary to *partition* or separate a set of elements into several equivalent subsets occur in such cases as

a) Making teams of 5 members each from the members of a class,

b) Separating a class into n teams, all the same size,

c) Dividing a sum of money into equal shares, or shares of a certain amount each; etc.

The teacher should accumulate 30 or more real situations of this kind. In all such partitioning problems, there are only two phases:

1. The number of equivalent subsets is known and it is required to find the number of elements in each subset.

2. The number of elements in each subset is known and it is required to find the number of equivalent subsets that can be obtained.

In any practical situation both these phases can be solved by the same process of separation of the objects. The distinction between phases is necessary only when we wish to interpret the answer in problem situations. Consider the partitioning of 24 pupils into 6 teams. We can select 6 pupils, one for each team (row A of the figure below) and repeat the process until all the pupils have been assigned.

```
        1   2   3   4   5   6
    A   O   O   O   O   O   O
    B   O   O   O   O   O   O
    C   O   O   O   O   O   O
    D   O   O   O   O   O   O
```

The result is 4 pupils on a team (count the rows). If, however, we desire to partition the class into teams of size 4 members each, we can select 4 members, enough for one team (column 1 of the figure) and repeat the process until all pupils have been assigned. In either case we have partitioned the pupils into a certain number of equivalent subsets. [Phase (1) has sometimes been referred to as *partitive* division and phase (2) as *quotative* or *measurement* division. This is merely a historical note. Neither the teacher nor the children need be concerned with these terms.]

The operation in arithmetic corresponding to partitioning a set into a number of equivalent subsets is called division. The *number* of elements in the set to be partitioned is called the *dividend*; the given number of elements in a subset (or of equivalent subsets) is called the *divisor*. The result, that is, the number of equivalent subsets (or the number of elements in a subset) is called the *quotient*. Thus we have

$$24 \div 4 = 6 \Rightarrow 24 = 6 \times 4$$
$$\Downarrow \quad \Downarrow \quad \Downarrow \quad \Downarrow \quad \Downarrow \quad \Downarrow \quad \Downarrow$$

Dividend divided by divisor equals quotient $\Rightarrow$ dividend = quotient $\times$ divisor.

$$\Uparrow \quad \Uparrow \quad \Uparrow \quad \Uparrow \quad \Uparrow \quad \Uparrow \quad \Uparrow$$
$$24 \div 6 = 4 \Rightarrow 24 = 4 \times 6$$

Mathematically, this can be described by comparing the set of whole numbers

$$C = \{0, 1, 2, 3, \ldots, q, q + 1, \ldots\}$$

with the set of products of each term of C and the divisor, d:

$$P = \{0 \times d, 1 \times d, 2 \times d, \ldots, q \times d, (q + 1) \times d, \ldots\}.$$

Eventually, if the partitioning is exact, and the original number of elements in the set to be partitioned is N, we shall find a product in set P, such as $q \times d$, which is equal to N. For $N = q \times d$, we say that $N \div d = q$. Thus, in the foregoing examples, since $24 = 6 \times 4$, then $24 \div 4 = 6$; since $24 = 4 \times 6$, then $24 \div 6 = 4$. Then we can also say this generally in symbols:

$$a \div b = c \quad \text{if and only if} \quad a = c \times b \quad \text{for some whole number } c$$

and

$$a \div \square = c \text{ if and only if } a = c \times \square \text{ for some whole number } \square.$$

This kind of division, when it is possible, is called *exact division*; there are no remainders. Then for each multiplication fact (where $a \times b$ is viewed as a unary operation, multiplying by b) there is an inverse division fact, obtained by dividing by b. For example, corresponding to $6 \times 4 = 24$ we have $24 \div 4 = 6$. Since multiplication is commutative, we also have another multiplication fact and a corresponding division fact. For example, corresponding to $4 \times 6 = 24$ we have $24 \div 6 = 4$. We shall refer to these four related facts as a multiplication-division family of facts. Of course, to $n \times n = n^2$ there is one related division fact, $n^2 \div n = n$.

The role of 0 in division is unique and quite different from its role in the other operations. First consider 0 as a dividend. It is quite easy to see that any partitioning of the empty set yields only the empty set. Hence

$$0 \div n = 0 \quad \text{since} \quad 0 \times n = 0.$$

Zero divided by any other number (not zero) yields a quotient zero. Next consider 0 as a divisor. It is evident that a nonzero number divided by zero is impossible, for if n is a nonzero dividend, then

$$n \div 0 = x \text{ implies } n = x \cdot 0, \text{ and since } x \cdot 0 = 0, \text{ then } n = 0.$$

This *contradiction* tells us that we should not use 0 as a divisor.

TABLE 6–1

Divisor, d

÷	1	2	3	4	5	6	...
0	0	0	0	0	0	0	
1	1						
2	2	1					
3	3		1				
4	4	2		1			
5	5				1		
.							
.							
.							

Dividend, n

$$n \div d = \boxed{q}$$

Again consider a case in which n is 0. Then

$$0 \div 0 = x \qquad \text{implies} \qquad 0 = x \cdot 0,$$

and here x can be any number. This ambiguity tells us that we should not use 0 as a divisor. Hence

Zero is never used as a divisor in cardinal-number arithmetic.

A portion of the exact division table is shown in Table 6–1. Note that 0 has been eliminated as a divisor. Also note the number of cells that are open, that is, the number for which an exact quotient does not exist (for example, $3 \div 2$, $5 \div 3$, $5 \div 2$, . . .). We say

The set of cardinal numbers is open under the operation exact division.

However, in everyday affairs, we certainly divide classes into a number of equivalent teams, even though the partitioning is not exact, and there is a part of the student body remaining, not enough to make another full team. To take care of these necessary partitionings with a remainder subset we resort to an arithmetic operation called *division with a remainder*. Here we find the largest possible quotient, called a *total quotient*.

Consider the problem $26 \div 4 = ?$. Surely there is no cardinal number n such that

$$26 = 4 \times n.$$

However,

$$26 = 4 \times 1 + 22,$$
$$26 = 4 \times 2 + 18,$$
$$26 = 4 \times 3 + 14,$$
$$26 = 4 \times 4 + 10,$$
$$26 = 4 \times 5 + 6,$$

or

$$26 = 4 \times 6 + 2,$$

but there is no cardinal number r to satisfy

$$26 = 4 \times 7 + r.$$

Hence the largest possible number by which 4 can be multiplied to give a product less than 26 is 6. We call 6 the total quotient and 2 the remainder. Thus we have an operation in which we are given an ordered pair of numbers $(26, 4)$ and the result is also an ordered pair of numbers $(6, 2)$, where 6 is the total quotient and 2 the remainder.

In general, consider any number N divided by d. First we write the set of cardinal numbers

$$C = \{0, 1, 2, 3, \ldots, q, q + 1, \ldots\}.$$

Then we form a new set, P, in which each of these elements of C is multiplied by the divisor d:

$$N$$
$$P = \{0 \times d, 1 \times d, 2 \times d, 3 \times d, \ldots, q \times d, (q + 1) \times d, \ldots\}.$$

1. If the division is exact we reach a number in set P, $q \times d$, which is equal to N, and q is the quotient; in this context, we say the remainder is zero.

2. If the division is not exact, we reach a number in set P such as $q \times d$, which is less than N, but the next number $(q + 1) \times d$ is greater than N. In this case q is the largest possible, or total, quotient. Also,

$$q \times d \leq N < (q + 1) \times d.$$

Subtracting $q \times d$ from each number of the inequality relation, we obtain

$$0 \leq N - q \times d < d.$$

But $N - q \times d$ is the remainder r. That is,

$$N - q \times d = r \quad \text{or} \quad N = q \times d + r, \quad 0 \leq r < d.$$

This formula defines division with a remainder.

Since, with the exclusion of division by zero, division with a remainder is *always possible*, it is the more common type of division used in everyday affairs. We can symbolize it for teachers in the following diagram:

$$\begin{array}{ccc}
\text{(dividend, divisor)} & \to & \text{(total quotient, remainder),} \\
(\quad N \quad, \quad d \quad) & \to & (\quad\quad q \quad, \quad\quad r \quad), \\
\underbrace{} & & \\
N \div d & \Rightarrow N = d \times q + r, & r < d, \quad 0 \leq r.
\end{array}$$

If $r = 0$, then the total quotient q is an exact quotient, and exact division may be considered a special case of division with a remainder.

In the foregoing explanation we used set operations, with the corresponding set language of partitioning, equivalent subsets, and remainder sets. We also used arithmetic operations with the corresponding arithmetic language of dividend, divisor, exact quotient, total quotient, and remainder. The teacher should understand this language and the distinction between terms used for set partitioning and terms used for operations on cardinal numbers.

6–2 READINESS ACTIVITIES FOR DIVISION

The concept of division is developed over a long period of time by a host of activities, both physical and mental, that enable the child to abstract and generalize the idea. In the very first years of schooling, children group themselves into teams or sections. Wise teachers have children observe the results; for example, 5 groups of 4 pupils, and perhaps 2 pupils not assigned: that makes 22 pupils. Or perhaps the pupils count off by fours and move into separate groups: one group of 4, and another group of 4, and another, and so on. Then they count the groups, saying, "We get 5 groups of 4 from 20 pupils." Such experience of counting by twos, fives, fours, sevens, and so forth, and using various kinds of objects—chairs, pupils, books, pegs, papers, etc.—establish a way of thinking about partitioning that serves as readiness for subsequent learning of the more formal aspects of division.

There are other readiness activities in which pupils can engage. One of these is counting backward, using a number line. Thus, instead of beginning with the origin 0 (which is a difficult starting point), start with point 20,

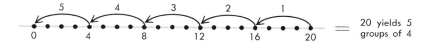

and count back 4 units, that is, 19–18–17–16, and repeat the backward counting until the number 0 is reached, or until it is impossible to count backward 4 more units. For example, suppose that we begin with 22:

This operation is analogous to an iterated subtraction process. Starting with a set of 22 elements, we first remove a 4-set, then another 4-set, and so on until all the possible 4-sets have been removed:

Children should say that when 5 groups, each of size 4, are removed from the collection of objects (the 22-set), 2 objects remain. They can further say: when one set is removed, 18 remain; if a new set of 4 is removed from these 18, then only 14 remain, and so on. Finally, they can say that if they start with 22 and keep subtracting 4, they can perform the subtraction 5 times and have 2 left. Note: *we do not say that 4 was subtracted from 22 five times.* This is a false statement. Note, in the example in the margin, that 4 was first subtracted from 22, then subtracted from 18, next from 14, and so on.

$$
\begin{array}{r}
22 \\
-4 \ (1) \\
\hline
18 \\
-4 \ (2) \\
\hline
14 \\
-4 \ (3) \\
\hline
10 \\
-4 \ (4) \\
\hline
6 \\
-4 \ (5) \\
\hline
2
\end{array}
$$

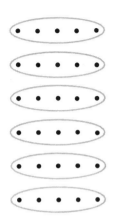

Some multiplication is taught before any division is taught, but in teaching multiplication we should pave the way for division. Thus, starting with sets of 5 elements, we join 6 of these sets and find that 5 × 6 = 30 [5 multiplied by 6 yields (or is) 30]. Then 30 objects partitioned into subsets of 5 objects each yields 6 of these sets. This serves as a check, and helps to achieve readiness for division. Teachers may find other activities in which the division idea occurs, but the important point is that, in all these activities, it is necessary to bring to the pupils' attention the relation between partitioning a set and the numbers relating to the partitioning. That is, pupils should know the difference between the number of the whole set, the number of equivalent subsets, the number in each subset, and the number of objects remaining after the partitioning.

6–3 TEACHING DIVISION FACTS

When the formal study of division begins, usually in Grade 3, the teacher must adhere to two principles:

1. The concepts of partitioning and of division of numbers must be developed simultaneously.

2. For each operation, partitioning and division, there is a correct and appropriate language. The learning of division is accelerated and becomes more meaningful if correct language and concepts are introduced simultaneously.

If pupils are to observe, select, abstract—and then generalize—by using all previously learned mathematics, we should begin our formal presentation with a study of partitioning of sets of objects into equivalent (same number of elements) subsets. There should be experience with sets that partition exactly, and with those that have a remainder set. The number of the elements in the remainder set, r, should always be compared with the number of elements in a part, d, so that pupils recognize that for a total partitioning:

$$0 \leq r < d \qquad (r \text{ is 0 or greater than 0, but must be less than } d).$$

In making partitionings, the pupils should always recognize that at the start they know the following two things.

1. A set to be partitioned and its number, called the *dividend*.

2. Either a number of subsets desired *or* the size of each desired subset, in either case called the *divisor*.

When they have completed the partitioning they have one result, namely:

3. The number of each subset *or* the number of equivalent subsets, in either case called the *total quotient*. If any elements remain unassigned, they constitute a remainder set, and the number of the remainder set is called the *remainder*. If the remainder set is empty (that is, if its number is zero), the total quotient is an exact quotient. If this remainder is not zero, then it is certainly less than the divisor; otherwise we do not have a total quotient. It must be emphasized that *the remainder is not a part of the quotient; it is the undivided part of the dividend*.

Examples of situations in which this language may be used are numerous, and illustrated by the following.

a) How many pencils can we buy for 30 cents, if pencils cost 6 cents each?

b) Suppose that we buy 5 pencils for 30 cents. How many cents does a pencil cost if we pay the same amount for each of the 5 pencils?

c) How many rows are needed for 46 chairs, if there are 7 chairs in a row?

d) How many chairs are in a row if 46 chairs are arranged in 6 rows?

As pupils discover the answers, they also learn to write and speak about the corresponding arithmetic operation. Thus, for the above illustrations, they say:

a) 30 divided by 6 is 5, or $30 \div 6 = 5$. We can buy 5 pencils.

b) 30 divided by 5 is 6, or $30 \div 5 = 6$. Each pencil costs (requires) 6 cents.

c) 46 divided by 7 is 6 with a remainder 4. $46 \div 7 = 6$, remainder 4.

d) 46 divided by 6 is 7 with a remainder 4. $46 \div 6 = 7$, remainder 4.

Such procedures relate division directly to problem-solving.

Since we cannot always count, subtract, or manipulate objects to solve a division problem (for example 3935 ÷ 41), we resort as we did in the other operations to learning fundamental division facts, which can then be used to find the total quotient and remainder for any division problem. Relying on previously learned concepts and facts, we use multiplication to learn the division facts. A few illustrations will enable pupils to construct or relate all the division facts to multiplication facts.

$$\diamond\ \diamond\ \diamond\ \diamond\ \diamond\ \diamond$$
$$\diamond\ \diamond\ \diamond\ \diamond\ \diamond\ \diamond$$
$$\diamond\ \diamond\ \diamond\ \diamond\ \diamond\ \diamond$$
$$\diamond\ \diamond\ \diamond\ \diamond\ \diamond\ \diamond$$

Consider one fact: $4 \times 6 = 24$, for which the diagram is a concrete representation. The same diagram may also represent $6 \times 4 = 24$ (if viewed from another angle). Hence the diagram may be used to develop $24 \div 6 = 4$ and $24 \div 4 = 6$. Thus there is established a family of facts:

$$a \times b = c \Leftrightarrow c \div b = a$$
$$\Updownarrow \qquad\qquad \Updownarrow$$
$$b \times a = c \Leftrightarrow c \div a = b$$

Having established this relation with a great many experiences for a new fact, the teacher can use sentences with frames. For example,

$$32 \div 4 = \square \quad \text{because} \quad 32 = \square \times 4,$$

and hence '$\square$' is replaced by '8' to make a true statement.

$$\square \times 8 = 32 \quad \text{so} \quad 32 \div 8 = \square,$$

and since $4 \times 8 = 32$, the frame may be replaced by '4'. Then we have a family of multiplication and division facts:

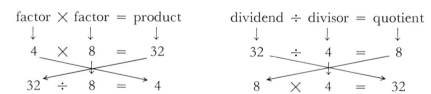

factor × factor = product   dividend ÷ divisor = quotient

At all times we should refer to the numbers by their mathematical names, either

$$\text{product} \div \text{one factor} = \text{the other factor}$$

or

$$\text{dividend} \div \text{divisor} = \text{quotient.}$$

When pupils have learned enough division facts (or have related them to multiplication) we can, as an enrichment activity, construct an exact division table, which is quite different from other tables of facts, and appears as shown on page 128. Thus exact division is not always possible. When it is possible, then the dividend is a whole-number multiple of the divisor.

The next step is to learn the division facts in relation to a remainder, or what is the same thing, to learn to solve a division example in which both the divisor and the quotient are single-digit numbers. Suppose that we are asked to find an answer to $17 \div 3$. Some teachers prefer to have pupils proceed by trial to get an answer. Any of the following processes would be accepted.

```
  3)17                    3)17                    3)17
 -  9   3                -  3   1                - 12   4
 ─────                   ─────                   ─────
    8                      14                       5
 -  6   2                -  3   1                -  3   1
r ← 2  5 → q               11              r ← 2   5 → q
                        -  3   1
                        ─────
                           8
                        -  3   1
                        ─────
                           5
                        -  3   1
                        ─────
         remainder ← 2   5 → quotient
```

This type of activity should be included within the informal readiness teaching. At the stage immediately preceding the learning of the algorism, we should relate all single-digit quotients and single-digit divisors to the exact quotients that have been learned, or to the corresponding multiplication facts.

Thus a child should learn that $17 \div 3$ has 5 as a total quotient because $3 \times 5 = 15$, but $3 \times 6 = 18$, which is greater than the dividend. He should recognize that 4 is not the total quotient, since $3 \times 4 = 12$ and $17 - 12 = 5$, a remainder which is larger than the divisor. One way to establish this is to write the possible partial quotients:

$$
\begin{array}{l}
3\overline{)17} \\
3 \quad 1 \\
\overline{14}
\end{array}
\qquad
\begin{array}{l}
3\overline{)17} \\
6 \quad 2 \\
\overline{11}
\end{array}
\qquad
\begin{array}{l}
3\overline{)17} \\
9 \quad 3 \\
\overline{8}
\end{array}
$$

$$17 = (3 \times 1) + 14 \quad 17 = (3 \times 2) + 11 \quad 17 = (3 \times 3) + 8$$

$$
\begin{array}{l}
3\overline{)17} \\
12 \quad 4 \\
\overline{5}
\end{array}
\qquad
\begin{array}{l}
3\overline{)17} \\
15 \quad 5 \\
\overline{2}
\end{array}
$$

$$17 = (3 \times 4) + 5 \quad 17 = (3 \times 5) + 2$$

In this way the pupil learns that 1, 2, 3, or 4 are partial quotients, since the remainder is greater than the divisor, but that 5 is the total quotient, since the remainder is now less than the divisor. Practice on the type of problems shown will develop not only the language and concept of the total quotient and remainder, but also the relation to the multiplication facts.

$$
\begin{array}{l}
5\overline{)22} \\
20 \quad 4 \\
\overline{2}
\end{array}
\qquad
\begin{array}{l}
6\overline{)23} \\
18 \quad 3 \\
\overline{5}
\end{array}
\qquad
\begin{array}{l}
7\overline{)54} \\
49 \quad 7 \\
\overline{5}
\end{array}
\qquad
\begin{array}{l}
4\overline{)28} \\
28 \quad 7 \\
\overline{0}
\end{array}
$$

$$22 = 5 \times 4 + \boxed{2} \quad 23 = 6 \times 3 + \boxed{5} \quad 54 = 7 \times 7 + \boxed{5} \quad 28 = 4 \times 7 + \boxed{0}$$

Dividend = (divisor multiplied by quotient) + remainder

divisor > remainder

The pupil should estimate the total quotient by trial use of the multiplication facts. Thus, in the second example above, he says: $6 \times 2 = 12$, $6 \times 3 = 18$, but $6 \times 4 = 24$ and this is too large, so 3 is the total quotient, etc.

In all the above examples the numeral for the quotient was placed immediately to the right of the numeral for the exact multiple of the divisor. Thus the numeral to the left of the quotient indicated the highest multiple of the divisor that is less than the dividend. In some commercial textbooks the partial quotients (as shown in the examples on page 135) are always written opposite the partial dividends, and the sum of these partial quotients given at the lower right-hand side of the algorism.

In other books, where it is desirable to develop a more efficient algorism, the partial quotients are written above the dividends. Thus the examples on page 136 would appear in the form

$$
\begin{array}{c}
\underline{4} \\
5\overline{)22} \\
20 \\
\hline
2 \text{ Rem.}
\end{array}
\qquad
\begin{array}{c}
\underline{3} \\
6\overline{)23} \\
18 \\
\hline
5 \text{ Rem.}
\end{array}
\qquad
\begin{array}{c}
\underline{7} \\
7\overline{)54} \\
49 \\
\hline
5 \text{ Rem.}
\end{array}
\qquad
\begin{array}{c}
\underline{7} \\
4\overline{)28} \\
28 \\
\hline
0 \text{ Rem.}
\end{array}
$$

In the following development we shall use this arrangement.

6–4 THE DIVISION ALGORISM

There are many ways to develop a meaningful algorism for division. To describe all the methods available would necessitate a separate book on this one subject. However, when we develop the algorism, at the start we should always relate the arithmetic to a set-partitioning situation. First we review the process of multiplying any number by 10, 20, 30, . . . , 100, 200, . . . , 1000, 2000, . . . , and so on. Then a problem similar to the following can be proposed.

Suppose that 97 programs are to be folded by 4 persons. If each person folds the same number, how many programs should each person be given? The problem then reduces to finding the quotient when 97 is divided by 4. It is readily seen that there can be more than 10 programs given to each person, since $4 \times 10 = 40$, which is less than 97. Suppose we write 10 as a partial quotient.

$$
\begin{array}{c}
10 \\
4\overline{)97} \\
40 \\
\hline
57
\end{array}
\qquad
\begin{array}{c}
\left.\begin{array}{c}10\\10\end{array}\right\}\,20 \\
4\overline{)97} \\
40 \\
\hline
57 \\
40 \\
\hline
17
\end{array}
\qquad
\begin{array}{c}
\left.\begin{array}{c}4\\10\\10\end{array}\right\}\,24 \\
4\overline{)97} \\
40 \\
\hline
57 \\
40 \\
\hline
17 \\
16 \\
\hline
1 \text{ Rem.}
\end{array}
$$

Then how many programs remain to be distributed? Of course, 97 − 40, or 57. We again recognize that the remaining programs are sufficient in number to distribute 10 to each person. We write another 10 as another part of the quotient and subtract 40 from 57. There remain 17 programs to distribute, and from previous work we know that 4 × 4 is the greatest multiple of 4 less than 17. We write 4 in the partial-quotient column, subtract 16 from 17, and have 1 remaining. Now the sum of the partial quotients gives the total quotient: 24. As a check we write

$$97 = (4 \times 24) + 1 = 96 + 1 = 97.$$

Once the example has been completed, we review every step we carried out, so that all students see how *the arithmetic explains the partitioning*. We should not end the discussion of this problem until we have interpreted the answer in terms of the problem situation: 3 of the 4 persons will fold 24 programs each; the fourth will fold 25.

A number of these examples can be given, especially those in which the partial-quotient column will have 4, 5, or more tens as partial quotients. This should lead to the problem of finding a more efficient method. Could we use 20, 30, 40, and so on, multiples of the divisor? The above example is then solved as:

$$4 \times 10, \quad \text{yes, } 40 < 97$$

$$4 \times 20, \quad \text{yes, } 80 < 97$$

$$4 \times 30, \quad \text{No, } 120 > 97$$

$$
\begin{array}{r}
4\rfloor \\
20\rfloor\ 24 \\
\hline
4\overline{)97} \\
80 \\
\hline
17 \\
16 \\
\hline
1\ \text{Rem.}
\end{array}
$$

So we immediately assign 20 programs to each person, subtract 80 from the dividend to obtain 17, and from here on the solution is the same. Now this same test is used to find the highest number of tens in similar problems. For example,

$$
\begin{array}{r}
4\rfloor \\
40\rfloor\ 44 \\
\hline
6\overline{)267} \\
240 \\
\hline
27 \\
24 \\
\hline
3\ \text{Rem.}
\end{array}
\qquad
\begin{array}{r}
9\rfloor \\
30\rfloor\ 39 \\
\hline
8\overline{)315} \\
240 \\
\hline
75 \\
72 \\
\hline
3\ \text{Rem.}
\end{array}
\qquad
\begin{array}{r}
40 \\
\hline
7\overline{)284} \\
280 \\
\hline
4\ \text{Rem.}
\end{array}
$$

Once the above process is mastered, it is easy to extend the division by single-digit divisors to three-, four-, or five-digit quotients. For example, the test for $2563 \div 8$ is

$$8 \times 10 = 80; \qquad 8 \times 100 = 800; \qquad 8 \times 1000 = 8000;$$

but 8000 is more than the dividend, so the answer is in the hundreds. Now try

$$8 \times 200 = 1600; \qquad 8 \times 300 = 2400; \qquad 8 \times 400 = 3200;$$

3200 is too large. Then 300 is the first partial quotient. The rest of the example is accomplished by exactly the same procedure as the two-digit-quotient process, previously mastered.

No attempt should be made to simplify this process until divisors of at least two digits have been introduced. It may well be that for the slowest pupils this process is sufficient for their life needs. It should be noted that the partial products are written as complete numerals and not as place-value digits in a particular position, for example, the '2' in '20' over the tens digit of the quotient. In so doing we avoid the so-called zero difficulties. We also avoid the "bringing down" of digits from the dividend. Thus, in the example in the margin, we did not bring down a '2', nor did we write a '0' in the hundreds place of the quotient as a separate step. To see how many difficulties are avoided, the reader should, by the process described, find the quotient and remainder for $48,026 \div 8$.

In this process (1) we develop the process of estimating, using mental multiplication by powers of 10, and decades of powers of 10, (2) we stress reasoning about the process, (3) we relate the process to a physical interpretation (for example, 3250 pupils distributed equally into 8 schools), and (4) we practice until children can do the process with confidence and accuracy.

The next step—and a difficult one to master—is to find the quotients for a two-digit divisor. The fact that in some cases the estimation of a partial quotient may be too high is unavoidable, and must be faced by starting the problem anew. However, at times the estimated quotient may be too small; but by the process taught, this can be remedied by continuing with the process. For

$$
\begin{array}{r}
20 \\
300\,\} \, 320 \\
\hline
8\,)\,2563 \\
2400 \\
\hline
163 \\
160 \\
\hline
3 \ \text{Rem.}
\end{array}
$$

$$
\begin{array}{r}
5 \\
20 \\
1000\,\} \, 1025 \\
\hline
8\,)\,8200 \\
8000 \\
\hline
200 \\
160 \\
\hline
40 \\
40 \\
\hline
0 \ \text{Rem.}
\end{array}
$$

example, let us consider $338 \div 46$. We round 46 to 50 and since $6 \times 50 = 300$, while $7 \times 50 = 350$, this method tells the child to try 6. We have

$$
\begin{array}{r}
1\!\!\rangle 7 \\
6\rfloor \\
\hline
46)\overline{338} \\
276 \\
\hline
62 \\
46 \\
\hline
16 \text{ Rem.}
\end{array}
\qquad
\begin{array}{r}
8 \\
\hline
46)\overline{338} \\
368 \text{ too much}
\end{array}
\qquad
\begin{array}{r}
7 \\
\hline
46)\overline{338} \\
322 \\
\hline
16 \text{ Rem.}
\end{array}
$$

If, however, the child uses 40 and finds $8 \times 40 = 320$, he arrives at the impossible subtraction $338 - 368$. Here the problem must be rewritten so that 1 less than 8, or 7, appears to be the correct quotient. Situations like this are not to be avoided, for they form good teaching material for reasoning about rounding off, approximations, and the process of estimation.

In introducing two-digit divisors, it is wise to start with examples that give single-digit quotients, and in which estimated quotients permit a mental operation to check the quotient. For example, $324 \div 69$. The children should be asked to explain, in light of previous knowledge, how they would do this. For mental estimation they should be encouraged to round off 69 to 70. Now it is easy to estimate that $3 \times 70 = 210$, $4 \times 70 = 280$, but $5 \times 70 = 350$ (too much). "Are you sure," you can ask, "since $69 < 70$, that 5 may not be too large a quotient?" Children can see that $69 < 70$ by 1, and $5 \times 1 = 5$, and $350 - 5$ is 345, which is again too large, so the quotient must be 4. Again the example should be illustrated by a practical situation of the children's own making. For example, 324 seats put into equal sections of 69 seats at an outdoor play means 4 sections, and 48 seats to be assigned to a special section.

After studying several examples, children should be allowed to practice situations in which rounding off is more difficult; for example, divisors ending in 4, 5, or 6, or divisors in the teens, such as 13, 15, 17. It should be apparent that rounding off 16 to 20 in the example in the margin gives 7 as a trial quotient, while 9 is the correct quotient. However, multiplying 16 by 10 would show the correct quotient at once.

$$
\begin{array}{r}
4 \\
\hline
69)\overline{324} \\
276 \\
\hline
48 \text{ Rem.}
\end{array}
$$

$$
\begin{array}{r}
2\!\!\rangle 9 \\
7\rfloor \\
\hline
16)\overline{154} \\
112 \\
\hline
42 \\
32 \\
\hline
10 \text{ Rem.}
\end{array}
$$

The second step is to introduce two-digit quotients; for example, $3145 \div 69$. The pupils should be asked to estimate a partial quotient and explain how they obtain it. Thus, from past work on estimation, one can expect, or suggest, that we round off 69 to 70, then try 70×10, 70×100 (too much) and then 70×20, 70×30, 70×40, and 70×50 (too much). Although 70 is used as a trial divisor, the real divisor is 69, and the product of 69×40 appears in the written example. The most reluctant learners may find it necessary to write the product at another place and then transfer it. For the other children, the teacher should provide practice in mental multiplication, with examples like $69 \times 40 = 2760$, before initiating the study of the algorism. Then these children should be encouraged to do the requisite multiplication mentally.

To estimate the units digit, the pupil may recognize from the previous estimation that $70 \times 50 = 3500$ and hence $70 \times 5 = 350$, and this yields 5 as the next partial quotient. The remainder, 40, is less than the divisor, 69, and hence the process terminates. The child can check by writing $3145 \stackrel{?}{=} (69 \times 45) + 40$, and simplifying the right-hand member. This method of checking reinforces the meaning of division, as well as giving practice in the multiplication algorism.

The first example, and a few like it (for example, $784 \div 23$, $6295 \div 73$, $247 \div 17$), should be studied in detail, and reviewed until the entire process is well comprehended. Then pupils must practice and solve problems, as well as create problems in which such division is necessary. The process can easily be extended to three- and four-digit quotients, and again the elimination of zero difficulties in the quotient is evident, as shown in the following examples.

$$
\begin{array}{r}
5 \\
40 \\
\hline
69)\overline{3145} \\
2760 \\
\hline
385 \\
345 \\
\hline
40 \text{ Rem.}
\end{array}
\quad 45
$$

$$
\begin{array}{r}
69 \\
40 \\
\hline
2760
\end{array}
$$

$$
\begin{array}{r}
1 \\
200 \\
\hline
23)\overline{4623} \\
4600 \\
\hline
23 \\
23 \\
\hline
0 \text{ Rem.}
\end{array}
\quad 201
$$

$$
\begin{array}{r}
3 \\
200 \\
\hline
48)\overline{9750} \\
9600 \\
\hline
150 \\
144 \\
\hline
6 \text{ Rem.}
\end{array}
\quad 203
$$

$$
\begin{array}{r}
50 \\
100 \\
7000 \\
\hline
14)\overline{100110} \\
98000 \\
\hline
2110 \\
1400 \\
\hline
710 \\
700 \\
\hline
10 \text{ Rem.}
\end{array}
\quad 7150
$$

The extension to three-digit divisors offers no new difficulties, only more complex computation. However, the refinement to a more efficient method of estimating the trial partial quotient and to writing the quotient in a single line do present situations that call for more concentration on the part of the pupil. Until the above procedure is mastered, however, no attempt should be made to develop a more concise representation of the algorism. This refinement can be delayed, for most pupils, until the sixth school year. A long-division algorism is, in the final analysis, a way of recording subtractions. Both the teacher and the pupil should know this, and the teacher should encourage the pupil to develop and use the most efficient algorism he can feel secure in using.

Estimating the number of places in the total quotient is easy, for the pupil has been doing this in every example in which he has determined the largest possible power of 10 as a multiplier of the divisor. The teacher may give a review of this process of determining the number of places in the total quotient by asking pupils to write the quotient digits above the dividend in such a way that the places—units, tens, hundreds, thousands, etc.—are in the same column. Doing long-division examples on lined paper held sideways helps to keep the appropriate figures lined up. Thus, in each of the following examples, the pupil indicates where the left-most digit of the quotient will fall, and he should know why.

$$\overset{\downarrow}{9\overline{)4673}} \qquad \overset{\downarrow}{28\overline{)1635}} \qquad \overset{\downarrow}{32\overline{)7546}} \qquad \overset{\downarrow}{67\overline{)29416}}$$

In each case the pupil determines the place, but not the trial digit for the place.

To determine the trial digit by continuing multiplication of the divisor by, for example, 100, 200, etc., until the product is too large is very time-consuming. Some children discover that they can reverse this process by dividing the first digit, or the first two digits, of the dividend (see margin) by the first digit of the rounded divisor. Thus, in the example shown, the pupil would obtain

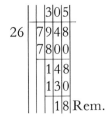

$7 \div 3 = 2$ as a trial digit and he knows the place is hundreds. Of course the estimate is too small. A better student would note that $3 \times 26 = 78$, which is less than 79, and hence use 300 as his trial or partial quotient. At the first attempt of refinement, the partial dividend should be written as '7800', since the digit '3' in the quotient represents 300.

Now the so-called zero difficulty appears. The next partial quotient cannot be in the tens place, since $10 \times 26 = 260$, which is greater than 148. But $15 \div 3 = 5$ gives the trial quotient, which must be written in the units column of the quotient. Since there were no tens in the quotient, it is necessary to indicate this by writing a '0' in this place in the quotient. Again the check

$$7948 = 26 \times 305 + 18$$

will help those children who *forget* to place the '0' in the tens place to discover their error.

Further refinement than that shown in the division algorism in the margin seems unnecessary for general use in written calcula-tion. Some commercial texts do resort to dropping the '0's in the partial dividends, and to "bringing down" the digits of the dividend as they are needed, but such refinement seems to be more confusing to most pupils than the added efficiency seems to warrant. Many good teachers adopt a policy of never telling a child he may omit the terminal '0's in the numerals for the partial dividends. If a child sees this himself, these teachers check to see that the child knows why he can do that and then let him do it.

In summary, the following steps appear to be necessary in developing an efficient, mature division algorism for cardinal numbers.

$$
\begin{array}{r}
742 \\
56\overline{)41{,}568} \\
39{,}200 \\
\hline
2{,}368 \\
2{,}240 \\
\hline
128 \\
112 \\
\hline
16
\end{array}
$$

1. In Grades K through 2 we develop readiness by grouping pupils into sets of 3, 4, or 5 each, finding the number of sets, and the number of pupils remaining that are not enough to make a set of the given size. We also decide to have 3, 4, or 5 teams or reading groups, and so on, in a class and find out how many pupils should be put on each team. Many similar devices are used to make equivalent subsets from a given collection of things.

2. In Grade 3, we develop the concept of partitioning of sets into equivalent subsets and the related concept of division with numbers. Here we develop the language 'dividend', 'divisor', 'quotient', and 'remainder', as well as the fundamental relation, $N = d \times q + r$, where $r < d$. We relate the fundamental division facts to the corresponding multiplication facts through families of facts and inverses. We study examples with single-digit quotients and divisors, with remainders. We do some work with multidigit quotients.

3. In Grade 4 we extend the work of single-digit divisors to include quotients, first from 10 to 20, and then to the hundreds and thousands. We do some work with 2-digit divisors.

4. In Grade 5 we teach 2-digit divisors, for mastery, first with quotients of a single digit and then quotients of 2 or 3 digits. We start with divisors other than those in the teens. Finally, we extend the algorism to include 3-digit divisors. In all the foregoing work we write each partial quotient as a distinct numeral and add the partial quotients to obtain the total quotient.

5. In Grade 6, the algorism is reviewed, and refined to writing the total quotient in a single line. No further refinement is deemed necessary for an efficient, serviceable, mature algorism.

At all times we relate the computational examples to practical problems of partitioning, and we pay particular attention to interpreting the answers of these problems.

6-5 FACTORS, PRIMES, AND COMPOSITES

Learning efficient algorisms for multiplication and division is necessary for a person who wants to use arithmetic in everyday affairs. There are, however, other aspects of multiplication and division that are fundamental to understanding the mathematical systems which are studied subsequently in high school. These aspects are also ones that evoke the imagination and interest of children in number relations, and thus have esthetic, as well as cognitive, value. Besides, the informal theory about numbers thus learned can serve as a basis for efficient computation with fractions and rational numbers. The part of number theory that is important to all children includes an understanding and an ability to use the ideas of *factor, divisor, multiple, prime number, composite number, exponent, complete factorization, greatest common factor, and least common multiple*.

The first task is to develop the meanings and interrelationships of *factor, multiple,* and *divisor*. As soon as the pupil has learned that the order in which one number is multiplied by another does not change the product (commutativity), both the multiplicand and multiplier may be called *factors of the product*. Thus, in the number fact $6 \times 5 = 30$, 6 and 5 are factors of the product, 30. Since $15 \times 2 = 30$, we also have 15 and 2 as factors of 30. Again, $3 \times 10 = 30$ reveals that 3 and 10 are factors of 30. Thus a product may have several different sets of two factors. To express a number as a product of two (or more) numbers is to express it in factored form. The teacher should give pupils practice in expressing numbers in factored form. The number 30 can be written as the product of two factors in the following different ways, not counting a rearrangement of the same factors as different ways: 1×30, 2×15, 3×10, 5×6. Thirty thus has eight different factors: 1, 2, 3, 5, 6, 10, 15, 30.

The number 1 plays a distinctive role in this work, since for any number, the product of it and 1 is that number. Thus $1 \times 2 = 2, 1 \times 5 = 5, 1 \times 8 = 8$, and finally children can write

$$1 \times n = n \times 1 = n, \qquad \text{where } n \text{ is any number,}$$

as a general rule of multiplication. We say that 1 is the *identity element* of multiplication because $1 \cdot n$ is always n. Since this law is true for all numbers (1 is a factor of every cardinal number), we generally seek the other possible factored forms of numbers. Some numbers do not have other factored forms. Children are asked to discover these numbers. Thus they arrive at a set of numbers which we call *prime numbers*:

$$2, 3, 5, 7, 11, 13, \ldots$$

We agree that 1 is not to be considered a prime number.

There are several ways to define prime numbers. One way is given above:

A number ($\neq 1$) is prime if it has no factors other than itself and 1.

(The exclusion of 1 is arbitrary, but definitions are subject to judicious choice; and as children work with prime numbers, they can see that including 1 as a member of the set of primes would be a nuisance more often than it would be helpful.) Another definition is:

A number n is prime if the only way to make a rectangular array of n objects is to have just one row or just one column.

(This is a good definition to use in the lower grades. Note that it automatically excludes 1 from the set of primes.) Another definition is:

A number is prime if it has exactly two different factors.

(Does this definition exclude 1?) You may know other definitions. Try several examples to assure yourself that all these definitions single out the same set of numbers.

Since the pupils have already learned the associative principle, which involves a product of three factors, the notion of factored form of a number may be extended. Thus, 6×5 may be written as '$(2 \times 3) \times 5 = 30$', or in the usual form

$$2 \times 3 \times 5 = 30.$$

Here 30 is expressed as a continued product of three factors. Since 2, 3, and 5 are prime numbers, it cannot be expressed by more than three factors. After a study of several similar examples, such as $2 \times 3 \times 7 = 42$, $2 \times 3 \times 2 \times 5 = 60$, the pupils can be led to construct factor trees, all of which lead to the same final set of prime factors. For example, for 60 we may have the following:

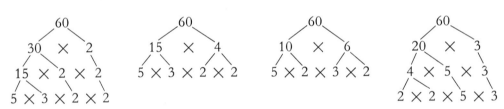

The final goal is to have children express any number as a product of prime factors. Although the tree is a way of finding this form, there are more systematic procedures. Children already know even and odd numbers and hence know that an even number has the factor 2, and an odd number does not. They know that a number which has its numeral ending in '5' has a factor 5 and that one ending in '0' has both factors 2 and 5. So we can use division to find factors. In this connection, they learn to use the word divisor in a special way. 'Divisor' is now applied to an exact division, one that gives an exact quotient. Thus 4 *is a divisor of* 20 because it yields an exact quotient, 5, but 4 *is not a divisor of* 23 because an exact quotient does not exist for $23 \div 4$, only a total quotient and a remainder. This use of the word divisor is learned by given examples:

Is 3 a divisor of 12? (Yes) of 15? (Yes) of 17? (No) of 19? (No) . . .

Is 8 a divisor of 8? (Yes) of 0? (Yes) of 16? (Yes) of 20? (No) . . .

Can 0 be a divisor of any number? No, 0 may never be used as a divisor.

As soon as this meaning of the word 'divisor' is established, in most cases the pupil may use the words 'factor of' and 'divisor of' interchangeably. That is, any divisor of a number is also a factor of the number, and any factor (other than 0) is also a divisor. Thus, since $42 \div 6 = 7$, 6 is a divisor of 42, but it is also a factor of 42; another factor is 7, because $42 = 6 \times 7$. Similarly, since $54 = 6 \times 9$, we know that 6 and 9 are factors of the product, but we also know that 6 and 9 are divisors of 54; that is, $54 \div 6 = 9$ and $54 \div 9 = 6$. In this way we learn a new vocabulary to use in speaking about multiplication and division.

Using the list of prime numbers, children can find the prime factorization of any number. For example, to find the factored form of 120, they divide as follows:

$$
\begin{array}{r|r}
2 & 120 \\ \hline
2 & 60 \\ \hline
2 & 30 \\ \hline
3 & 15 \\ \hline
  & 5 \text{ is prime}
\end{array}
\qquad \text{and} \quad 120 = 2 \times 2 \times 2 \times 3 \times 5.
$$

Also, given 1092, they divide as follows:

$$
\begin{array}{r|r}
2 & 1092 \\ \hline
2 & 546 \\ \hline
3 & 273 \\ \hline
7 & 91 \\ \hline
  & 13 \text{ is prime}
\end{array}
$$

Of course, 273 is readily recognized as not having the divisor 5, and hence the next prime number to try is 7. Thus $1092 = 2 \times 2 \times 3 \times 7 \times 13$. In all cases, pupils can check by carrying out the multiplication to yield the product.

When a number is expressed in factored form, we quite frequently refer to the number as a multiple of one of its factors. Since $20 = 4 \times 5$, one can say that 20 *is a multiple of* 4 (4 multiplied by 5 yields 20) or 20 is a multiple of 5 (5 multiplied by 4 yields 20). This reinforces the language and meaning of 'multiplied by'. Similarly, since $30 = 2 \times 3 \times 5$, 30 is a multiple of 2 (2×15); of 3 (3×10); of 5 (5×6); and of course also of 6, of 10, and of 15. Thus a number is a multiple not only of its prime factors, but of any product of several of its prime factors.

At some appropriate point, all children should realize that the following three statements convey the same information:

1. k is a factor of w;

2. k is a divisor of w;

3. w is a multiple of k.

Whenever one of them is true, the other two are true.

Children should study a number of similar examples, and then they are in a position to write the set of all possible factors of a number. Since, as a product of prime factors, $60 = 2 \times 2 \times 3 \times 5$, we have the following statement:

The set of all factors (or divisors) of 60 is

$$F_{60} = \{1, 2, 3, 4, 5, 6, 10, 12, 15, 20, 30, 60\}.$$

Of course 1 is a factor of every number, and for this same reason a number is a factor of itself, and hence both 1 and the number itself are members of the set of all factors of the number. When a factor set has been produced, it should be examined by questions of the following type:

a) Is 60 a multiple of 3? (Yes) What multiple? ($60 \div 3 = 20$, the multiple 20.)

b) Is 60 a multiple of 12? (Yes) What multiple? ($60 \div 12 = 5$, the multiple 5.)

c) Is 60 a multiple of 24? (No) Why not? ($60 \div 24$ does not yield an exact quotient.)

d) If 2 and 3 are factors of 60, are all multiples of 2 and of 3 also factors of 60? (No) (8 is a multiple of 2 and 8 is not a factor of 60.)

e) Is the prime-factorization set the same as the set of factors of 60? (No) Why not? (The prime-factorization set forms the product 60. The set of factors is the set of all divisors of 60.)

f) If 1 were allowed as a prime factor, how many prime factors would there be in the prime-factorization form of 60? (Any number. For example, $2 \times 2 \times 3 \times 5 \times 1 \times 1 \times 1 \times \cdots$ forever.)

g) Since 1 is not considered a prime number, how many prime factors are there in the prime-factorization form of 60? (Four: $2 \times 2 \times 3 \times 5$.)

The teacher can undoubtedly think of other, similar questions.

A very useful activity now is to use 0, 1, the prime numbers, and the operation multiplication to write the names of all the cardinal numbers in order (up to a reasonable limit). The set begins as follows:

0, 1, 2, 3, 2×2, 5, 2×3, 7, $2 \times 2 \times 2$,
3×3, 2×5, 11, $2 \times 2 \times 3$, 13, 2×7, ...

If any number in this sequence is not represented as a product it must be 0, 1, or a prime number. All the other numbers are expressed as products of prime numbers, and hence are called *composite numbers* because they are composed of products of prime numbers.

As the pupils will discover later when they begin to simplify fractions, and add and subtract them, it is convenient to discover the greatest number that divides exactly into (is a divisor of) two given numbers. It will also be convenient to find the least number which is some multiple of two or more given numbers. The first of these is called a *greatest common factor* and abbreviated to GCF. The second number is called the *least common multiple* and abbreviated to LCM. However, the study of these two ideas is interesting in itself, especially to brighter pupils.

To find the greatest common factor, we do the following:

1. Find the *factor* set of each number.

2. Find the set of factors *common* to both sets.

3. Find the *greatest* number in the common set.

Children should discover these steps rather than have them given to them as a rule of procedure.

A first approach is to give two numbers and ask the pupils to find the factor sets. Then they may be asked to compare the factor sets, according to which factors they have in common, which factors not in common, the smallest factor (other than 1) in each set, the greatest factor in each set, and finally to examine how the set of common factors behaves when we consider the quotients of the given numbers divided by these common factors in each case. For example, given 84 and 60, the pupils find that

$$F_{84} = \{1, 2, 3, 4, 6, 7, 12, 14, 21, 42, 84\},$$
$$F_{60} = \{1, 2, 3, 4, 5, 6, 10, 12, 15, 20, 30, 60\}.$$

The set of common factors, called the *intersection* of the two sets, is

$$F_{84} \cap F_{60} = \{1, 2, 3, 4, 6, 12\}.$$

The largest number in this set is 12, and hence 12 is the GCF of 84 and 60. Suppose we divide 84 and 60 each by 12; the results are 7 and 5, which have no common factor. If, however, we divide 84 and 60 by 6 (another common factor) we obtain 14 and 10, and these numbers have a common factor, 2. In this way pupils come to recognize the important property of a GCF. That is, in the quotients that are obtained by dividing the numbers by the GCF, there can be no common factor.

Another way of finding the GCF is to use the prime factorization of each number. Thus

$$84 = 2 \times 2 \times 3 \times 7, \qquad 60 = 2 \times 2 \times 3 \times 5.$$

The factors common to these two forms are 2, 2, 3, and hence

$$(2 \times 2 \times 3) = 12$$

is the greatest common factor. The pupils must discover that when a common factor occurs more than once in each number, for the greatest common factor we use each factor only the number of times it is in common with each factored form. Thus, in the example

$$84 = 2 \times 2 \times 3 \times 7 \qquad \text{and} \qquad 90 = 2 \times 3 \times 3 \times 5,$$

the greatest common factor is $(2 \times 3) = 6$, since the factors 2 and 3 are *in common* only once in the factored forms.

A common multiple of two or more numbers is certainly their product, for this is the way we use the word multiple. Thus, for 84 and 90, the product $(84 \times 90) = 7560$ is a common multiple.

But there may be a smaller number which is a common multiple, for example 3780 is, because $90 \times 42 = 3780$ and $84 \times 45 = 3780$. Is there a smallest number which has both 90 and 84 as divisors?

We can link the answer to finding the prime factorization of these numbers. Any number for which 84 is a divisor must contain all the prime factors of 84, and similarly for 90. Thus the least number which divides both 84 and 90 is one that contains at least all the factors of both numbers. Further, it must contain any factor as many times as it occurs in each number, but no more. Thus for 84 and 90, the LCM is $2 \times 2 \times 3 \times 3 \times 5 \times 7$, or 1260. Pupils should explain why we need the factors 2 and 3 each twice, but no more and no less.

A good strategy for finding the LCM of two (or more) numbers, say 484 and 66, is to write each in prime factorization form:

$$484 = 2 \times 2 \times 11 \times 11, \qquad 66 = 2 \times 3 \times 11.$$

Start with either indicated product, preferably the one which looks "longer," and ask, "What do I need for the other numbers that I do not already have?" If we start with $2 \times 2 \times 11 \times 11$, we already have the '2' and '11' we need for the other number; we still need a '3'. The LCM of 484 and 66 is $2 \times 2 \times 11 \times 11 \times 3$, or 1452. If there are more than two numbers, continue in the same way.

Finally pupils should compare the two ways in which they used the prime factorization of two numbers to find the GCF* and LCM. The first, for the GCF, is to select only those factors common to both numbers, and use them as many times as they are in common. The second, for the LCM, is to select all factors which are in both numbers, and use them the greater number of times they occur in one of the factors.

6-6 EXPONENTS

Pupils should be introduced to exponents as indicating a new operation in arithmetic, called *raising to a power*. Thus they already know what $4 + 2, 4 - 2, 4 \times 2$, and $4 \div 2$ mean. We now have

---

* The GCF is also referred to as a GCD, or *greatest common divisor*.

a new operation,

$$4^2 \qquad \text{which means} \qquad 4 \times 4, \qquad \text{so} \qquad 4^2 = 16.$$

Similarly,

$$2^3 \qquad \text{means} \qquad 2 \times 2 \times 2, \qquad \text{so} \qquad 2^3 = 8,$$

but

$$3^2 \qquad \text{means} \qquad 3 \times 3, \qquad \text{so} \qquad 3^2 = 9.$$

The second number in each case, written in a superior position, is called an *exponent*. The first number is called the *base*. The meaning is clearly shown by examples. The exponent shows the number of times the base is to be used as a factor to obtain the result called a *power*:

$$3^2 \qquad\qquad \to 9$$
$$\text{base}^{\text{exponent}} \to \text{power}.$$

At the start children must be taught to use the appropriate language. Thus

$3^2 = 9$ is read "the second power of 3 is 9," or "3 squared is 9."
$2^3 = 8$ is read "the third power of 2 is 8," or "2 cubed is 8."
$4^3 = 64$ is read "the third power of 4 is 64," or "4 cubed is 64."

There is no special name for powers higher than 3; 2^5 is read "the fifth power of 2." Next the procedure should be reversed and the expressions to the right of 'is read' should be translated into the symbolic form to the left. Finally pupils should give the factored form of a power, such as

$$3^5 = \underbrace{3 \times 3 \times 3 \times 3 \times 3}_{5 \text{ factors}}$$

or simplify a factored form into exponential form, such as

$$2 \times 2 \times 2 \times 3 \times 3 = 2^3 \times 3^2.$$

For the purposes of number work in elementary school no further extension of the use of exponents is necessary.

Now, we can write a factored form of a given number in a more abbreviated style. If we wished to factor 504, we could proceed in the following manner:

$$504 = 2 \times 252 = 2^2 \times 126 = 2^3 \times 63$$
$$= 2^3 \times 3 \times 21 = 2^3 \times 3^2 \times 7,$$
$$540 = 2 \times 270 = 2^2 \times 135 = 2^2 \times 3 \times 45$$
$$= 2^2 \times 3^2 \times 15 = 2^2 \times 3^3 \times 5.$$

Then the GCF of 504 and 540 is

$$2^2 \times 3^2 = 4 \times 9 = 36$$

and the LCM of 504 and 540 is

$$2^3 \times 3^3 \times 5 \times 7 = 8 \times 27 \times 35 = 7560.$$

It is in this fashion that exponents and number theory give much practice in multiplication and division, as well as deeper insight into the processes themselves.

EXERCISES

1. Describe two procedures for partitioning a set of elements into equivalent subsets (or parts) which could be used to develop the concept of division of cardinal numbers. Describe the precise language you would use in each procedure.

2. a) Show that the division operation is not an inverse of the binary multiplication operation; that is, that some products have several different ordered pairs of factors.
   b) Show that a single exact division fact has a unique multiplication fact related to it, and hence the unary operation of multiplying by 4 has an inverse operation: dividing by 4.
   c) Explain how you would teach division facts by using previously established facts in multiplication.
   d) Explain how, once the meanings of the two processes are established, you might teach new multiplication and division facts together; that is, as multiplication-division families.

3. Explain how you would teach children that zero may not be used as a divisor. How do you teach zero as a dividend?

4. If $8 \div 4 \div 2$ means $(8 \div 4) \div 2$, show that division is not associative.

5. Compare the algorism of division as explained in the text with the following description as to (1) understanding, and (2) efficiency:

Round 28 to 30. Divide 3 into 13, quotient 4.

$$
\begin{array}{r}
480 \\
28\overline{)13456} \\
112 \\
\hline
225 \\
224 \\
\hline
16
\end{array}
$$

Place the '4' above the '4' in the dividend and multiply 28 by 4. Subtract 112 from 134. The difference is 22. Compare it with 28. Since it is less than 28, bring down the '5' from the dividend. Divide 3 into 22, quotient 7. Try 7. $7 \times 28 = 196$. Subtract from 225. The difference is 29. This is too large compared with 28. Erase and use 8 as trial quotient number. $8 \times 28 = 224$. Subtract from 225. Remainder 1. Bring down the '6' from the dividend. 16 is less than 28. Put a '0' in the ones place in the quotient. Answer: 480 R 16.

6. The best way to practice a computational procedure is to use it in acquiring a new procedure. Show in this respect how one practices estimation, multiplication, and subtraction when one is learning the division algorism.

7. Discuss the pros and cons of teaching the number theory of prime factorization, GCF, LCM, and exponents before formally presenting operations on fractions. Consider the use of the material and the motivation.

8. Show how you would rationalize the Euclidean algorism for finding the LCM of 24, 35, 30. Here a common factor is removed from the numbers, and if a number does not have the factor, that number is retained until a factor of it occurs. Would you teach this? Defend your answer.

2	24	35	30
2	12	35	15
2	6	35	15
3	3	35	15
5	1	35	5
7	1	7	1
	1	1	1

LCM $= 2 \times 2 \times 2 \times 3 \times 5 \times 7 = 840$

9. a) Illustrate by a diagrammatic device how the four operations on cardinal numbers are related.
   b) Make an outline of the order in which the operations are learned, the fundamental principles of the operations, and their relation to fundamental operations on sets.

154

10. A short method of division by a single-digit divisor is shown in the margin. Explain the algorism. Would you teach this method in the elementary school? If so, why, how, and when would you present it to a class?

$$\begin{array}{r} 841 \text{ R } 4 \\ 8\overline{)67^33^12} \end{array}$$

REFERENCES

FEHR, H. F., "Sense and Nonsense in a Modern School Mathematics Program," *The Arithmetic Teacher* **13,** February 1966, pages 83–91

LUNG, C., "Division Made Easy," *The Arithmetic Teacher* **10,** November 1953, pages 453–454

PECK, L. C., and D. NISWONGER, "Measurement and Partition—Commutativity of Multiplication," *The Arithmetic Teacher* **11,** April 1964, pages 258–259

RUDDELL, A. K., "Levels of Difficulty in Division," *The Arithmetic Teacher* **6,** March 1959, pages 97–99

fundamentals
of
geometry

One of the major differences between the old and the new programs in elementary school mathematics is the inclusion of appreciable amounts of geometry in the new programs, beginning in kindergarten. The word *geometry* comes from two Greek words meaning "earth measure" and the origin of this subject dates back several thousand years to the time when lands were remeasured after floods had obliterated established boundaries. Little by little the general properties of boundaries, shapes, and sizes were refined and expanded into an abstract theory of the world as it appeared around us. For two thousand years, this geometry, as represented by Euclid, was the only geometry in existence. Today there are several different geometries, all of which have little or nothing to do with land measurement. However, most geometries have both nonmetric (shape, position, relation) and metric (size, distance) aspects.

All the geometric things (entities) which we shall discuss are to be considered as subsets of a *space*. By a space we merely mean a set of all points under consideration. We make no attempt to define 'point'. We say that a point has no size, and no shape, and the word 'point' is roughly synonymous with 'place' or 'position'. The space we study in elementary school is roughly the set of points everywhere about us, and it is called *Euclidean space*, and the properties of this space comprise Euclidean geometry. While it is the same geometry that most persons studied in high school, we do not teach it to young children the same way it is taught in high school. In this chapter we shall investigate those aspects of Euclidean geometry which are not particularly concerned with measurement. We shall speak of relations which have something to do with size, such as congruence and order, but not ways of measuring geometric objects.

7-1 REASONS FOR STUDYING GEOMETRY

The daily life of all persons involves spatial relations, both qualitative and quantitative. Every child has a modest amount of geometric knowledge learned from experience, and this experience, guided by a well-conceived instructional program, can teach him more, with less effort, than he is likely to learn by himself.

It seems likely that the geometry taught in high schools in the coming decade will be based on the assumption that students enter the course with a knowledge of the facts of Euclidean geometry. This implies that these facts must be learned in elementary school. Furthermore, geometric intuition is an important prelude to working with a deductive system. A student who is to understand the proofs of his high school geometry, and more important, to devise proofs of his own, will be at a great advantage if his geometric intuition has been developed over a period of years.

Geometry provides one of the best vehicles for developing intuitions about mathematical relations of all kinds. It lends itself admirably to a laboratory approach, by which children can learn methods of inquiry. They can be taught to observe (to see what is there), to record pertinent observations, to make predictions and conjectures, and to test these and formulate conclusions.

Through the ages geometry has been an important tool for all sorts of vocational applications—from carpentry to physical science to art—and it remains so today. Qualitative intuitions of spatial properties and quantitative understandings applied to measurement and properties associated with measurement are probably more necessary for the non-college-bound student than for the college-bound.

By no means the least compelling of reasons for teaching geometry in the elementary school is that young children invariably enjoy it, provided that the geometry they are learning does not consist entirely of a long list of terms. Geometric vocabulary is valuable in itself, but it is no more a substitute for geometry than a dictionary is a substitute for a novel. If we let children explore the world around them, and give enough guidance to channel their explorations toward some sort of possible future organization of their discoveries, they are happy and productive, and furthermore have facts and understandings that they can use in their daily lives, whatever their chronological ages.

The first goal of instruction in geometry in the elementary school is that students become acquainted with the facts of geometry. They name, they classify, they generalize, they discover properties of figures of one, two, and three dimensions; they acquire concepts which are immediately useful to them as well as a storehouse of knowledge for future use.

7–2 GEOMETRY FOR ELEMENTARY SCHOOL PUPILS

Geometric entities, like numbers, are abstract. Just as no one has ever seen the number 3, although he may have seen three objects which he could use in studying about the number, so no one has ever seen a point or a line, although he may have seen objects which he could use to study these, and other, geometric entities.

The geometric entities we study are sets of points. A line is a set of points; a triangle is a set of points; a plane is a set of points; a cylindrical region is a set of points; but we cannot pick up a point and show it to someone. We represent a point by a dot. The dot is not a point. The most puny dot we can draw covers millions of points. Similarly, we represent a line by a streak made by a pencil or crayon. The streak is not a line, because the thinnest streak we can make has some width and some thickness, and a line has neither. Nevertheless, for the young child, we do not belabor these distinctions. We call the dot a point; we call the streak a line; we call the surface we use to picture the interior of a triangle together with its boundary a region.

The teacher must understand the role of definition, the difference between a definition and a description, and the use of undefined terms. The teacher must understand, also, that erudite talk about undefined terms and classifying an object and distinguishing said object from other members of its class, and the like, means little to young children. Descriptions should be refined as a child grows more mature, and careful descriptions can lead into precise definitions eventually.

From a kindergarten child we have the following description of a rectangle: "A rectangle has two same longs and two same shorts, and if it has four same longs, it's a square." Young children should learn the geometric names of the shapes they see. This kindergarten child could surely pick out models of rectangles in his classroom, or anywhere else. His description is fine for a five-year-old. It would not be acceptable from a ten-year-old. Why not? Can you draw a picture of an object which fits his description and which is not a rectangle? Possibly, when the same kindergarten child gets to be about seven years older, he will describe a rectangle as a quadrilateral with congruent diagonals each of which bisects the other and a square as a rectangle whose diagonals are perpendicular.

The wise teacher does not start out with definitions, or even with descriptions, of geometric figures. He shows several examples. He uses models he can let the children see and feel. The children learn to recognize the shapes they call triangles, rectangles, circles, and so on, in the same way that they learn to recognize the shapes they call chairs, and to *use* their geometric vocabulary just as they use their general vocabulary. As they acquire more experience, they refine their concepts of these terms. Each time we classify an object, we are recognizing its membership in some set. Whether we realize it or not, we spend a large part of our lives in becoming aware of sets, and we cannot expect a young child to have the same degrees of awareness as an adult.

Up to the age of eleven or twelve years, children should consider geometric figures to be things you can see or feel. It is all right, perhaps even desirable, to speak occasionally of the abstractions (a line is not hot or cold, it is not heavy or light, it is not blue or pink, you cannot see it but you know it is there, and so on), but geometry at elementary levels is physical, concrete. We use physical models of the abstractions which are the geometric entities, but we do not keep reminding the children that it is models we are using. They fold paper and the creases become segments or lines, depending on the *use* they have for the creases at the time. They pick up solid figures, feel the edges, count the corners, feel the surfaces, name the shapes, speculate *what might happen if* the thing were cut in a certain way, and so on.

7–3 DEVELOPING GEOMETRIC CONCEPTS

Elementary school geometry has its origins in the world of *things*. The modern mathematics classroom is, in a real sense, a laboratory. It is not possible to assign a grade level or even a specific sequence to the topics under discussion. A concept in geometry is not an either-you-have-it-or-you-don't entity; it is a matter of degree. Descriptions are refined over a period of years until they become precise definitions. The same pupil should learn more each year about the geometry he has already had, as well as some topics which may be new to him. *A long period of informal acquaintance with a topic should precede its formal presentation.*

Before we can have a geometry lesson at any level, we have to be sure the children can make appropriate classifications and see simple relations. One way to determine this is to put two or more boxes on a table, dump out a heap of something (scrap lumber, small toys, play money, almost anything which is convenient and safe for children to handle) and ask the children, one at a time, to put the objects into the boxes. Before each one starts, he is to have some sort of plan. The other children are to try to figure out what his plan is. One child may classify by color, another by size, another by shape, another by weight, another by the kind of material (if not all objects in the heap are made of the same material), another by the use he envisions for the object, another by its position on the table, and so on. There are no correct or incorrect "plans" in this activity. There is always more than one way to classify something, depending on the attributes which are chosen as bases for classification.

It is relevant to question whether one plan may be more useful than another. Then the next question is, "useful for what?" A great deal of learning can come from discussing the variety of plans and from checking to see whether a child has really followed the plan he had. If a part of his plan was to "put all the three-cornered things in this box," we should find out what he means by *corner*, and then the other children should check to see whether all the things in that box have three corners, and, just as important, whether there are any three-cornered things which are not in that box.

Sometimes we need to find out what ideas the children have about something before we attempt to do a lesson on it. For example, one second-grade teacher drew pictures like these on the chalk-board and asked the children what they saw.

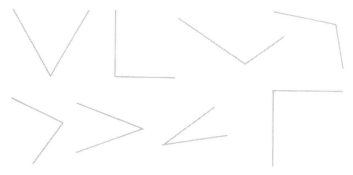

Here are some of the replies: birds; sea gulls; roofs of houses; airplanes; children playing "freeze"; corners; *some of them are angles.* The class as a whole agreed that each of these replies was "okay." Now for the revealing feature: which ones are angles? (First we'll number the pictures so we don't have to run up and point.) Everyone agreed that the first one (top left) is an angle, and the fourth one (top right) is not. There was some disagreement about the second one and the last one (the right angles). To these children—and they are typical of children at their maturity level—an acute angle is an angle, a right angle is a square corner but you may call it an angle if you insist, and an obtuse angle is something else. Is this the time to tell these children that, whether they like it or not, an angle is the set of points which is the union of two noncollinear rays with a common endpoint?

It might be wiser to give each child a piece of paper, ask him to fold it once just any old way, and then fold it again, but this time crease it so that the first fold falls along itself. Then ask the children what kind of corner they have folded (a square corner; a right angle by the most impeccable mathematical standards, one of four congruent angles surrounding a point of a plane). Now we can tell the children that 'right angle' is another name for square corner and that they can classify the pictures on the chalkboard, and all sorts of other objects in the room, according to whether these objects are or are not examples of right angles. How do they determine this? They take their sample right angle and place it appropriately against whatever they may be testing. If it just fits, the other object is classified under 'is'; otherwise the objects belong in the 'is not' category. Note that this activity involves no consideration of angle measure.

For an example not only of how revealing it may be to ask the children about a topic before you start to teach it but also of how much fun it can be, consider the following dialog which took place in a third-grade class. (Supply appropriate gestures.)

T: Tell me what you know about a circle.

P_1: It's round.

P_2: It doesn't have points like a triangle.

P_3: If you draw it on a piece of paper, and you turn the paper around, it looks the same to you any way you turn it.

P_4: It's plump.

P_5: It has to roll, like a tire.

P_6: It won't roll unless the paper is stiff.

P_1: It's something like a ball, but it's not the same as a ball.

P_2: It's smooth, no bumps, no dents.

P_7: Yes, it's the only thing you can use for a wheel and get a smooth ride.

. . .

T (hoping to evoke the thought of an oval or ellipse): Can you think of something which is somewhat like a circle but which isn't really a circle?

P_1: Well, if you took a hexagon and smoothed those corners off, . . . (!)

T: How do you draw an egg?

P_3: That's something like a circle.

P_7: So's a watermelon.

. . .

T: Look around the room and see if you can find something shaped like a circle.

P_s: (almost in unison) Your face.

Most of the courses of study for elementary school mathematics in the United States in the late nineteen-sixties treat geometry components as they are treated in the sample units prepared by the School Mathematics Study Group for elementary grades. This

approach imposes a point-set vocabulary, together with a few re-
finements, on Euclid's way of looking at space. Other approaches
are being tried, and in a few years, geometry based on isometries
(distance-preserving mappings) or vectors may even be available
for use with elementary school children.

Unless a classroom teacher has both the talent and the time to
develop a creditable, structured course of his own for his class to
use, he is well-advised to follow the development outlined in his
textbook or a course of study. He can supplement the course by
suitable extensions and even by presenting a different point of
view for some topics, but he should be sure his lessons include the
mainstream of the course of study.

Regardless of the approach to geometry used in the course of
study, the teacher should have on hand all sorts of things for the
children to see and handle. Scrap lumber or plastic or metal
sheeting (no splinters and no sharp edges), scraps of soundproofing
material or pegboard, an assortment of hardware items, a bag of
assorted building blocks of different sizes and shapes, pieces of
dowel sticks, strips of poster paper or tag, masking tape: in short,
all sorts of things which can be used as models, or to make models.
The teacher should make learning aids for his class.

7-4 ESSENTIAL PRIMITIVE CONCEPTS

The primary teacher, as well as the teacher of pre-first-grade
classes, should discuss with the children the sizes and shapes of all
sorts of objects in the classroom. Technical vocabulary is not
important at these levels. Pick out things in the classroom which
are "just alike." Are these objects the same size? Are they the
same shape? What is meant by "same shape"? For these children,
the faces of blocks are squares, the block itself is a cube, sides of
boxes are rectangles, the doorway is a rectangle, the face of the
clock is a circle, probably, and so on. All squares are the same
shape; so are all circles. All rectangles are not the same shape.
The children need an intuitive grasp of these ideas. There should
be discussions about which of two blocks is larger and how you can
tell which. Perhaps they are the same size. How can you tell that?

Children should have much experience with casual use of
geometric terms before these terms are taught or discussed point-

edly. A child does not need to know how to describe a circle before he can recognize the shape of a circle, for example. He can find points inside the circle, outside the circle, and on the circle. He can be given worksheets with instructions to color in each circle, trace the lines which make pictures of squares, mark just one point on each triangle, and so on.

After children have done things like this and have handled objects on which they have felt the corners and the edges, compared the shapes and sizes, classified some of the objects under 'same shape' and/or 'same size', they may be ready to discuss informally the attributes an object must have if it is to be called by a certain name.

Experiments have shown that young children will recognize as having the same shape two squares, for instance, which are different sizes, but are "sitting the same way" long before they recognize the similarity of two squares which are the same size but are "sitting different ways."

Until a child has reached a certain maturity level, arrived at, under average circumstances, at about age seven, he does not realize that the same tile which he recognizes as a square in one position still has the same shape if he rotates it less than a quarter turn. Most people who work with young children believe that the process by which a child reaches certain maturity levels can be speeded up by properly constructed activities. The alert teacher seizes every opportunity to begin sentences with "what if . . ." or "suppose. . . ." "What shape is the bottom of this box? What if I hold it this way? . . . Suppose I hold it behind me so that you can't see it. What shape is it then? . . ."

7-5 TEACHING GEOMETRIC TERMS AND SYMBOLS

When children have arrived at the stage at which they are ready to describe the attributes an object must have if it is to be classified as a square (or any other specific figure), they have been through the stages of aural recognition and oral use of the word, at least. Possibly they have also seen how it is written and they know how, or are ready to learn, to read it. Hearing, saying, seeing, reading, learning to spell a word, all depend on clarity of perception. Whatever techniques are used in the reading program should be used in teaching geometric vocabulary. Even primary school children can be helped by appropriate descriptions of the derivation of words. Take the word 'triangle', for instance. Ask the children what other words they know that have the little word 'tri' in them. They surely know 'tricycle', and they probably know others. How is a tricycle different from a bicycle? What does 'triangle' mean? Three angles, literally. Children can learn to use this word correctly and to read it long before they can learn to spell it. (Spelling it requires them to differentiate between 'angle' and 'angel'.)

Over a period of years, the children should learn to appreciate the technical vocabulary. Properly used in its technical sense, it has a precise meaning, and frequently the use of the technical word is the only way this precise meaning can be expressed without a long and cumbersome discourse. Technical words are economical. A child mature enough to learn the word 'isosceles' will think it pretty neat that "two sides alike" is all in that one word.

Some children love to learn long words. Syllable counts notwithstanding, teachers know that 'parallelogram' is easier to contend with than 'which' or 'with'. Middle graders can even learn to spell 'parallelogram' and other long words which are easier to spell. One fifth grader whose teacher had trouble remembering whether the 'r' or the first 'l' was doubled explained, "Write it in manuscript (**parallelogram**) and you can see two little parallel lines."

Geometric symbols are extremely easy to learn, because most of the time they are little pictures of the objects or relations they represent. How do you read '$\overline{AB} \perp \overline{XY}$'? Just read the pictures: Segment AB is perpendicular to segment XY. How do you read '$\triangle ABC$' or '$\odot C$'? Read the pictures. How do you write 'is parallel to'? Just make two parallel strokes with your pencil: ‖. At first the symbol for 'is congruent to' may have to be learned by brute force ($\cong$), but when the children have learned about similarity, they may notice that the symbol for 'is similar to' looks like a letter 'S' (lying down backward, the way it is printed in most books) and 'S' is the first letter of 'similar'. Then they may deduce that congruent figures are not only similar, but "equal" in a certain sense (a congruence is a restriction on a similarity; the ratio of similitude is 1); and if you combine the symbols for similarity and equality, you get the symbol for congruence.

There are many mnemonic devices, some of them seemingly farfetched or even ridiculous, which help children remember words and other symbols. The teacher should ask different children to share their schemes for remembering these things. This usually helps the other children, and sometimes it helps the teacher.

7–6 LINEAR FIGURES

It is hard to find anyone who will advocate teaching fractions before whole numbers, but it is easy to find people who will argue that lines should be taught before segments, and vice versa. Consistent, understandable treatments of geometry can be developed either way. A similar remark can be made about other geometric entities. We shall give some suggestions for teaching a few concepts, expecting the reader to extrapolate, and recognizing the existence of productive alternatives which space (in a book of this kind) prohibits our describing.

Suppose we wish to develop the meaning of 'segment', perhaps in a primary class. One way to do this is to mark two spots on the floor, ask the children if it is all right if we call these spots 'points' (they always agree), and have different children show different ways they can walk from one point to the other. Keep doing this until at least one child walks "straight" from one point to the other. Draw on the chalkboard pictures of the paths the children have taken. Then ask the children to pretend they have wings and *think* what other paths they might take. These paths cannot be pictured realistically on the flat chalkboard, but gestures will suffice. Now ask, "Of all the possible paths, is there at least one shortest path? Is there exactly one shortest path? Which path is that?" Explain that we call the set of points along this shortest path (we do not quibble at this time on what 'shortest' means), together with the two points we had at first, *a straight line segment*, or *segment* for short. If we wish to talk about, or write about, this segment, we have to give it a name. First, we had better tag the points. Let's use capital letters as names for the points. Be sure the children understand that, in pictures, the dots are the points; the letters are just names. Now we can name the segment which has these points as *endpoints* by using the word 'segment' and the names of the two points.

This picture shows the line segment PQ. (It also shows the line segment QP.)

P •————————————————————• Q

We practice drawing and naming segments. Somewhat later, we want a shorthand way to write 'segment PQ', so we write the letters with a little picture of a segment across the top of them: $\overline{PQ}$ or $\overline{QP}$.

If we wish to develop the concept of a *line* from what we know about a segment, we can start with two points again, on the floor, on a desk, or on any flat surface. We ask the children to pretend that they are magic people and that each of them has a magic car. This magic car can go everywhere. Nothing stops it. It can go through anything: wood, stone, bricks, dirt, air, water, even empty space. Furthermore, it never runs out of gas.

Now, each of them is sitting in his car on top of one point and headed for the other. He just gets started when the steering mechanism locks. How far can he go in the direction he is headed? If the steering mechanism is the only thing wrong with the car, can it back up? How far can it go backward? The set of points along the path the car can go forward and backward is called the line through the two points we started with. A line has *no endpoints*. How can we draw a picture of a line when we wish to show that it goes on and on forever in both directions? We need some way of showing that the ends of our picture do not show the ends of the line. Here are two ways to do this:

How can we name a line? We could pick two points of the line, name them, say 'A' and 'B', and then call the line containing them *line AB* (or *line BA*). (Does it matter which points of the line we pick or what letters we choose to name them?) We could use a single letter, conventionally lower-case, and speak of *line l* (or *m*, or whatever).

Once we have lines, it's easy to define a *ray*. The only thing to be particularly alert for here is to make sure the children understand that each point of a line can be the endpoint (or vertex) of two rays, and that in naming a ray, we always say the name of its endpoint first.

We use the children's intuitive notions of the words to discuss the distinction between straight lines and curved lines, curves. Apparently, so long as a line bends in some way, it does not matter to them whether it bends gradually or abruptly. They are comfortable in referring to either of the two pictures in the margin as curves.

Now they can pick out *open figures* and *closed figures*. If we want them to, they will call any closed figure a *closed curve*. Closed figures have an inside and an outside. If they are *simple closed figures* (or *curves*) it is possible to pick out points of the *interior* and *exterior*. Try it with these.

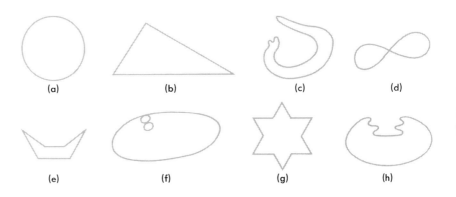

In drawings (d) and (f), one may ask of a given point, "Which part of the closed figure is it inside of?" When this question is necessary, the figure is not one we call *simple*. Since a simple closed figure "never crosses itself anywhere," we can color in the figure without lifting the crayon or crossing its boundary.

In elementary school, the simple closed figures we deal with most often are circles and polygons.

A circle (or other closed curve) may be defined as a region of a plane, but most current programs define it as a line figure. Polygons are a particular kind of union of segments. As such, each polygon has a length, the length of the segment you would get if you cut the polygon at any point and straightened it out. A circle also has a length, the length of the segment you would get if you cut the circle at any point and straightened it out.

To lead up to a mathematical definition of a circle, we may have children make drawings or stand in prescribed positions, depending on their maturity level. The teacher may stand with his arms stretched straight out at the sides and ask two children to come up and stand in a place so that each of the teacher's longest fingers touches one nose. The teacher then rotates his body about 30° and asks two more children to do the same thing. He repeats this until there is no room for any more children. How are the children standing? In a ring? In a *circle*? Where is the teacher? In the middle? In the *center*? Suppose we had exceptionally thin children. Could more of them stand *in the same circle*? It is easy to see how to do a comparable activity on a piece of paper, or on the chalkboard. For measuring the distance of each point from the center, it is better to use something other than a ruler: a certain kind of pencil or a filing card, perhaps.

When we are teaching the names and properties of the different polygons, it is important to have some organizational scheme running through the development so that the children are not faced with the impossible task of learning a myriad of unrelated facts. Charts or tables, Venn diagrams, tree diagrams, and the like should be used extensively to help the children structure their knowledge. The following several paragraphs describe one "for instance."

Children discover easily that the smallest number of segments that can be joined end to end to make a closed figure is three. They know that the name of a figure like this is *triangle*. At some point, they learn that triangles are classified in two ways: by the relative lengths of their sides and by the relative sizes of their angles.

They learn that any figure which is the union of segments in the same way that a triangle is the union of segments (joined end to end, and having no points of intersection other than endpoints) is called a *polygon*. They learn that all four-sided polygons may be called *quadrilaterals*. Now they can agree that if they had a barrel (imaginary, of course) which contained all the polygons in the world, there would be some quadrilaterals in that barrel. They might even say that the set of quadrilaterals is a subset of the set of polygons. This relation among polygons and quadrilaterals may be pictured as shown in the diagram in the margin. What takes up the rest of the space inside the loop for polygons? Put in some more loops and label them with other names of polygons the children know. Make it very clear that the relative sizes of these loops have nothing to do with the relative sizes of the subsets. All the loops do is show relations among classi-

Polygons

Quadri-
laterals

fications, and at elementary levels, the loops should not overlap if the intersection of the corresponding sets is empty.

When the children have learned subclassifications of quadrilaterals, the diagram can be expanded, in stages, until (probably in sixth grade) it looks like this:

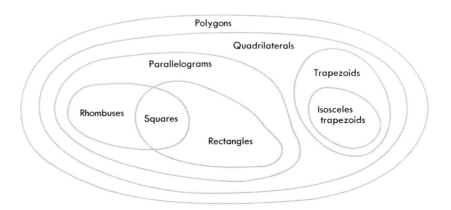

A child who understands a diagram like this will be able to make statements such as: All trapezoids are quadrilaterals. Not all trapezoids are isosceles. (Note how important it is to place the word 'not' where it belongs in a statement like the preceding one. "All trapezoids are not isosceles" means something entirely different. It is, in fact, a false statement.) Rectangles are special kinds of parallelograms. We could make a great big loop outside all these and label it 'simple closed curves'. Depending on the definitions given, a square is a rhombus, a rectangle, a parallelogram, a quadrilateral, a polygon, and a simple closed figure.

The teacher should make profuse use of graphic devices to show classifications and relations, and should encourage his pupils to invent graphic devices of their own. A child who even thinks about how to show something pictorially or graphically is forced to organize his knowledge, and if he completes the chart, he helps others as well as himself.

For three or four years, a plane is just a flat surface which goes on and on, as a line does. Plane regions, like segments, are bounded. Eventually, a situation will arise wherein the concept that a surface has no depth must be introduced. Perhaps the best physical analogy to use for that is a shadow. With a flashlight and a cardboard cutout of a rectangle, the teacher can make a shadow on some flat surface. The children can *see* this shadow; they can move their hands over the surface of the shadow; they can even measure its length and width. They can neither feel nor measure any depth, or thickness.

Any solid object which can be held in the hand, by an ordinary person or by a super-giant, is a model of a region of three-space.

7-7 ORDERING BY SIZE

When children attempt to compare the size of a first object with that of a second object, the results may fall into four categories: smaller than, larger than, same size, can't tell. A comparison may fall into the 'can't tell' category for two reasons: (1) the children do not have available for use at the time the criteria (e.g., appropriate definitions) to enable them to make the comparison, as might be the case if they tried to compare the volumes of two differently shaped solids, or the areas of a square and a circle; (2) the meaning of size with respect to the object may not be clearly understood.

The criteria for making comparison of sizes first come from manipulating the objects or tracings of the objects, or cutouts, and fitting the property to be tested. If we are comparing lengths or areas, we place one object alongside of or on top of the other object. If a first object fits inside a second object, it is smaller than the second; if it fits outside (encloses) the second object, it is larger than the second. It is the *same size* if it *just* fits. If the regions cannot be fitted, that is, if a part of one is inside and a part outside the other, one cannot always tell how the sizes compare. Later, in working with three-dimensional objects which cannot be placed one inside the other, the children have to devise ways of determining relative sizes. They should decide what attributes it makes sense to compare. They learn concepts, and vocabulary, such as *longer than*, *has a smaller surface than*, *has the same volume as*, and the like.

Very soon after they really comprehend the notions of relative size, the children should develop a nonverbal awareness of the transitivity of the *order relation*. The teacher can help them develop this. "John's pencil is longer than Harry's pencil. Harry's pencil is longer than Pete's. Without looking at the pencils, what can you tell me about John's pencil and Pete's?" "Sue is the same height as Ethel. Ethel is the same height as Jean. If what we just said is true, what do we know for sure about Sue and Jean?"

Once children have the primitive concept of comparison at their command, they can learn to make progressively more refined and more complex judgments. Most elementary school programs treat this later work adequately, to the extent that they treat it at all. Here we are calling attention to the fact that all the above considerations are subsidiary understandings which must precede the level at which some programs start.

7–8 CONGRUENCE

Congruence is one of the most important relations in all geometry. To a mathematician, a congruence is a distance-preserving mapping. That is, if two figures are congruent, they have corresponding points such that the distance between two points of one figure is the same as the distance between the corresponding points of the congruent figure. To a child not above sixth-grade level, the noun 'congruence' has implications too sophisticated for him to digest. He can deal with the adjective 'congruent' or the verb 'is congruent to'. He thinks of two figures as congruent if one figure fits *exactly* on the other, or if one figure could be *a carbon copy* or a *tracing* of the other, or if they could have been *made from the same pattern* (no alterations).

The word 'congruent' may be introduced as soon as the children have adequate concepts of size and shape. When children are comparing cutouts (which in the interest of honesty, and for the purpose at hand, should all be made of the same material) and fitting one on the other, they may make remarks like: "Yes, it just fits." "If these two things were the same color, you couldn't tell them apart." "They match all over." "They are exactly alike." "Whoever made these cut them from the same pattern." At this time, the teacher may say, "We have a word which means all the things you have been saying. The word is *congruent* (con gru'ent). Say 'congruent' with me." Then the teacher picks up two congruent cutouts, shows the appropriate matching and says, "Look, these triangles are congruent. These racing cars are congruent. . . . Are these two stars congruent? . . ."

Next the children may check for congruence two pictures which are on separate pieces of paper. How can they do this? Put one piece of paper on top of the other, hold them up to the light, and see if they can make the drawings match. At first, the pictures should be in approximately the same relative location and position on the two pieces of paper. Later, one drawing might have to be turned (rotated) before the pictures will match. Still later, the pictures may be made so that one piece of paper has to be turned over (flipped) before they will match.

When a number of pictures on the same piece of paper are to be tested for congruence, children should be asked for suggestions about how to do this. They may suggest cutting the pictures out. This is a good suggestion, and if the pictures are not on a page in a book, the children might try it. They may find out that, if the pictures differ from one another in some small detail, they have not been able to cut them out carefully enough to guarantee the results they are getting. Then, someone is sure to suggest tracing one figure and comparing the tracing with the other figure. This suggestion really pays off, even when the tracing has to be turned or flipped to make it match the second figure. With this technique, finite sets of discrete points, line figures, and plane regions may be tested for congruence.

From many activities in which they test for congruence a variety of displays of dots, of segments, of lines, of polygons, of circles, of angles, of blobs which indicate the interior of certain bounded figures, and so on, children acquire the intuitive feeling that if two sets are congruent, all their corresponding subsets are congruent. They find out that all lines are congruent, even though the pictures they make of lines may not be. Similarly, all rays are congruent. Two segments are congruent if and only if they have the same length. Two circles are congruent if certain segments associated with the circles (radii and diameters) are congruent. Two squares are congruent if just one side of the first square is congruent to one side of the other. The same criterion does not work for rectangles. Two triangles are congruent when corresponding sides and corresponding angles are congruent.

The children can discover the basic congruence theorems. In this way they get an idea of minimal conditions. A sixth-grader made a significant statement in this connection when he said, about triangles, "If you have three pairs of congruent sides, it forces you to have three pairs of congruent angles. It does not work the other way." He did not know it but he was stating one version of the side-side-side congruence theorem and was saying, in effect, that a converse of that version is not true. In the fifth and sixth grades, the children may be encouraged to make statements of minimal conditions for congruence of all kinds of figures. Consider two regular hexagons. They are congruent if just one side of the first is congruent to one side of the second. Consider two hexagons which are not regular hexagons. Does just one pair of congruent sides guarantee congruence of these hexagons? Why not? (The other necessary congruences are implied in the definition of a regular polygon: all sides and all angles congruent.)

It is hard to develop experimental techniques for testing three-dimensional figures for congruence. The most productive intuitive notion is "could have been made from the same pattern." To achieve more precision than that requires a lot of preliminary work on determining correspondences under three isometric mappings of a space onto itself: slides (translations), turns (rotations), and flips (reflections). When the children have become proficient in finding images of points of a figure under one or more of these transformations (all intuitive and informal at this level), they can devise ways of testing the distances between all possible pairs of corresponding points to see whether these distances are the same. Wallpaper samples are excellent material for the study of congruence, similarity, and symmetry.

7-9 SIMILARITY

The word 'similar' has a precise meaning in geometry. The teacher should avoid using this word in a nontechnical sense in a mathematical context.

'Congruent' is sometimes said to mean 'same size, same shape'. This is fine for some purposes, but what might a person mean if he said that two angles were the same shape, for example? In the same vein, 'similar' is sometimes said to mean 'same shape, but not necessarily the same size'. There are times when that does not tell us what we need to know.

We need measurement to define similarity adequately, but we can develop intuitive notions of similarity before measurements of

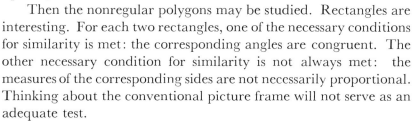

segments and angles are introduced. We do this by the same techniques we used with congruence. If teachers know that a congruence is a restriction on a similarity, they see to it that the initial activities they plan for dealing with similar figures do not make use of this sophisticated concept. They start with circles, perhaps, no two the same size. The children place one of these on top of another and they notice two things: (1) one is smaller than the other; (2) if the smaller is placed on top of the larger, it can be positioned so that "there is the same margin all the way around," or "it looks like a picture frame." Activities of the same kind can be done with the various regular polygons, equilateral triangles, squares, and so on.

Then the nonregular polygons may be studied. Rectangles are interesting. For each two rectangles, one of the necessary conditions for similarity is met: the corresponding angles are congruent. The other necessary condition for similarity is not always met: the measures of the corresponding sides are not necessarily proportional. Thinking about the conventional picture frame will not serve as an adequate test.

The inventive teacher can plan fascinating activities which develop intuitive notions of similarity for all sorts of irregular figures. When a photograph is enlarged, or printed in any variety of sizes from the same negative, all such prints are similar. (Prints of the same size are congruent.) Properly constructed scale models of any object are similar to the original and to one another. In particular, all scale drawings of the same object are similar.

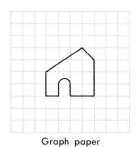

Graph paper

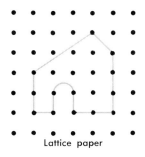

Lattice paper

Children from about fourth grade up can make a larger or smaller scaled version of the same drawing by the simple expedient of using graph paper with more or fewer squares to the square inch. Lattice paper can serve the same purpose.

Obviously this technique saves the children from having to do any measuring or any computing with fractions. All they have to do mentally is to think something like this: "Let's see. If I start here, go over three and up two, I have this point. Now, from here, I go . . ."

An overhead projector can be used to advantage in many situations, and the topic at hand is a case in point. The projected image, if not distorted, is similar to the original. With a specific projectural, moving the machine forward or backward produces images similar to one another. Think what a teacher might do with such images projected on the chalkboard instead of on a screen.

A word of caution about the use of an overhead projector may be in order. It should not be used so extensively that mathematics becomes, for the children, a spectator sport.

7–10 SYMMETRY

Whenever the children make a cutout of any kind by using a pattern of half of it laid along a fold of a piece of paper, they are making a symmetrical object. In these cases, the objects have line symmetry, *symmetry about a line*, the line being that of the fold in the paper.

Teachers know that there are three kinds of symmetry: symmetry about a point, symmetry about a line, and symmetry about a plane. When a figure (a single object or a collection of objects) has one or more of these symmetries, each point of the figure is the *reflection* (*in* the point, line, or plane) of some other point of the figure, and conversely.

A sphere is sometimes described as having perfect symmetry. It is symmetrical about a point (its center), about countless numbers of lines (any line through its center), and about countless numbers of planes (any plane through its center). The test for symmetry is essentially the same for all cases. Consider a sphere and its center. Pick any point on the sphere, go to its center, go that same distance past its center in the same straight line, and you always land on another point of the sphere. Consider a sphere and a line through its center. Pick any point on the sphere. Go from that point to the line by the shortest possible route (along a line perpendicular to the given line), go the same distance past the line, and you always

176

land on another point of the sphere. Consider the sphere and a plane through its center. Surely the reader can supply the next sentence.

The word 'reflection' suggests the phrase 'mirror image'. The use of mirrors, real or imaginary, is useful in studying symmetries, and particularly so in the case of line symmetry of a plane figure. A line of symmetry is also called an axis of symmetry. Children can locate axes of symmetry in plane figures experimentally by using small hand mirrors. For instance, given an equilateral triangle, they can find three places to put the mirror, each perpendicular to the plane of the triangle, so that the part of the triangle they can see together with its mirror image makes the whole triangle. Given an isosceles triangle, they can find just one such place. For a scalene triangle, there are no such places. In these experiments the line of symmetry is the line in which the mirror meets the paper.

Even better than a mirror for this purpose is a piece of thin clear plastic sheeting. This should be just thick enough to have the rigidity needed for this purpose. (If it is a bit too thick, you get multiple images.) With the plastic, the image of one half of a figure reflects onto the other half. You can see an original and its image at the same time!

Equally useful in exploring line symmetry in plane figures is the technique of tracing them on transparent paper and trying to find ways to fold the paper so that two parts of the figure look like one if you hold the paper up to the light.

Using the "equal distance" idea, middle-grade children discover readily that a square has point symmetry. This does not surprise them. When they discover that any parallelogram has point symmetry, they are usually surprised. They can use any of the techniques described in the preceding paragraphs in exploring plane figures for line symmetry. With a little bit of practice, they get very good at predicting the locations of lines of symmetry. They should always test their predictions. Whenever a plane figure is symmetrical about a line, it is also symmetrical about the plane containing that line and perpendicular to the plane of the figure.

Three-dimensional figures are harder to test for symmetry experimentally. More of the work has to be done mentally. A right circular cone, the only kind of cone children work with, has an axis of symmetry "straight down the middle." It is also symmetrical about any plane containing this line. A cube is symmetrical about a point, about several lines, and about several planes. Making a solid figure out of modeling clay and cutting it up with a knife sometimes helps in discovering planes of symmetry. You see how many ways you can cut it so that one half is a "mirror image" of the other.

7-11 PARALLELISM AND PERPENDICULARITY

Some concept of parallelism and of perpendicularity is required in order to classify polygons and some of the solid figures. For most purposes, an informal description suffices. Two coplanar (that is, in the same plane) lines, or two planes, and also a line and a plane, are parallel if they never intersect. (Remember that both lines and planes are infinite in extent.) Two segments or two plane regions are parallel if the lines or planes of which the segments and regions are subsets are parallel. Two lines or two planes, or a line and a plane, are perpendicular if they meet at right angles (for little children, they make a square corner). Intersecting segments, rays, and plane regions are perpendicular if the lines or planes of which these are subsets meet at right angles. Most geometry programs, especially those developed for elementary school children, do not treat coplanar segments or rays which do not intersect, but are contained in lines that meet at right angles.

So long as parallel lines are discussed only from drawings on paper or the chalkboard, the lines either intersect or they are parallel. Railroad tracks are parallel. How else can we describe railroad tracks? They have to be everywhere the same distance apart, measured along the crossties, if the wheels are to stay on the tracks. This, without using the word, suggests that parallel lines have to be coplanar. The line where a wall of a room meets the floor is parallel to the line where the same wall meets the ceiling. It is not parallel to the line where an adjacent wall meets the ceiling. (These are skew lines.) It is parallel to the line where the opposite wall meets the ceiling, because, if you had a big enough piece of paper, you could trace the relevant segments on that piece of paper and the lines of which these segments are subsets do not intersect; they are everywhere the same distance apart, "straight across."

7–12 AN ILLUSTRATED SEQUENCE OF GEOMETRIC STUDY

All the aspects of congruent figures, symmetry, similarity, per-pendicularity, parallelism, and order, may be brought out by a few sequential lessons on a very limited topic in the second or third school year. The cautions in use of definitions and vocabulary given earlier should be carefully heeded in the teaching. The key words for teaching are: observation, description, manipulation, intuition. The following sequence is for a more intensive study of the square and rectangle either as line figures or as regions. Similar developments can be prepared by the teacher for study of other quadrilaterals, triangles, polygons, or angles.

7–13 THE STUDY OF THE SQUARE AND THE RECTANGLE

1. Talk about square-shaped objects, and show some models both of line (wire) figures and regions (square sheet of paper). Do the same for rectangular shapes. Use counter-examples—a rhombus and a rhomboid (parallelogram not a rectangle)—so that children can distinguish between objects that are in the shape of a square, a rectangle, or not either one.

2. Show many (at least 15) four-sided regions. Ask children to identify the squares and prove that they are square.

Do the same for identifying rectangles. (Here a rectangle is different from a square; only later do we talk about a square as being a special kind of rectangle.)

3. Show designs and drawings containing squares. Have children bring to class similar examples. Do the same for rectangular designs.

4. Use square sheets and fold into smaller squares.

Open

Do the same with rectangles. Compare sizes of squares, and compare length of diagonal and of a side by folding; the diagonal is longer than the side, about half again as long.

5. Give children many small square tiles (1 in. or 1 cm) and make designs. Place squares in all different kinds of positions.

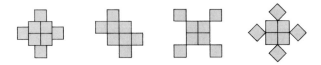

Do the same with small rectangular tiles, 1 cm × 2 cm.

6. Order the square regions by size, decreasing and increasing.

Tell how you do this. Try the same with rectangles. Does it always work? Which is more?

7. Make a square shape out of a rectangular sheet of paper. Check to be sure it is a square by folding each side over on each of the others.

Now make a square from any piece of paper,

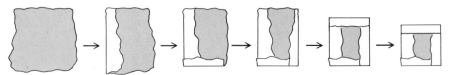

using what you have learned in making a square from a rectangle.

8. Finally compare rectangles and squares by cutting and measuring:

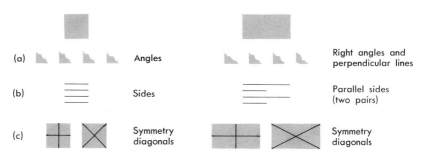

(a)	Angles		Right angles and perpendicular lines
(b)	Sides		Parallel sides (two pairs)
(c)	Symmetry diagonals		Symmetry diagonals

9. Review all the properties given in (1) through (8) above.

7–14 THE COMMON SOLIDS

Solids are usually classified by attributes associated with the shapes and relative positions of their surfaces.

A sphere looks the same any way you turn it. It is absolutely smooth. An ellipsoid is absolutely smooth, too, but "it is longer one way than the other." Any way you cut it in half, though, the two halves are just alike. Not so for an ordinary egg, because although it is oval-shaped, it is not an ellipsoid. A cylindrical solid is smooth around the side and it has a smooth flat top and bottom. The top and bottom are congruent curves (usually circles) and furthermore, the planes containing these curves are parallel. A cone has one flat surface and one smooth surface. Also it comes up to a point, the kind of point we eventually learn to call a vertex. Boxes have smooth sides (faces) and their opposite sides are parallel; also their opposite sides are congruent. Boxes have edges and corners. Some edges of a box are parallel, other edges are perpendicular, other edges are neither. If you look at one corner of an ordinary box, you can see three right angles. . . .

The reader surely realizes that we do not spend seven years at the level indicated in the preceding paragraph. We have merely described some of the observations children have to make before they are ready for a more formal study of solids and for the use of a more technical vocabulary. Many of these observations, fortunately, take place during preschool years.

7–15 SUMMARY

There is no one carefully constructed treatment of Euclidean geometry for elementary school pupils which is clearly superior to all other carefully constructed treatments. Geometry curricula are changing, and this is no cause for alarm. The properties of specific geometric figures remain constant through the ages, although the names by which they are called and the vehicles used for approaching them and making their acquaintance may differ at different times and in different places.

The modern elementary school teacher must operate on the premise that geometry, like a large part of all mathematics, has its origin in the world of things. The modern mathematics classroom is, in a literal sense, a laboratory. The children must learn to observe, to record pertinent observations, to make predictions and conjectures, to test these, and to formulate conclusions. They must learn, and use, vocabulary which is just as precise as their level of understanding allows, and no more.

There is no prescribed sequence for teaching most of the topics in geometry, although some concepts are prerequisite for some others and should be handled accordingly. A long period of informal acquaintance with a topic should precede its formal presentation, and this informal acquaintance should broaden and deepen as the pupils mature. Most topics can be treated in some appropriate way at all grade levels. The emphasis is on observation, on description based on manipulation and sensorial realizations.

Through the use of physical models (things they can see and feel) of geometric abstractions, the children learn the facts of Euclidean geometry. Properly guided, they build this knowledge into a structure in which all the parts fit together. Both the geometry and the way they have learned it are useful to them, immediately and in the future.

EXERCISES

1. Approximately what fraction of an elementary mathematics course should be devoted to geometry? Give reasons for your answer.

2. It is frequently asserted that a principal reason for teaching geometry is the development of mathematical intuition. What does this imply for instruction?

3. You are teaching a sixth-grade class. You are immersed in decimals during your mathematics periods. It is Wednesday. The principal announces that beginning next Monday, the sixth-grade classes will have a special treat: instead of their regular mathematics classes, for three days, they will have televised lessons on the nine-point circle. You have no idea what it is. What do you do? ("Panic" is not an acceptable response.)

4. At what grade level would you introduce the word 'congruent'? At what level would you introduce the concept? How important to the study of mathematics is the concept of congruence?

5. Choose a grade level and list the materials you regard as (1) essential and (2) desirable for teaching geometry at that level. If an annual budget of $50, not including those supplies which a school usually stocks for general use, will not cover your essential items, revise your list.

6. Make a tree diagram, or some other kind of chart, to show classifications of simple closed curves, as alternatives to the Venn-diagram approach to organizing such concepts suggested on page 170.

7. Describe a lesson in which children could learn something about congruent figures, similar figures, and/or symmetrical figures while making decorations for Halloween, Christmas, or some other occasion. Mention the acquaintance with these relations you would expect the children to have before this lesson starts.

8. Make a simple line drawing and describe the way you would teach children to enlarge or shrink it (i.e., make drawings similar to it, in the mathematical sense) by using graph paper or lattice paper.

9. Describe a learning unit in which children explore a variety of quadrilaterals for line symmetry and point symmetry.

10. Would you use the words 'parallel' and 'perpendicular' with children below third-grade level? If not, how would you handle the associated concepts? If so, how would you introduce the words?

REFERENCES

D'AUGUSTINE, C. H., "Topics in Geometry and Point Set Topology," *The Arithmetic Teacher* **11,** October 1964, pages 407–412

FEHR, H. F., and T. J. HILL, *Contemporary Mathematics for Elementary Teachers*, Boston: D. C. Heath, 1966

PHILLIPS, J. M., filmstrip G, "Segments and Polygons," filmstrip H, "Congruent Figures," in *Seeing the Use of Numbers, Set VII*, Eye Gate Productions, Jamaica, N.Y.

ROBINSON, G. E., "The Role of Geometry in Elementary School Mathematics," *The Arithmetic Teacher* **13,** January 1966, pages 3–10

SKYPEK, D. H., "Geometric Concepts in Grades 4–6," *The Arithmetic Teacher* **12,** October 1965, pages 445–449

measures
and
metric geometry

There are two stages in the learning of measures in the elementary school program. The first stage, taught in the first few grades, enables a child to learn the names and uses of common units of measure which he meets in everyday life. Whether he learns this in a science lesson or in a mathematics lesson is of no consequence. The second stage takes place in Grades 4, 5, and 6, where a theory of measure is developed that gives deeper insight into the process. Here the measures of length, area, angular size, and volume properly belong to the study of mathematics. However, measures of weight, capacity, speed, and the like may well be left to science instruction.

8-1 FIRST STEP IN MEASURE

Every child, at an early age, must learn to *tell* time, to *count* money, to *measure out* food, to *weigh* objects, and so on. This learning treats fundamental everyday usage of units of these measures and is learned by using sight, touch, comparison, and interpretation in real situations. In a sense, this is not mathematics, but elementary experimental science, and as such it constitutes a readiness activity for the subsequent mathematical study of measure. At this stage children learn how to *use* measures and may get no more than an intuitive notion of their essential meaning.

Before a child can use these measures intelligently he must first have developed a usable concept of the conservation of matter. In handling a cup of sand, he must know that whether he pours it in a long narrow tube or in a shallow dish or on the table in a pile, although the sand is redistributed in different shapes or spread over a larger surface, the amount of sand has not changed. This same concept is necessary before a child can understand how to count; the number of objects in a set is the same regardless of their arrangement. In this sense, counting the members of a set of objects is finding the measure of the set, the *number* of things in it, *how many*. However, when we wish to find the amount of a quantity of continuous (or almost continuous) matter, such as its length, its area, its volume, its fluid capacity, and the like, we cannot count to find how many units are in it; we *measure* to find *how much*. This type of measure in any practical situation has an *approximation* feature which is in contrast to the *exactness* of counting. So right from the start we stress this approximate nature of measures that tell how much.

Because very early in their social life children are constantly using different amounts of liquid food—milk, water, soda—and they see differently shaped containers of liquids, liquid measure offers a good topic with which to start. For purposes of experimenting and demonstrating the teacher should have available a collection of containers to measure a cup, a pint, and a quart. Containers of other capacities should also be available for the purpose of comparison. By pouring a cupful of water into a flat pan or dish, children come to recognize that it is not the *shape* of a container that tells how much there is. The child's goal is to come to know that as a standard measure, a cup (or cupful) is a fixed amount, the same for all people. As a measure there are no large cups, or little cups, but only the fixed amount in a standard cup up to the mark. All standard cups hold the same amount.

Exactly the same amount? Now children can be introduced to the approximate nature of the measure *one cup*. They argue about whether or not a few more drops should be added to fill the cup up to the mark, or whether a little liquid should be taken out. Look at the mark. How wide is it? Since it is soon recognized that different persons have a different point of view as to when it is exactly one cup (or one unit of measure), we can never be sure that the same person at two different times will get exactly the same amount as one cup. We have *about* one cup, as close as we can measure it. It is impossible to be exact in this kind of measure.

Finally, without memorizing a table, but by observation, children learn that 2 cups is (as much as) 1 pint, and 2 pints is 1 quart. (The use of the verb 'is' in the preceding sentence was deliberate. When referring to quantities, not to containers, 2 cups or 2 pints or 2 quarts is one quantity and takes a singular verb.) Using these standard units and pouring water (or rice or sand) into other containers of different shapes and sizes, the children find which containers hold more, or less, than others and about how much they hold in terms of standard units. They have learned something about how to measure and to use measures of liquid capacity.

In a similar way children learn how to name and use money units in a counting situation that tells how many. The terms of one cent, five cents, one dime, and one quarter dollar which occur in U.S. coins should be used. Although play money should be available, it is necessary that real coins and exchange of coins be used from time to time. The children learn that a cent is also called a penny, 5 cents a nickel, and that a dime is equal in value to 10 cents, a quarter dollar to 25 cents. Finally, other equivalent exchanges are learned by finding their value in cents. Thus a dime has the same value as two nickels, a quarter as five nickels (or two dimes and one nickel), and so on. Finally, the children learn to count a sum of money by cents, nickels, dimes, and quarters. In learning these equivalents the children play games—store, cafeteria, savings bank, and so on—all activities which children enjoy and which yet serve as learning situations.

Children learn quite early to talk of their height and weight. They usually do this in terms of pounds and inches, respectively. Although the metric system of measurement is growing in importance and use, the teaching of metric units should be delayed until children have a firm knowledge of the decimal system of numeration, including decimal fractions.

Before a unit of length (or height) is introduced, pupils should compare various "pieces" of length—line segments, sticks, edges of tables, edges of pieces of paper, parts of lines running along the floor or walls of the room—to determine which are longer or shorter. Children can compare their heights by marking the levels of the tops of their heads on a piece of paper fastened along the wall. They come to recognize that standing on a chair does not make them taller in terms of their own height, it only enables them to reach a point that is higher above the floor than a point they could reach while standing on the floor. The teacher should constantly call attention to the actual length or size they are talking about as being that of a line segment from one point to another, from a point at the level of the soles of their feet straight up to a point at the top of their heads, in the instance just described.

To find a better comparison, the teacher introduces standard units—the inch, foot, and yard—by using a tape with these units marked. At first the inch is the smallest unit used. Children measure to the nearest inch, and the teacher is careful to select distances that are nearly a given whole number of inches. Later children estimate a third or a half of an inch after they have been taught the meaning of these fractions. Finally they learn to draw pictures of segments having a given measure in inches. By using the foot and the yard in similar exercises, they come to know that 12 inches is equivalent to 1 foot and 3 feet to 1 yard.

Weight offers more difficulty in teaching because it involves a physical principle of density. A large volume of feathers appears to be, and is, so much more in volume than a small volume of lead, yet they may weigh the same. A pound of butter, a pound of coffee, and a pound of cornflakes all have the same weight. Children learn that weight means how heavy something is and they experience this by lifting different weights (objects) from the floor to the desk top, and also by holding various weights in their hand. The teacher should have a set of eight one-ounce weights, two half-pound ones, and a one-pound weight for demonstration. Using a balance, children learn that a half-pound of putty is always a half-pound, no matter into what shape you may press the putty. They learn that whether they stand on a scale with two legs, or with one leg held up, they still weigh the same.

Children can best learn to tell time if the teacher uses a demonstration clock along with the clock on the wall in the class-room. Time has two meanings for children. One meaning is that time is a method of telling them when an activity is to take place, i.e., an instance during the day such as the time a recess starts. The other is that time is an elapsed period of duration, such as a recess of 15 minutes. Both ideas are important and should be taught. The goal is to have all children, by the end of second grade, tell what time it is by looking at the clock, and to tell how much time elapses in a given instance by advancing the hands of the clock from one position to another in the direction that all clock hands take, upper left to upper right to lower right to lower left and around again the same way.

The teacher first teaches the pupils to distinguish the hour hand (small) from the minute hand (large, i.e., longer). They note that when the small hour hand is on an hour mark, the large minute hand is always at twelve. They set the clock for a given hour and learn to say the given hour when anyone else sets the clock. Next they learn to say and read the half-hour language, "half past two o'clock," "half past seven o'clock," noting that in every case the minute hand is always at the six-hour mark, and that the hour hand is midway between two consecutive hour marks. They also learn that when the hour hand moves from one hour mark to the next hour mark, the minute hand makes a complete turn.

Next children study the minute divisions on the clock, which are not numbered. They learn that there are 5 minute spaces between any two consecutive hour marks and they count by fives to find 60 minutes in one hour. Why? Because in one hour the small hand goes from 2 to 3, but the big hand rotates through all 12 hour markings. Then pupils learn to tell time to the nearest 5 minutes, and finally to the nearest minute. Right from the start of this last learning, they should say time as it is generally used in the adult world, for example, at 20 minutes past 8 o'clock they say "eight-twenty" and write 8:20. Note the colon and its use to separate hours from minutes. While "quarter to five" is allowed, it is written 4:45 and read "four forty-five." At the end of Grade 2, all children should be able to read a clock to the nearest minute of time.

8–2 DEVELOPING THE THEORY OF MEASURE

In Grades 4, 5, and 6, as the theory of measure and measurement is developed, the vocabulary used should be one which conveys very precise and correct concepts. For example, if you were called on to define or describe the meaning of "length," could you do it? Is length a physical object? Of course not. Is it a geometric figure? No. Does a geometric figure have length? Some do and some do not. In fact, length is a characteristic or property possessed by line segments (or any geometric lines such as a circle, a loop, a spiral, etc.). This length may be named through a process of measuring. This name is usually an expression which consists of a number, called the *measure*, and a selected piece of the line called the unit of measure. For example, we may say, "The length of the segment is $5\frac{3}{8}$ inches," for a case in which the measure is $5\frac{3}{8}$ and the unit piece of measure is an *inch*.

In the study of measure, such words as *quantity*, *amount*, *measurement*, and *magnitude* will occur. In general, these words are used synonymously as the "how-muchness" of the thing we are concerned with. However, the word most commonly used in science is *magnitude*, and it is used in two senses. First, anything such as length, weight, time, light, and so on, is called a *magnitude* if it possesses the property of "size," that is, of "muchness." Second, the size, muchness, or measurement of the entity is also referred to as its *magnitude*. Thus we can speak of weight as a magnitude, but we can also speak of the magnitude of a piece of metal as 2 pounds. Thus we see that we can have different kinds of magnitudes.

Length is the magnitude of a bounded portion of a line (1-dimensional region).

Area is the magnitude of a bounded portion of a surface (2-dimensional region).

Volume is the magnitude of a bounded portion of space (3-dimensional region).

Angular magnitude is the property of the size of an angle (or better, an angular region).

In an elementary school mathematics program, all these magnitudes are studied. The most important of all is length.

If there is to be any need to measure physical or geometrically described objects, it is essential that at least two pieces of the thing exist. Then we can compare one piece with another piece to see which is more, or less, or if they are the same in terms of some appropriate magnitude. This is the beginning of the theory of measure. Next we can select a piece of line, for example, and calling it a unit, compare every other piece of line with it by finding the *number* of unit pieces needed to cover another piece without any overlapping. This *number* is called the *measure*. A measure is always some number, and just a number. If we give the measure and cite with it the unit, the result is called a *measurement*. A measurement is a measure with the name of the unit used to find the measure. The measurement of the magnitude is also its magnitude or size, or "how much" there is. Note that one may report the length of a segment as 36 inches, or as 3 feet, or as 1 yard. In each case, the *measure is different*, the *unit is different*, but the length (magnitude) of the segment is the same. The magnitude does not change because we take different units and thus come up with different measures. The same situation holds for reporting other magnitudes, such as area or volume.

Everyone who is expected to count in some situations and to measure in others must recognize the essential difference between situations in which counting is appropriate and those in which measuring is appropriate in finding answers to questions of *how many* and *how much*. Young children should not be required to verbalize the requisite understanding. There is some counting involved in measurement; the *measure* of an object in terms of some unit is a count of those units contained in the object, although this number is seldom arrived at by counting the units one by one. When can we count? Do the objects being counted, each as 1 thing, have to be alike in any way? Can you count the objects in your living room? Does the piano "count" just as much as the tiny statuette sitting on an end table? The only thing these objects must have in common is membership in a given set: in this case, the set whose members are all objects, and only those objects, which are in your living room. If you are to count them, they must be separate, distinct, *discrete*. Each object, regardless of kind or size, is a counting unit. Can you count your weight, your age, the distance from your house to the school? Well, no, but. . . . These are measurement situations. How do they differ from counting situations? In a measurement situation, you are dealing with some sort of *continuum* which must be divided up somehow—usually not literally separated—into countable units. If the results of measurement are to be useful, only a few different units should be used in a single instance, and these few had better be closely related, if not just alike.

The preceding two sentences suggest two important principles of measurement: (1) A measuring unit must be of the same nature as the object being measured. Thus, we use a unit of length (a little piece of length) for measuring length, a unit of time for measuring time, a unit of weight for measuring weight, and so on. (How, then, shall we measure intelligence?) (2) When we wish to make more precise measurements (e.g., closer approximations to a true length), we subdivide the chosen unit. Sometimes the names given these smaller units have no apparent relation to the name of the parent unit (rod, yard, foot, inch) and sometimes the names include an explanation of the way the original unit was divided (meter, decimeter, centimeter, millimeter). Fractions of any given unit, as well as whole-number multiples, are also used, of course. The great usefulness of having both a light year and a millimeter as units of length, for instance, is that they, together with the other units of length, allow us to avoid very large numbers and very small numbers as measures.

Young children can develop reliable judgment about the measuring units which make sense in given situations. They know they should not attempt to measure the length of a table with a clock. They would not try to find their weight with a ruler. They know that it seems better to report their height in inches, or feet and inches, than in fractions of a mile. They sense that tons are more appropriate than ounces for a unit to use in reporting the weight of an ocean liner, even when they do not really know how heavy a ton is. At any rate, they know they could not lift it. They usually need some guidance to realize that the only feature of a ruler relevant to its purported purpose is its length, and that the part of the ruler they should pay attention to is the very edge at which the calibrations are marked. All the rest of the ruler serves as a handle so that we can pick up the part we want to use.

8–3 TEACHING LINEAR MEASURE

Concepts of length, and progressively more structured experiences with what it means to measure a length and with what the results of this measurement imply, are dealt with throughout a child's school experience. Each of the first six of the eight steps described in this section should be treated in some appropriate way at all grade levels, beginning in the first grade at the latest. Some applications require that the children be able to work with common fractions or decimal fractions, and the placement of these applications is determined accordingly.

In Grade 4, when we teach children for the first time a mathematical approach to the study of line measure, we need not use the words 'magnitude', 'quantity', or 'amount'. We need only to speak of *length*, *unit of length*, and how much. The words 'measure', 'measuring', and 'measurement' will enter naturally into the discussion. Since length is fundamental to both mathematics and science as well as to the study of other measurements, since it is easy to give laboratory approaches to the study of length, since children are already familiar with rulers and with drawing and measuring segments, and since the whole procedure we use to develop the theory of measuring length is exactly reproduced when we study other measurements, length is a proper magnitude for introducing the theory of measure.

There are a number of steps which, taken in proper sequence, can lead to the construction of a useful and meaningful concept of length. A suggested sequence of steps is the following:

1. *Review counting.* Compare collections of objects (a) by matching to give order relations greater than, equal to, or less than, and (b) by counting to find the number which is the measure of the set. (How many?)

2. *Compare segments.* This can be done (a) by placing line segments alongside each other and comparing them to give order relations greater than, equal to, or less than, and (b) by suggesting a way in which a number can be used as a measure of a segment. (How much?)

3. *Develop the concept of unit of length.* Select an optional unit and "lay it off" along a segment. Eliminate exactness and discuss the approximate character of how many units cover a segment.

4. *Develop the concept of measure and measurement.* Show that for a given segment, which maintains a unique length, differently selected units give rise to different measures; hence the need to report a measurement in the conventional manner.

5. *Develop standard units.* Combine a brief historical account of the need for standard units with practice in the use of selected standard units.

6. *Use the English system of measuring units.* Develop the inch, foot, yard, and mile (rod optional). The ruler, yardstick, and tape are used to measure and to draw or lay off segments with given lengths.

7. *Apply the theory.* Measure perimeters, circumferences, and objects encountered in practical home and business situations. Calculate with measures and transform from one unit to another (addition, subtraction, multiplication and division by a number).

8. *Introduce the metric system of measures.* Make approximate transformations from the metric to the English system, and vice versa.

Let us now examine each of these steps in further detail.

1. The goal in teaching length to children is to have them correctly interpret the words *measure, unit of measure,* and *measurement,* and to apply these concepts in practical everyday situations. To reach this goal we begin with the familiar idea of counting, reshape the thinking and the language so that they apply to measurement, and then adapt the process to the idea of length. Thus the first activity is to have children compare sets of objects (by matching) and arrange the sets in order. What does this order arrangement tell us? For each two sets, which set is more, whether they are equal, and which is less.

Then the children count the collections of chairs (or other objects in a set) in the room and report to the class. Here a report of '30' is a measure of the set, but reported in this form it tells very little. A week later we shall not know what the units were to which the '30' refers. So we amend the report to read '30 chairs'. This is the *measurement of the set* and tells *how many units,* specifying the unit, which is *chair.* This type of activity should be repeated until children differentiate well the ideas:

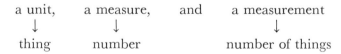

a unit,	a measure,	and	a measurement
↓	↓		↓
thing	number		number of things

2. Now we ask children to look for a way of reporting the sizes of parts of lines: segments, pieces of cord, edges of desks or sheets of paper, and so on. We ask them to recall what we did to compare sets of separate things. The start can well be to compare the drawings of two segments on the board, $\overline{AB}$ and $\overline{CD}$, as in the example in the margin. It appears that $\overline{AB}$ is more line than $\overline{CD}$ and we can prove it by marking off $\overline{CD}$ on a straightedge and placing it along $\overline{AB}$ with C matched to A. Then, since point D falls between A and B, we know that $\overline{AB}$ is more than $\overline{CD}$. If we ask, "More of what?" children reply, "More line." Cord (string which does not stretch but can be curled around in various shapes on top of a desk) is also valuable for developing an intuitive sense of "amount of line." The *amount* is the same no matter what shape it takes, and if we pull it *taut* into a straight line (no stretching, for it will break), we can compare it with other pieces of string. A rubber band is a good counterexample at this time— for we can get more *line* by stretching it—so long as it does not break. We cannot compare things that do not maintain a certain amount of line (at least not at this stage).

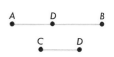

Children relate this method of telling which is more or less line with that of matching elements of two sets to tell which is the greater. In the sense of matching, the procedures are alike, but in the sense of individual matching versus continuous mapping they are different. We used only endpoints to match parts of lines, but we used object to object in matching collections of objects.

If a curved wire is to be compared with a segment, we must proceed with it as with the string, that is, bend it (without stretching) into a straight line segment. Again it should be stressed that the amount of line does not change as we change its shape. Now we can agree to call the *amount of line* (a property of the segment, not the segment itself) the *length*. Much practice should be given in making order comparisons of length of segments, using string, wire, drawings, or tapes, preferably not marked or calibrated.

As a final activity at this stage, we ask children if they can invent a way of finding the *measure* (a number) for a line segment, similar to the way they counted a set. Since some children have already used a ruler marked off in inches, they will suggest using a ruler—if one is handy—but the teacher should see that *just at this moment no rulers or yardsticks are available*. What shall we do?

3. The children are now ready to create their own units of line, and to do their own measuring. Select a line segment in the room, a segment which for some purpose or other you need to know "How much?" A good beginning is the edge of the teacher's desk, either edge or all of them. We can tell *how long* the edge is by comparing it with some smaller segment used as a unit. Some suggested units are the lengths of a piece of chalk, an unsharpened new pencil, an edge of a book, a chalkboard eraser, or any object with which a fixed segment can be *laid off* along the edge of the desk. By laying off, we mean: "place endpoint to endpoint along the edge with no overlapping." Even a stretched end-of-thumb-to-end-of-little-finger handspan could be used. At the start, we cover the edge only to the lower whole-number approximation; that is, we stop counting when the next whole unit would extend beyond the end of the object we are measuring.

Different numbers occur as different units are used. Thus the children may find that the edge of the desk has

$$\left.\begin{array}{r} \text{14 chalk units} \\ \text{9 eraser units} \\ \text{6 pencil units} \\ \text{7 handspans} \end{array}\right\} \quad \begin{array}{l} \text{These all name} \\ \text{the same size} \end{array}$$

and so on. They note that with each different unit, there is a different number. Then they are told that the number is the *measure* and the number of units is the *measurement*. To name the length we use the measure and the name of the unit. Unless the unit accompanies the name of the measure we cannot possibly convey to others an idea of just how long the desk really is.

In this type of activity, children learn that (a) if a different unit is used, the measure (number) will be different, (b) differently named measurements can name the same length, and (c) all measurement of this type is approximate. We cannot be exact. Even if the endpoints of the desk edge and the last applied unit appear to be the same, all we can say is that it is nearly exact. At this time no extended discussion of accuracy should be made. We practice measuring with these arbitrary units and naming the lengths until children have grasped the procedure fairly competently, both in doing the operation and in reporting it.

4. Knowing the nature of a unit of length, children can construct their own rulers. Each child can select his own unit and give it his last name. Thus Bob Savage has a *savage* unit which he selects.

Bill Smith has a *smith* unit. Of course, many other ways can be devised for naming a unit. Each child is given a narrow strip of cardboard. Then he selects a unit of length. The teacher should help children not to take too small or too large a unit, but something like the length of the first joint of the thumb. This is marked off from the left end and a 1 is placed at the other end-point of the unit. Then the cardboard is placed across lined paper so that the left end and the 1 point are on parallel lines. By making the same number of spaces between 1 and 2 as there are between 0 and 1, the 2-units point is marked. This is continued to the end of the strip of cardboard, as shown in the diagram. Children must be helped with this process, but they gain proficiency by making several different rulers. A different unit must be given a different name. At first only whole units should be named, but the diagram shows how, at a later stage, half-units can also be named.

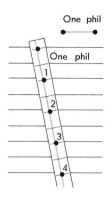

   Now the pupils, using these rulers they have made themselves, find the lengths of several segments drawn on paper prepared by the teacher and record their answers. If they have several different rulers, they can write;

Unit	Measure	Length	
phil	3	3 phils	For segment (a)
smith	4	4 smiths	

and so on for the other segments to be measured. The children should also do the reverse problem of constructing a segment of a given *measure*, using their own units and recording the result.

Measure = 4

phil

Length = 4 phils

5. The various measuring units devised by the class would lead to confusion if they wanted to buy a certain length of ribbon or cord at the local store. They would have to take their unit of length with them. Here the teacher can give a brief discussion of the need for and the development of *standard* units of all kinds of measurements. The teacher can find this adequately described in encyclopedias and books on the history of measurement. This leads to the study of the English system of linear measurement.

(The meter and centimeter can be mentioned but not stressed at this point, unless there is an immediate use for them in an activity the children will be engaged in.) The teacher should introduce the 6-inch ruler, foot ruler, and yardstick, and point out that the inch may be subdivided into halves, quarters, and eighths.

The proper choice of a unit for measuring certain lengths should be discussed. The width of a sheet of paper would probably be measured in inches and parts of an inch, the length of a desk in feet and inches, the length of a room in feet, or yards and feet, a running track in yards, etc. The yard, foot, and inch should be used as directed in (4) above.

6. In studying the system of English measurement, we shall say "12 inches = 1 foot" because these can be looked upon as being the same length. That is, '12 inches' and '1 foot' name the same length. Similarly, we say "3 feet = 1 yard." It is also of value to know that 1 mile = 1760 yards = 5280 feet. With this system, we can record and use measurements in a manner similar to the way we use the decimal system of numeration to record the number of, and operations on, collections. Thus 12 inches may be exchanged for 1 foot and vice versa; 3 feet for 1 yard and vice versa. A measurement of 19 inches is also $(12 + 7)$ inches or 1 foot 7 inches. When we abbreviate foot (or feet) to *ft*, and inch or inches to *in.*, we write 1 ft 7 in. Similarly, 52 in. is $(48 + 4)$ in. or 4 ft 4 in. But 4 ft is $(3 + 1)$ ft or 1 yd 1 ft. Hence 52 in. is 1 yd 1 ft 4 in. We can reverse the process and say that 1 yd 1 ft 4 in. is $(1 \cdot 3)$ ft 1 ft 4 in.; or 4 ft 4 in.; or $(4 \cdot 12)$ in., 4 in., which is 52 in. Note that 52 in.; 4 ft 4 in.; 1 yd 1 ft 4 in. are different names for the same length. Children should practice this conversion, both ways, until they can do it with ease and confidence.

Usually it is desirable, and sometimes it is necessary, to estimate a distance. For this purpose, children can measure the first joints of their fingers, one of which will be about an inch. Their shoe size will help them estimate a foot, and a *big* step helps to estimate a yard. Children should be encouraged to give other ways of estimating units of length and finding approximate measures.

7. Children can now apply the theory they have learned to finding perimeters (lengths of the paths) of triangles, rectangles, and other straight-line figures. To do this we usually measure

198

parts of the figure and then combine the lengths. We can add the measures of the same unit, but we do not add units. We add a *number* of inches to another *number* of inches and the sum is the *number* of inches in the combined lengths. The addition of measures involves merely working with another system of numeration, in which exchanges are made according to the system of units used.

Thus suppose that one strip of cloth is 2 ft 7 in. and another is 3 ft 9 in. If the strips are laid end to end, how long will the combined length be? Placing measures of like units in a column, we add the measures.

$$
\begin{array}{ll}
2 \text{ ft} & 7 \text{ in.} \\
3 \text{ ft} & 9 \text{ in.} \\
\hline
5 \text{ ft} & 16 \text{ in.} = 6 \text{ ft } 4 \text{ in.} = 2 \text{ yd } 4 \text{ in.}
\end{array}
$$

We could also change each length to a number of inches:

$$
\begin{array}{ll}
2 \text{ ft } 7 \text{ in.} = (2 \times 12 + 7) \text{ in.} = 31 \text{ in.} \\
3 \text{ ft } 9 \text{ in.} = (3 \times 12 + 9) \text{ in.} = 45 \text{ in.} \\
\hline
\phantom{3 \text{ ft } 9 \text{ in.} = (3 \times 12 + 9) \text{ in.} =} 76 \text{ in.} = (2 \times 36 + 4) \text{ in.} \\
\phantom{3 \text{ ft } 9 \text{ in.} = (3 \times 12 + 9) \text{ in.} = 76 \text{ in.} } = 2 \text{ yd } 4 \text{ in.}
\end{array}
$$

Subtraction proceeds in the same way. Thus

$$
\begin{array}{l}
\; 2 \text{ yd } 1 \text{ ft } 4 \text{ in.} \\
-\; 1 \text{ yd } 2 \text{ ft } 8 \text{ in.} \\
\hline
\end{array}
\Rightarrow
\begin{array}{l}
\; 1 \text{ yd } 3 \text{ ft } 16 \text{ in.} \\
-\; 1 \text{ yd } 2 \text{ ft } 8 \text{ in.} \\
\hline
\phantom{-\; 1 \text{ yd } 2 \text{ ft }} 1 \text{ ft } 8 \text{ in.}
\end{array}
$$

Here 1 ft was exchanged for 12 in., making 16 in., then 1 yd was exchanged for 3 ft. Now every measure in the minuend is greater than or equal to the corresponding measure in the subtrahend and no difficulty is encountered. Of course, each measurement could be converted into inches and then the subtraction would be as usual.

A length can be multiplied or divided by a number, just as a segment is multiplied or divided by a number. This number is called a *scalar*. Thus, if the segment *U* is multiplied by 4, we obtain 4*U*.

If the length of U is 4 ft 3 in., then 4 times this length is:

$$4(4 \text{ ft } 3 \text{ in.}) = 16 \text{ ft } 12 \text{ in.} \quad \text{or}$$

$$\begin{array}{r} 4 \text{ ft} \quad 3 \text{ in.} \\ \times \qquad 4 \\ \hline 16 \text{ ft } 12 \text{ in.} = 17 \text{ ft.} \end{array}$$

Note that each measure is multiplied by 4. If the teacher illustrates on the board a few segments and multiplies each by whole numbers (scalars), as shown above, and follows this by the corresponding scalar multiplication of the lengths of the segments, this will be sufficient for developing this concept.

Since dividing by a whole number is equivalent to multiplying by the reciprocal of this number, division by a scalar presents no new problem. Thus $\frac{1}{3}U$ is a segment V such that $3V = U$:

$$\overset{\frac{1}{3}U}{\bullet\!\!-\!\!\bullet} \qquad\qquad \overset{U}{\bullet\!\!-\!\!\!-\!\!\!-\!\!\!-\!\!\bullet}$$

Hence $(4 \text{ ft } 6 \text{ in.}) \div 3 = (4 \text{ ft } 6 \text{ in.}) \times \frac{1}{3} = \frac{4}{3} \text{ ft } \frac{6}{3} \text{ in.}$, which is $1\frac{1}{3}$ ft 2 in. or 1 ft 6 in.

With these concepts and skills, a child has all the fundamental knowledge of length (linear measurement) he needs for practical purposes. He should, of course, know that distance is another word for a special kind of length, usually the length of the line segment joining two points, or a combination of such lengths. Problems of all sorts can now be introduced.

One important category of problems in which a length or a distance must be used is problems which involve the perimeter of a polygon. The perimeter of a polygon is its length; conceptually, for children, it is the length of the segment you would get if you could snip the polygon at any point and straighten it out. Some children find it helpful in remembering the meaning of 'perimeter' to notice that this big word contains the little word 'rim'. There is no need to develop formulas for perimeters of any of the polygons (circles, treated in Chapter 13, are a different story). If the children know what is meant by *perimeter*, and if they know that measures in terms of the same unit may be added in the same way that any of the numbers of arithmetic are added, they can find the perimeter of any polygon. When a polygon has two or more sides of the same length, there are shortcuts which may simplify the computation. Children should be encouraged to look for such shortcuts.

An important mathematical application of the concept of length is a definition of congruent line segments: Two segments are congruent if and only if they have the same length. Thus measurement furnishes a test for congruence of segments. It is the rare child who does not see this for himself.

8. It is necessary that pupils have a fairly good understanding of, and some skill in, operating with one system of linear measure before they compare different systems. The only other system of linear measure of importance is the metric system. The fundamental unit in this system is a *meter*. This system is used widely throughout the world and almost totally by scientists in their work. A history of the metric system and its fundamental units can be found in any encyclopedia, or in pamphlets available from the U.S. Bureau of Standards, Washington, D.C. The length of a meter is given by the distance between two fine markings on a platinum-iridium bar kept in the Bureau of Standards in Washington. The official meter is kept at the International Bureau of Weights and Measures, in Sèvres, France. For practical purposes, we define

$$1 \text{ meter} \approx 39.37 \text{ inches},$$

where '≈' indicates that the measure in inches is correct only to the nearest hundredth. Hence, for comparison purposes, we may say that the meter is about 3.37 inches longer than the yard, roughly $3\frac{1}{3}$ inches longer.

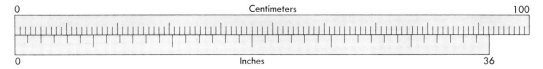

The meter is subdivided into ten congruent units, each called a *decimeter*. The decimeter is divided into ten congruent units, each called a *centimeter*. The centimeter is divided into ten congruent units, each called a *millimeter*.

Thus the metric system of measure, with the meter as a unit, is constructed so that every measure can be represented by a decimal numeral.

$$0.1 \text{ m} = 1 \text{ dm (decimeter)}$$
$$0.01 \text{ m} = 1 \text{ cm (centimeter)}$$
$$0.001 \text{ m} = 1 \text{ mm (millimeter)}$$

201

A measurement of 2.476 meters can be read as "2 meters, 4 decimeters, 7 centimeters, 6 millimeters."

When children are learning this system, there should be several meter sticks in the classroom, and each child should have a cardboard ruler either 1½ or 3 decimeters in length, divided into centimeters and millimeters. First children learn the units and their names.

CENTIMETERS

Next they measure as they did with the inch ruler, writing a result in decimeters, centimeters, and millimeters. For example, 1 decimeter, 2 centimeters, 6 millimeters, would be written as:

$$1 \text{ dm } 2 \text{ cm } 6 \text{ mm.}$$

After measures of this kind are made we can convert them into only one of these units. Children know 10 cm = 1 dm, and 10 mm = 1 cm. Hence

1 dm 2 cm 6 mm becomes 126 mm or 12.6 cm or 1.26 dm or 0.126 m.

Note the digits in all these measurements. A few exercises of this type show the decimal character of the metric system. It works just like the decimal system of numeration, with the following analogy:

$$\text{ones} \rightarrow \text{meters}$$
$$\text{tenths} \rightarrow \text{decimeters}$$
$$\text{hundredths} \rightarrow \text{centimeters}$$
$$\text{thousandths} \rightarrow \text{millimeters}$$

We also refer to the Latin derivation of the prefixes *deci*, *centi*, and *milli*, so that an association to tenths, hundredths, and thousandths may be established.

Children may ask if the system of units can be extended to the left in a manner similar to the decimal system of numeration. Of course it can, and for those who desire to know the names of the units (of measure) we can cite:

$$10 \text{ meters} = 1 \text{ dek}a\text{meter}, \quad 1 \text{ ten meters (note the } a)$$
$$10 \text{ dekameters} = 1 \text{ hectometer}, \quad 1 \text{ hundred meters}$$
$$10 \text{ hectometers} = 1 \text{ kilometer}, \quad 1 \text{ thousand meters}.$$

The prefixes *deka* (sometimes written *deca*), *hecto*, and *kilo* are Greek words meaning ten, hundred, and thousand, respectively. However, the only important unit here is the kilometer, since it is used quite widely around the world as a unit of measure of large distances, in the same way that we use mile as a unit of length for large distances.

As a final part of this work, pupils should learn how to convert a measurement in one system to an equivalent measurement in the other system. The most common usages are to change inches to centimeters and vice versa, and to change kilometers to miles and vice versa. We ask children how they can find a way to do this from the fundamental equivalence,

$$100 \text{ cm} \approx 39.37 \text{ inches}.$$

The ratio of the *measures* is $100 \div 39.37$, or 2.54 (see margin). This means that 2.54 cm is equivalent to 1 inch. If we place a ruler divided into centimeters alongside one divided into inches, we can verify this result.

$$
\begin{array}{r}
2.54 \\
39.37\overline{)100.0000} \\
78\ 74 \\
\hline
21\ 260 \\
19\ 685 \\
\hline
1\ 5750 \\
1\ 5748 \\
\hline
2
\end{array}
$$

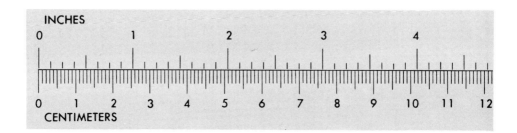

Now children can also derive the fact that

$$1 \text{ cm} \approx 0.3937 \text{ in.}, \quad \text{or nearly } 0.4 \text{ in.}$$

Next we challenge children to show the relation between a mile and a kilometer (or a kilometer and a mile). This can be accomplished by transforming 1 mile to 63,360 in. and multiplying by 2.54, then dividing by 100,000. Thus we find

$$1 \text{ mi} \approx 1.609 \text{ km} \quad \text{and} \quad 1 \text{ km} \approx 0.621 \text{ mi.}$$

From these transformations, children learn a rule of thumb. They know that $\frac{5}{8} = 0.625$. The transformation shows that 1 km $\approx$ 0.621 mi. Since 0.625 $\approx$ 0.621, we have the approximation rule:

> To change a number of kilometers to a number of miles, multiply by $\frac{5}{8}$; to change a number of miles to a number of kilometers, multiply by $\frac{8}{5}$.

Suppose we have a problem such as, "The speedometer shows 96 km per hour. How fast is that in the U.S.A.?" Some children are helped by thinking as follows: "Multiplying by $\frac{5}{8}$ gives a smaller number; multiplying by $\frac{8}{5}$ gives a larger number. A mile is longer than a kilometer, so it takes fewer miles than kilometers to measure a given distance. A speed of 96 kilometers per hour would be some-number-less-than-96 miles per hour. I can find this number by multiplying 96 by $\frac{5}{8}$ ... 60 miles per hour. Yes, that makes sense."

The work in linear measure begins very early, in some cases before kindergarten. The serious study of measure usually begins in Grade 4, but it does not end there. The topic is repeated each year and extended into high school study of geometry. As other magnitudes are studied—angular, area, volume—the theory of measure of these is related to that of linear measure, and in this way the general concepts of magnitude, measure, and unit of measure grow deeper and broader.

8–4 MEASURE OF ANGLE

For the purpose of developing angular measure, it is simpler and quite correct mathematically to conceive of an angle in a manner analogous to a line segment. A line segment consists of two endpoints (or boundary points) and all points on the line between the endpoints. This region of a line, called a *segment*, is the thing we measure. Thus an angle may be considered a region of a plane. The angle consists of two rays $\overrightarrow{OA}$ and $\overrightarrow{OB}$ having the same origin (endpoint, vertex) and all the rays bounded by these two rays

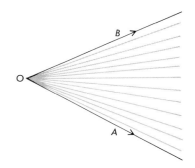

(lying between them) and having the same origin, O. This point is called the *vertex* of the angle. Thus an angle becomes a convex sector region of the plane. An angle is always less than a half plane. With this definition of an angle, we are in a position to study its measure in a manner that uses the same sequence of ideas we used in learning the nature of length. (In a similar way, in space which is of three dimensions, a convex solid conical region enables us to study space angles.)

Before we study the measure of an angle, we must develop an intuitive feeling for the size of an angle. This will enable us to compare angles. Among ideas that we can use is the distinction between a geometric object and a drawing of it. Just as we drew a picture of a line, so we draw a picture of an angle as a part of a plane. A line is infinite in extent and we measure a finite part of this line. A plane is infinite in extent, and the child must come to see that an angular part of the plane, although it is infinite in extent, since the rays go on forever, covers only a certain part of the plane.

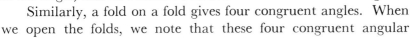

He must also come to consider an angle as convex; that is, "If any ray is extended in the opposite direction from the vertex, the extension is outside the angle."

1. When we use the sector region as an angle it is easy to compare angles by folding the paper. If a paper is creased so that every crease passes through a point O, by folding one edge of an angle over another we can tell which angular region is more than (it overlaps), less than (it fits inside), or the same as (it just fits) another. When the children do this, they note that the length of the creases (representations of a small section of the boundaries of the angle) has no relation whatsoever to the size of the angle.

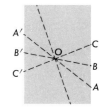

Similarly, a fold on a fold gives four congruent angles. When we open the folds, we note that these four congruent angular

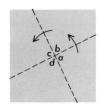

regions completely fill the plane, and we say that each of these angles is a right angle (see diagram in margin). Now any angle can be compared with a right angle to see whether it is greater than, equal to, or less than a right angle. Here the word *obtuse* (greater than a right angle) and *acute* (less than a right angle) may be introduced. Children can now indicate angles in the classroom, draw angles (copy them) indicating the boundary and the interior, and compare them. Although compasses may be used for copying angles, they are not necessary. A tracing serves the purpose.

2. Referring to the way we measured segments, we now ask children to invent a way to measure angles. Of course, they must use a unit angle and cover the angle to be measured with non-overlapping unit angles. A unit measuring angle (the child's own unit) may be cut from cardboard. The unit is placed on the angle with vertices coinciding and with one side on $\overrightarrow{OA}$, so that it covers part of the angle. A point C on the other side of the unit angle is indicated on the paper and ray $\overrightarrow{OC}$ is drawn in the angle.

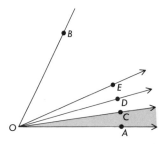

Now the process is repeated with the unit angle placed with one side along $\overrightarrow{OC}$ and the other side covering some more of the angle AOB. A mark is made on the other side of the unit angle at D, and then ray $\overrightarrow{OD}$ is drawn. This is continued until the angle is covered as closely as the unit will allow.

Then the number of unit angles (not overlapping, only having a side in common) is counted. What is this number? It is the measure. Do all children get the same measure for the same angle? No. Why? They have used different unit angles. How do we make sure that all answers indicate the one size of the angle? Use the name of the unit with the name of the measure. Thus for a given angle the size (magnitude) is the same but one can have many different measures, and hence different measurements. Thus 1 big, 3 angs, or 7 anglets may all name the size (or how-muchness) of the same angle because big, ang, and anglets are different unit angles.

Further discussion shows that the measurement of a segment has a name: length. Later the child learns that the measurement of a finite bounded region of a surface has a name: area. An angle is not a segment, nor is it a finite bounded region. What do we call the measurement of an angle? No special name has been given, so we merely call it *angular measurement*. We note also that $\overline{AB}$ is a geometric figure but that the measurement of the figure is reported as a name: so many linear units. This may be written:

The length of AB is 22 inches.

If the measure of $\overline{AB}$ is 22, we write

$$m(\overline{AB}) = 22.$$

We have already learned that a measure is of little value unless we know the unit of measure. Similarly, the measure of an angle may be given in the form

$$m(\angle AOB) = 7.$$

But without the unit of angular measure this has little value. So when we report the result we write the measurement (measure-unit) in the form:

The angular measurement of $\angle AOB$ is 7 *units*,

where children can give their own name to their angular unit.

3. If we are to communicate information to other people about the measurement of angles, or the construction of angles, we must establish some common units for angular measure. The teacher can discuss the selection of a standard unit from a historical point of view, referring to 360 degrees as the number of unit angles that cover the whole plane about one point as a vertex. This is related to the almost-same number of days ($365\frac{1}{4}$) that it takes the earth to sweep around the sun in one year. It may be of interest to know that in one day the earth always sweeps through an arc, so that the sector areas for any two days are equal. Thus a solar day is not the same length throughout the year, as the clock day is.

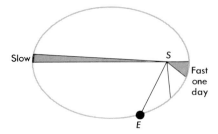

Since an angle is an infinite region, we make use of a circle to measure our angles. At the vertex we draw a circle which intersects the angle in the arc AB. (Note that the intersection of these two figures is an arc.)

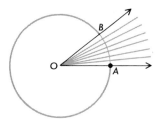

If the angle were just two rays $\overrightarrow{OA}$ and $\overrightarrow{OB}$, what would the intersection be? Just points A and B. We shall use the arc $\overarc{AB}$ (a line figure) to measure the angle. In this way we can use an analogy between linear measure and angle measure. The length of arc is not given in standard linear units, but in some appropriate fraction of a circle. Once we know what fraction of what circle, we may measure the arc as we would measure a segment.

We could use a right angle as a unit of angular measure. This would amount to using the circular arc which is one-fourth of a circle. But it is too large a unit for practical purposes; it would be similar to using a yard as a measuring unit for finding the width of this page, a case in which an inch is a more appropriate unit. So we select a smaller angle. Here we tell pupils that down through the ages the degree has been found useful as a unit. There are other units (the mil, grad, radian) but they need not be mentioned at this stage. Just as the inch is subdivided into smaller congruent units, the degree is also divided into 60 congruent angles, each called a minute of angle (not a minute of time). Even smaller units exist, for a minute is divided into 60 congruent angles, each called a *second* (not a second of time).

In teaching the degree of angle, we merely say that a right angle is divided into 90 congruent angles, each called a degree of angle. Thus if the measure of a right angle is 90, the unit is a degree and we write:

The angular measure of a right angle in degrees is 90.

To construct angles or to measure angles, we introduce an angle-measuring tool called a *protractor*. Protractors are manufactured in a variety of sizes and shapes. Some are circular (360°), some are semicircular (180°), and some are quadrants (90°). When any of these is used in the conventional way, the center of the circle from which the protractor was cut is to be placed on the vertex of the angle. There is a theorem in geometry which states that an angle with its vertex at the center of a circle has the same measure (in degrees or in any other appropriate units) as the arc which the sides of the angle cut off on the circle. This is the principle which governs the design of a protractor.

When we are teaching the use of a protractor, the hardest thing to get children to do consistently is place the center of the protractor on the vertex of the angle. The teacher's job is easier if the children use 360° protractors, at least to begin with. A teacher who can order the protractors he prefers is wise to choose this kind. However, most schools buy 180° protractors, and these present a problem because, on some of them, the center is on the edge of the protractor, and on others, the center is at another place (see drawings, page 210). Experienced teachers know that it is close to impossible to ensure that all children in a class have protractors which are just alike. The teacher has to help the children understand how a protractor is meant to be used and to insist that they form the habit of locating the center of each protractor they are to use. The teacher must also check to see that they place the center of the protractor on the vertex of each angle they are measuring. Why should they then line up one side of the angle with a 0-mark on the protractor? They don't have to do this. The analogy between the ruler and the protractor applies again. If we want to read a measure directly from a ruler, we place the 0-point of the ruler (usually unmarked) at one end of the segment we are measuring; otherwise we would have to make two readings and subtract. So it is with the protractor: we can read the angle measure directly if we line up one side of the angle with a 0-mark; otherwise we have to make two readings and subtract.

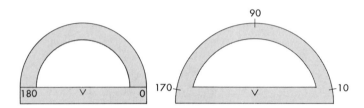

The teacher who remembers the theorems about angle and arc measures from his geometry courses can devise, for bright sixth-graders, discovery sequences leading to the conclusion that one can place a circular protractor (360°) on an angle "just any old way" and have a way of computing the measure of the angle from the readings on the protractor. For average classes, it is enough to develop proficiency in using a protractor in the conventional manner.

The teacher should have a large demonstration chalkboard protractor and a straightedge available for illustrating the use of a protractor. The children should see that a protractor works for angles the way a ruler works for line segments. The units of measure are different, but the measuring process is the same. The protractors the children are using are calibrated in degrees; the unit of measure is a degree.

Now the pupils select angles in the room, draw angles on their paper in various positions and sizes, and then use the protractor to measure the angles. If the sides of the angle drawn on the paper are not long enough to intersect the protractor, then the pupils can use a straightedge to extend the sides to sufficient length. Why can they do this? The sides of an angle are rays, not segments.

Finally, the children should be given some practical problems in drawing and measuring angles (less than 180°). In a summary lesson, they should compare their study of measuring angles with that of measuring segments and should then be tested for correct concepts of (a) the geometric object, (b) the comparison of like objects, (c) the meaning of a unit of measure, (d) the measure of the magnitude in either arbitrary or standard units, and (e) the ability to apply these ideas in practical and mathematical situations.

A large number of applications of angle measure involve measuring angles associated with triangles (and other polygons) and using relations which exist among these measures. First, we have to establish what we mean when we speak of an angle *of* a triangle (or other polygon). Strictly speaking, a triangle has no angles; an angle is determined by two rays, and a triangle is a union of segments. But each pair of segments whose point of inter-section is a vertex of a triangle determines two rays, each with that same vertex, and these rays determine an angle. Thus there are three angles *associated with* each triangle, and it is to these angles that we refer when we speak of the angles *of* a triangle.

There is a theorem in Euclidean geometry that states: The sum of the degree measures of the angles of any triangle is 180°. The teacher can help the children to believe this theorem in several ways.

One way is to have the children measure carefully the three angles of a number of triangles and find the sum of the angles in each case. If they have measured carefully, the sum will always be close to 180°. Now is a good time to discuss the difference between an *error* and a *mistake*, as those concepts apply to measure-ment. In childish language, an error is not your fault (it is a necessary concomitant of the approximate character of numbers arrived at by measurement) whereas a mistake *is* your fault (you did something incorrectly). Then most children are ready to believe that if these angles could be measured exactly, the sum would be 180°. Those who remain skeptical are to be respected. No one has proved to them that the exact sum is not 179°.

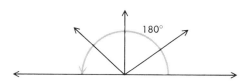

Other ways to demonstrate that the sum of the angles of a triangle is 180° depend on the fact that the sum of the nonover-lapping angles surrounding a point in a plane is 360°, so the sum of adjacent nonoverlapping angles at a point in a line covering the half plane about this point is 180°.

The same result is apparent if two right angles are placed side by side. Now if the children cut out triangles having a variety of shapes, tear off each of the "corners" and place the angles side by side as shown in the figures, they find that the three angles always form a half plane; that is, the sum of their measures is 180°.

More convincing to some pupils is the following demonstration, again done on triangles of a variety of shapes. Cut out of a piece of paper a triangular region and locate the midpoint of two of the sides, either by measuring or by placing two vertices together and pinching the place where a fold would be made if the paper were to be folded that way (a). Fold the segment which has these two midpoints as endpoints (b). Now fold the two parts of the third side, each on itself. This makes two rectangles, one of which is in three pieces (c) and furthermore, the three angles of the triangles you started with "just fit" on one side of a straight line.

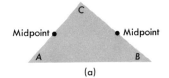
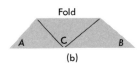
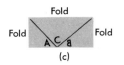

Once the angle sum for a triangle is established, the angle sum of other polygons is easy to find. Any quadrilateral can be partitioned (in two ways) into two nonoverlapping triangles (see margin). What is the sum of the angles of one of these triangles? What is the sum of the angles of both of them? Then what is the sum of the angles of the quadrilateral? Would you get the same results no matter what quadrilateral you chose? Do you see how to find the sum of the angles of a pentagon, a hexagon, an octagon, any polygon?

Now here is a discovery exercise. Complete this table. As soon as you see a way to proceed without making drawings, test it, and if it is sound, use it.

Number of sides of a polygon	Number of nonoverlapping triangles	Sum of the measures (in degrees) of the angles of the polygon
3	1	180
4	2	360
5	.	540
6	.	.
.	.	.
.	.	.
.	.	.
n	.	.

Can you give a rule for any polygon for finding the sum of the measures of its angles?

It is evident from the manner in which the measures of angles was established that two angles having the same measurement are congruent.

8–5 AREA MEASURE

A teacher who has grasped the nature of measure for length and angle needs no extensive direction on how to teach area and volume. All that is needed is a correct conception of the nature of a unit of area and a unit of volume, and a belief that following a sequence and procedure with these magnitudes analogous to those used with length or angle will lead to the desired results. In the following, we merely give some suggestions for developing these measures of area.

1. Before they come to the study of area, children have had experience with regions in a plane: those bounded by triangles, squares, circles, and so on. Before they can come to a realization of what area is, a measure of a portion of a surface, they must be able to compare regions as to their relative size. This is more difficult for regions than it is for lines or angles because regions of the same size can take on many shapes. For example, all the regions depicted at the top of the next page cover the same amount of surface, but they appear to be quite different in this respect.

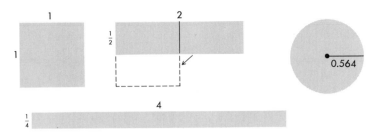

Thus in order to compare regions we must frequently dissect a region into parts and then rearrange the parts with only edges in common between any of the parts. The newly arranged figure may be almost a square region, thus allowing a better comparison. Quite a good deal of time should be spent on dissection of regions, using scissors and rearranging the parts to form a new region which has the same measure as the original figure.

2. After a review of linear and angular measure, children realize that they must take some piece of plane region as a unit of measure. A discussion of the best type of unit—considering disks, rectangular regions, triangular regions and so on—will lead to the square region as a good unit to use. Here children can make their own square unit out of cardboard or use cross-sectioned paper from which they can take a square region of their own choice. If the area of a region bounded by a closed curve is to be found, a square region (one, four, nine, even 100 little squares) cut out of cross-sectioned paper may give us a unit for measuring the area. The pupils count the number of square units and parts of square units in the area and get an approximate measure of the region. In all this work the teacher stresses (1) a square unit of area, (2) the measure of the region which is a number, and (3) the measurement which is so many of the given square units.

3. Next we discuss the standard units used to find an area. The units can be a square inch, square foot, square yard, square mile (section), square centimeter, or square meter. All these units are plane regions. Be sure that children distinguish between a *unit square* (a line figure, one linear unit on each side) and a *square unit* (the amount of surface bounded by the unit square). Also a unit square has only one shape, while a square unit may have many shapes (see the preceding figure). Have on hand models of a square inch, square foot, and square centimeter. Use these

models to find or estimate areas of regions drawn on paper. Also, show that the smaller the square unit, the more precise is the measure of the region.

4. Develop the systems of square measure:

144 sq. in. = 1 sq. ft	100 sq. cm = 1 sq. decimeter
9 sq. ft = 1 sq. yd	100 sq. dm = 1 sq. meter
43,560 sq. ft = 1 acre	100 sq. m is called an *are*
640 acres = 1 sq. mi = 1 section.	

Allow children to illustrate the size of an acre in terms of city lots. They should learn to change square feet into square yards and square inches, and vice versa. Finally, they should have some conception of the ratio of a square inch to a square centimeter by drawing these two regions and then partitioning the square inch into square centimeters. The figures will indicate that 1 square inch ≈ $6\frac{1}{2}$ square centimeters. Then, by calculation, $2.54 \times 2.54 \approx 6.45$, which verifies the estimate. All this study prepares the way for developing formulas for finding the area of certain regions from certain linear measures in the region. This is an illustration of indirect measurement.

The measurements of length, angular region, and area as presented so far are called *direct measurements* because we applied a unit directly to the magnitude to be measured. If, however, we measure some aspects related to a figure and from these measures by calculation alone find the measure of another magnitude, it is called *indirect measurement*.

5. Using cross-sectioned paper, we can use indirect measurement to develop the calculation of the area of a rectangular region from the direct measure of the length of the two adjacent sides. On a sheet of paper, we can mark off a rectangular region 6 units long and 3 units wide. Let the unit of measure of the region be one of the square regions. It is easy to see that 6 of these square units cover the bottom row of the region, forming a rectangular area with measure 6. Since the given region is 3 units wide, it can be covered by 3 of these rectangular rows. Hence the number of square units in the entire region is

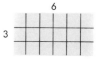

$$3 \times 6 = 18.$$

After the study of several examples of this type, the pupils abstract
the rule:

> The product of the measure of the sides (in linear units) is the
> *measure* of the rectangular region in *square units*.

The stress and meaning given to the italicized words in this rule
are necessary for correct conceptualization of the rule.

At an appropriate time, rectangular regions are represented
for which the measures of the sides are not whole numbers. We
call the lengths of the two sides the *dimensions* ($di \rightarrow$ two, *mension* $\rightarrow$
measures) of the rectangle. For a rectangle, either length may
also be called a base and the other an altitude. If pupils study
the parts of square units, or cut and rearrange these parts, they
discover that the same rule applies for finding an area of a rectangular region from its linear dimensions:

$$(5 \times 3) + (5 \times \tfrac{1}{2}) + (3 \times \tfrac{2}{3}) + (\tfrac{1}{2} \times \tfrac{2}{3}) = 19\tfrac{5}{6},$$
$$3\tfrac{1}{2} \times 5\tfrac{2}{3} = 19\tfrac{5}{6}.$$

This aspect of the study is now represented by a formula. In
the formula, the letters are symbols that may be replaced by the
names of numbers:

$$A = b \cdot h,$$

where b stands for the measure of one side of a rectangle and
h stands for the measure of the adjacent side of the same rectangle;
since b and h represent linear measures, their measurement is in
linear units. On the other hand, A stands for the measure of the
area of the rectangular region. Since A stands for an area measure,
its measurement is in *square units*. For a square region, $b = h$,
and the formula becomes

$$A = b \cdot b \qquad \text{or} \qquad A = b^2.$$

To find a formula for a triangular region, we must redefine
the measures b and h. If a triangular region is cut out of paper,
we can always bend one side over on itself so that the crease goes
through the opposite vertex. This crease represents a segment and
we call the measure of its length the *altitude* of the side of the
triangle which was bent over on itself. The measure of this side
of the triangle is called the *corresponding base*. By making a number
of creases the pupils will discover that a triangle has three altitudes

216

and three corresponding bases. (If one of the angles at the end of the base is obtuse, it is a good exercise to let children discover how to find the corresponding altitude.)

Now we show that any such triangle is exactly half of a rectangle which has as two adjoining sides the same base and altitude as the triangle. Hence the formula for the measure of a triangular region is given by $A = \frac{1}{2}(b \cdot h)$. No other polygons need be treated specifically in elementary school work, since most common regions can be separated into disjoint triangular and rectangular regions and the sum of the area measures of the parts equals the measures of the area of the given region.

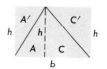

In all work with areas, it is helpful to use graph paper, or lattice paper, so that the children can actually see, or easily draw in, representations of the square regions they are using as measuring units. This is absolutely essential in initial treatments; if children continue to use it for several years, it is, at worst, harmless.

8–6 VOLUME MEASURE

A region in space is considered as being all the points bounded by a closed surface. Good examples are a solid (not hollow) cube, a baseball, or a piece of cylindrical rod. A closed box is not an example of a space region. If, however, we think of the box and all its interior points, we can have an illustration of a space region. When we compare two space regions, again the difficulty arises: how do we intuitively recognize differently shaped regions as having the same measure? We also have the added difficulty of trying to "cover" a space region. A line segment, angle, or plane region can be covered by superimposing a physical unit on it. But we cannot put a physical solid unit on or into a solid to find the number of solid units needed to fill it.

So we resort to using the boundary or shell of a solid region and fill it with some flexible but inelastic material (water or sand, for example). By emptying the material into a container selected as a unit until the unit is filled and repeating the process until all the material has been poured out of the region, we can find a measure and thus compare regions. We must not, however, use weight to compare volumes. Why? Think of using rice for one container and liquid mercury for the other! The weight of the smaller region could thus be much more than the weight of a larger region.

The magnitude of a space region is called its *volume*. Among the standard units are a cubic inch, a cubic foot, a cubic yard, and a cubic centimeter. The development of these units of volume, and their applications to space regions, should be analogous to that for the other magnitudes developed in this chapter. The only formula to be developed in the elementary school is that for a rectangular prismatic solid, or box. The linear measures of three adjoining edges are sufficient to enable us indirectly to find the volume.

Consider an ice tray which is one unit high and whose rectangular base has linear measurements l and w. Then in one column there are w cubic units and in l rows of these columns there are $l \times w$ cubic units.

Now if h of these trays were piled on top of each other to form a rectangular solid there would be $h \times (l \times w)$ cubic units. Hence

$V = h \times l \times w$ (measure of a rectangular prismatic region).

For a cube, all measures of the edges are the same, and we obtain

$$V = e \times e \times e = e^3.$$

In Chapter 13, we shall present an intuitive development of the formulas for the surface and volume of a cylindrical region. We shall also show how the formulas for rectangular solids and cylinders are related, and how to derive certain other formulas from these as enrichment activities.

Further development of areas and volumes should be deferred to the secondary school curriculum. Other measures such as weight, time, liquid volume, etc., are properly physical magnitudes and extensions of the treatment of them described in this chapter should be developed in the science courses where, and in the way, they are used.

The following summary of concepts and magnitudes* shows the goals and fundamental understandings that the study of measure should achieve in the elementary school.

8-7 GENERAL CONCEPTS

The unit for measuring must be of the same nature as the thing to be measured. A line segment is used as a unit for measuring line segments, an angle as a unit for measuring angles, a region of a plane for measuring surfaces, etc. For convenience in communication, standard units (foot, meter, degree, square foot, square meter, etc.) are used.

The measure of a geometric object (line segment, angle, plane region, solid region) in terms of a unit is the number (not necessarily a whole number) of times the unit will fit into the object.

Measurement yields underestimates and overestimates of measures in terms of whole numbers of units. In the case of line segments, angles, regions, and space regions, they also yield approximations to the nearest whole number of units.

Segments, angles, and regions can be thought of as mathematical models of physical objects. Physical terms are used to describe the physical objects and the physical terms are also used in discussing mathematical models. This is acceptable, provided that the correct mathematical interpretation of the physical terms is understood.

A curve in space has length. A surface in space has area.

Some measures of a figure may be calculated from other measures of that figure.

---

* Adapted from SMSG, *Elementary Mathematics*, Books 4, 5, and 6; Pasadena, Calif.: Vroman, Inc., 1963.

Length

A line segment is a set of points consisting of two different points *A* and *B* and all points between *A* and *B* on the line containing *A* and *B*. Sometimes we say "segment" when it is clear that we mean "line segment."

We use a line segment as a unit for measuring line segments.

We use the word "meter" to name the segment which is accepted as the standard unit for linear measurement. We use "inch," "foot," and "yard" to name certain other units which are defined with relation to the standard unit.

The measure of a line segment in terms of a unit is the number (not necessarily a whole number) of times the unit will fit into the line segment. The unit segments may have common endpoints but must not overlap.

In the measurement of a line segment, as the unit becomes smaller, the interval within which the approximate length may vary decreases in size. The precision of a measurement depends on the size of this interval. The smaller the unit, the smaller the interval and the more precise the measurement.

The length of a line segment in terms of a unit consists of (1) the measure of this segment in terms of this unit together with (2) the unit used. Example: the length of this segment is 5 inches; its measure (in inches) is the number 5.

Many of the familiar curves in a plane or in space also have length. We can bend a wire to the shape of the curve and then straighten the wire to represent a segment.

We can calculate the *perimeter* of a triangle or other polygon. If the measures of the sides of a triangle (where the unit of measurement is the inch) are 4, 5, and 6, then the perimeter of the triangle is measured by the number 4 + 5 + 6, or 15. We say that the perimeter of the triangle is 15 in.

A figure consisting of several segments that do not touch may have length. The measure of the figure in terms of a given unit is the sum of the measures of the separate segments in terms of that unit.

8–8 THE USE OF A STRAIGHTEDGE AND A COMPASS

A straightedge is described by its name, 'straightedge'. It refers to an unmarked edge of something which is straight. We can use the edge of a ruler as a straightedge when we just draw a streak along this edge and pay no attention to the marks on the ruler. The edge of a filing card, a strip of tag, a strip of plastic sheeting, and other similar objects can serve as straightedges for use in the classroom whenever we do not have rulers at hand, or whenever we wish to be sure the children are not using the ruler as a measuring instrument in problems we wish them to solve in some other way.

We speak of drawing a line, for example, rather than of drawing a picture of a line for two reasons:

1. In elementary school, no major emphasis is given to the abstract nature of points and sets of points.
2. The word 'draw' implies 'picture', and there is no need for redundancy except for emphasis.

It is not easy for most children to draw a line through two points on a piece of paper. For one thing, they are likely to use large dots for the points. The teacher must encourage the children to make small, "healthy" dots. Then there must be practice in laying the straightedge down below, or beside, the dots, *allowing for the width of the pencil point*, so that the line will go through the center of these dots. The children should practice drawing lines and segments determined by pairs of points in all sorts of relative positions on a sheet of paper. (The teacher who is not skillful may need to practice the same sort of thing on the chalkboard.)

A compass, according to the dictionary, is "an instrument for describing circles or transferring measurements consisting of two pointed branches, or legs, joined at the top by a pivot; called also compasses, a pair of compasses, or dividers." The instrument most of us think of as a compass has a pencil point at the end of one of its legs and a sharp metal point at the end of the other. A compass is essentially an instrument for marking a point, or a sequence of points, at a given distance from a fixed point. The metal point is placed on the fixed point, the legs of the compass "step off" the given distance, and the pencil point makes the desired mark.

A compass may be used in constructing a segment congruent to a given segment. The length of the given segment is the given distance. All we have to do is open the compass so that its legs span the desired distance and then decide where to place the sharp point of the compass. With any kind of straightedge we can draw a segment which our eyes tell us is longer than the segment we wish to copy.

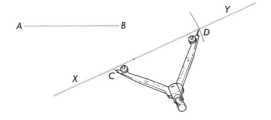

Suppose that we wish to construct a segment congruent to $\overline{AB}$ and having one of its endpoints at C. We can draw just any segment (such as $\overline{XY}$) through C. Then we place the sharp point of the compass at C (we have already opened it to the required distance) and mark a point on $\overline{XY}$ on either side of C. If we label this new point D, then $\overline{CD}$ is the required segment. How do we know that $\overline{CD} \cong \overline{AB}$? By definition, congruent segments are those which have the same length, and the construction makes $\overline{CD}$ the same length as $\overline{AB}$. It is now a simple matter to construct a segment any given whole number of times the length of any specified segment; we just use the compass to lay off that number of congruent segments end to end.

Using a compass to copy a segment is an easier job physically than using a compass to draw a circle. Children of all ages like to work with compasses. Doing what the children call playing with compasses is often a fine thing to do. The teacher must make plain at the start that the compass is one of the tools used in studying geometry and that it is not to be used by anyone as a weapon or a can opener. Some first- and second-grade children can become very skillful in using compasses. Others (and some of these are among the academically talented) simply do not have the requisite muscular control and cannot be expected to achieve proficiency until they mature a bit more in that regard. A teacher is well advised to have primary-level children make their circles by drawing around a disc or a circular cylinder of some sort. The teacher who passes out compasses and paper and merely tells the children to practice using the compasses to draw circles will have a classroom full of marred desk tops, frayed dispositions, torn paper, and unproductive activity.

The teacher should provide some sort of backing sheet, such as a piece of cardboard, thin plywood, or heavy paper. Then the teacher must show the children how to hold the compasses: by the top, and between the thumb and first finger of one hand. The other hand is used to hold the paper. The metal point of the compass should pierce the paper just enough to anchor the compass firmly. Whatever weight is placed on the instrument should be largely on the leg which is on the pivot point (the center of the circle being drawn) with just enough pressure on the pencil point to make a mark. The first few times the children use compasses, the teacher should expect no more from the children than the development of a reasonable skill in making the compass draw where they want it to. Those who acquire this skill quickly may be encouraged to experiment with making designs. When they get a design which appeals to them, they may copy it on clean white paper (unlined), color it, and put it in their mathematics notebooks or on the bulletin board. All children should do this eventually.

When children have learned to use a compass well, there are a number of interesting constructions they can do. Only one basic construction will be described here; others will be treated in Chapter 13. Give each child a piece of unlined paper, preferably the size of typewriter paper. Ask him to *plan* how to draw in the middle of the paper a circle large enough to come within "this much" (about half an inch) of the sides. Then have him draw this circle and keep his compass set. Have him choose a point anywhere 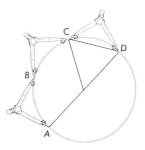 on the circle, mark that point, place the metal point of his compass on it and "march around the circle" with the compass. (See drawing in margin.) If he works very carefully, he finds that six steps with the compass get him back to the point at which he started. The marks he has made with the compass have divided the circle into six congruent arcs. Have him use his straightedge to connect pairs of marked points in order. The children will recognize the regular hexagon. If he connects each vertex of this hexagon to the center of the circle, he has six congruent equilateral triangles. He should measure the angles with vertices at the center of the circle and decide whether the results are what he should expect.

With the same basic construction, the child can construct an equilateral triangle (as in the illustration on the left). He can measure with his protractor each of the angles of this triangle, and the results should give him an idea of how to construct an angle of 60°. (The last sentence of the preceding paragraph suggests another way to construct a 60° angle.) If he connects the points as shown in the illustration on the right, he has a six-pointed star. The class should observe and discuss the triangles and other polygons which are seen in this star.

Children should be encouraged to explore other things they can do with just a compass and a straightedge and this basic construction. They can go outside or inside the circle, change the setting of the compass or not, and see what they get. They always get some pretty pictures, but the teacher should not let that be the end of the activity. He should ask questions such as: "Why did it come out like this? Why does this circle go through the center of the other circle? Are these two segments congruent? Are these angles congruent? Can you be sure without measuring?"

There is a compass-and-straightedge construction which amounts to dividing a circle into five congruent arcs, for a five-pointed star, but it is complicated. The interested teacher who wishes to draw a regular pentagon or a five-pointed star may draw a circle, draw any radius (lightly), divide 360 by 5, and measure five nonoverlapping 72° angles around the center of the circle. (How can you be sure five 72° angles will just fit?) The points at which the sides of these angles cut the circle are the vertices of a regular pentagon or a five-pointed star, depending on how you connect the points. This technique of course works for regular polygons with any number of sides.

8–9 MEASURE AND THE CONGRUENCE THEOREMS

After children have had a long period of acquaintance with the concept of congruent figures and a lot of experience in testing for congruence by using cutouts, tracings, paper folding, and the like, they may use all the measuring techniques they know in exploring the properties of congruent figures, with particular attention paid to triangles. They should discover that, for any two congruent figures, corresponding angles have the same measure and all corresponding segments have the same measure, in terms of appropriate common units in each case. Since "same measure" defines congruence for angles and segments, this discovery should reinforce their awareness that corresponding parts of congruent figures are congruent. In the cases of triangles and regular polygons, and of polygons which are either equilateral or equiangular, they soon find out that they can guarantee the congruence of two figures by testing just a few corresponding parts. They should formulate generalizations beginning in the following ways:

Two triangles are congruent if . . .
Two equilateral triangles are congruent if . . .
Two squares are congruent if . . .
Two regular hexagons are congruent if . . .
⋮
Two rectangles are congruent if . . .
Two rhombuses are congruent if . . .

At first they should be allowed to complete these general statements in any way that produces a true sentence. Then they should be encouraged to minimize the conditions listed. They should always test their completed statements. Sometimes they leave out too much, and they should discover this. Sometimes they leave in too much, and in testing the statement, they often discover something like, "Oh, I didn't have to say this. It comes with some other things I said." The final version of any of these statements is a congruence theorem.

At almost any level, the children should experiment with strips of wood, plastic, or stiff paper and angles drawn by using a protractor or represented by "corners" cut from the same material as the strips to see how many different sizes and shapes of polygons they can make with a given number of specific pieces.

For triangles, the children soon find out that if they pick up these strips (lengths) at random, there are times when they cannot make a triangle at all. How can they be sure it is possible to make a triangle with three given lengths as sides? Compare the lengths and be sure that each of them is shorter than (i.e., neither the same length as nor longer than) the other two laid end to end. When it is possible to make a triangle with three given strips, they should put these strips together in all possible ways, always intersecting only at endpoints, of course. They soon find out that, however they do this, they get models of the same triangle in different positions. Get the "local magician" to change the strips into line segments, make a statement beginning, "If three sides of one triangle are congruent respectively to three sides of another . . ." or "if two triangles have their three sides congruent in pairs . . . ," and you have the side-side-side congruence theorem for triangles. After the children have acquired the requisite skill with rulers, protractors, or compasses, they can demonstrate the same theorem with accurate drawings.

The other two basic congruence theorems for triangles may be developed experimentally in an analogous fashion. Take two specified lengths and specify the size of the angle between them. Make a model of a triangle having those specifications. How many sizes and shapes of triangles can you make? Just one. You have exactly one choice of length for the third side and exactly one choice for each of the other two angles. Make a general statement of what you have just found out and you have an acceptable version of the side-angle-side congruence theorem. The development of the angle-side-angle theorem is left as an exercise for the reader.

Why should we wish to develop these theorems informally with young children? For one thing, children think it's pretty neat that when a few conditions are met, other conditions follow. As some of them say, "When you buy this much, you get the rest free." For another thing, children cannot help acquiring some appreciation for those characteristics of mathematics which make it so fascinating to so many people. Also, these theorems can be postulated and, in sixth-grade classes, used in simple formal proofs. In this connection, statements of theorems the children discover should be refined as time goes by until these statements are made eventually in 'if-then' form.

Experimenting with models and using measurements should probably never stop. In particular, it should not stop before children have discovered that two triangles having three pairs of congruent angles are similar, but not necessarily congruent.

EXERCISES

1. Give a precise description of each of the following:
   a) Magnitude   b) Quantity   c) Measure
   d) Unit of measure   e) Measurement   f) Length
   g) Area   h) Angular magnitude   i) Volume

2. Outline a procedure that could be used in teaching time to children from kindergarten up to second grade, and indicate the equipment you would need for the method you propose.

3. Make a list of the important measurements children should learn in the primary school. Select two of these measurements and tell how you would develop them and test the pupil's understanding.

4. *Precision of measurement depends on the unit of measure used.* Discuss the meaning of this statement with respect to measuring a line segment and outline a procedure for teaching the meaning of precision in Grade 4 with English units and in Grade 6 with metric units.

5. Accuracy of measurement is a relative property and depends on the ratio of the measure obtained to the probable *exact* measure of the magnitude. Look up the meaning of accuracy in an encyclopedia under the heading *metrology* and tell to what extent you would use this idea of accuracy in teaching in elementary school.

6. Make a complete list of the metric system of units for length, area, and volume. Tell which of these units you would introduce in elementary school, giving reasons.

7. In teaching measures in Grades 4, 5, and 6, it is important to have measuring tools and materials. List the tools and supplies, for teachers and for pupils, that you would require for teaching (a) length, (b) area, (c) angular measure, and (d) volume.

8. Describe at least two ways, other than that given in the text, for developing formulas for the area of rectangles and triangles. Show how you would extend your methods to develop the formula for the area of a parallelogram.

9. Make a list of desirable goals that most pupils should achieve in the study of measures, by the end of Grade 6. For each goal listed, give at least one test situation that would measure the achievement of the goal.

10. An excellent activity for showing the difference between a square foot and a foot square starts with supplying each child with a foot-square piece of blue paper, a larger-area rectangular piece of yellow paper, a pair of scissors, and paste. Describe the instructions you would give a class so supplied. Describe the difference it would make, if any, in your instruction if the area of the yellow paper were 1 sq. ft.

11. Discuss the use of the symbols '=' and '≈' in: (a) systems of measurement, (b) reporting measurements, and (c) transforming measurements from one system to another. Tell how you would teach the proper use of these two symbols.

12. Consider the summary given on page 220 under *length*.

    a) Rewrite the first item so that it is a definition of angle instead of segment. In each succeeding section, change just a few words so that the summary will apply to angular measure instead of to linear measure.

    b) Make analogous alterations in the summary so that the summary will apply to area measure. Insert a section which has to do with computing area measure from linear measures.

    c) Repeat (b) for volume measure.

REFERENCES

BOTTS, T., "Linear Measurement and Imagination," *The Arithmetic Teacher* **9**, November 1962, pages 376–382

BOWLES, D. R., "The Metric System in Grade 6," *The Arithmetic Teacher* **12**, 1, January 1964, pages 36–38

HOLLISTER, G. E., and A. G. GUNDERSON, *Teaching Arithmetic in the Primary Grades*. Boston: D. C. Heath, 1964, Chapters 9 and 10

KEEDY, M. L., and C. W. NELSON, *Geometry: A Modern Introduction*. Reading, Mass.: Addison-Wesley, 1965, Chapter 8

OSBORNE, R., M. V. DEVAULT, C. C. BOYD, and W. R. HOUSTON, *Extending Mathematics Understanding*. Columbus, Ohio: Charles E. Merrill Books, Inc., 1961, Chapter 11

PHILLIPS, J. M., "Equidecomposable Figures," filmstrip E from *Seeing the Use of Numbers*, Set VI; "Congruent Figures," filmstrip H from *Set VII*, Eye Gate Productions, Jamaica, N. Y.

SCHOOL MATHEMATICS STUDY GROUP, *Mathematics for Elementary School; Teacher's Commentary*, Grade 4, 5, and 6. New Haven: Yale University Press, 1963

SMART, J. R., and J. L. MARKS, "Mathematics of Measurement," *The Arithmetic Teacher* **13**, April 1966, pages 283–287

WREN, F. L., *Basic Mathematical Concepts*. New York: McGraw-Hill, 1965, Chapters 8 and 9

the teaching
of fractions

There are a number of ways in which one can conceive of a fraction, but in elementary school we shall first of all think of a fraction as referring to a part of something. This is the context in which children know, before they come to school, some of the vocabulary used with fractions. In any fraction, an ordered pair of whole numbers is involved. This pair of numbers is represented in common-fraction form by two numerals, one written above a bar, the other below a bar, where the bar is called a *fraction bar*. The reader is familiar with this form and knows that the second numeral is never a '0'. The following are numerals for fractions:

$$\frac{2}{3}, \quad \frac{5}{8}, \quad \frac{0}{4}, \quad \frac{12}{29}.$$

For the present we shall avoid the use of the words *fractional* and *rational*. Only after the child thoroughly understands what a fraction is will it be possible for the teacher to talk about these concepts of number.

Although a fraction, as a number, can be defined in an abstract mathematical fashion, this is not the way to introduce it to children. We first understand that meanings can be given to a fraction according to the way it is used in describing physical ideas, and the way it enters into operations. From these various meanings there can gradually evolve the concept of a fractional number. Before taking up the teaching of fractions, let us review some of the meanings that every teacher should have clearly in mind before instruction begins.

9–1 PRELIMINARY IDEAS FOR TEACHERS

1. Consider some element as a unit, as one of a kind of thing. Choose something easy to divide into pieces of the same size and shape. Examples are a one-inch segment, one length of cloth, one square region, one bar of candy, and so on. We now partition the element into a fixed number of parts, all of which are congruent. Then we select a certain number of these parts for consideration. To represent these parts, in terms of the unit with which we started, we use a fraction, for example $\frac{2}{5}$, in which the upper number tells the number of congruent parts we are referring to, namely 2, and the lower number tells us the number of congruent parts in the whole unit element, namely 5. Thus, just as 2, 8, or 73 tells us the number of elements in a set, the fraction $\frac{2}{5}$ indicates the number of congruent subdivisions of a unit. In general we may look on

$$\frac{x}{y}, \qquad y \neq 0,$$

as denoting x of the y congruent subdivisions of a unit element. Now try explaining $\frac{3}{7}$, $\frac{9}{9}$, and $\frac{21}{13}$ by this meaning of a fraction. We need this interpretation when we work with fractions on a number line, as well as in other situations.

2. Suppose that, instead of one unit or element, we had more than one (a whole number) of them, for example 3, 5, or 13. Now we pose the problem of how to partition all the elements into a certain given number of equivalent parts, that is, parts that have exactly the same magnitude. Consider the problem of dividing 3 by 5 without resorting to a remainder. From the theory of whole-number division, we know that if $3 \div 5$ were to have an exact answer, the answer would tell the size of one of the equal subdivisions. Thus $3 \div 5$ can be looked on as designating the size of one part, when 3 elements or units are partitioned into 5 equivalent parts.

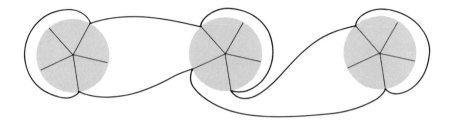

The diagram shows that when we divide each of the 3 units into 5 congruent sections, we have 15 sections, and hence $15 \div 5 = 3$, the number of sections in each part. But by the meaning of fractions given above, this is $\frac{3}{5}$. Hence we can look on the fraction $\frac{x}{y}$ as meaning:

1. One of the parts when x units are subdivided into y equivalent parts, or

2. The exact quotient of $x \div y$. (If $x = q \cdot y$, then $\frac{x}{y} = q$.)

3. An excellent way to think of fractions, and a way in which they are most commonly used, is to conceive of them as *operators*.* This is in reality just a combination of the two above meanings given to a fraction. Consider a unit segment U. We shall think of multiplying this segment by a whole number as *stretching* U.

In the illustration shown, when U is multiplied by 1, it is left identical to itself. If we multiply it by 3, the segment is stretched so that it can be divided or partitioned into 3 segments, each congruent to U, and so it goes for multiplying by 2, by 6, or by any whole number. (Incidentally, multiplying the segment by 0 causes it to vanish.)

Now we shall introduce a new operator which we shall designate by a numeral for a nonzero whole number with a bar above it: $\bar{2}$, $\bar{8}$, $\bar{1}$, etc.

---

* See Fehr, H. F., and T. J. Hill, *Contemporary Mathematics for Elementary Teachers*, Boston: D. C. Heath, 1966.

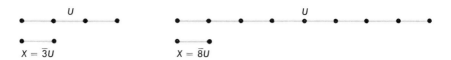

$$X = \overline{3}U \qquad\qquad X = \overline{8}U$$

These operators are defined as follows: $\overline{3}U$ is a segment X such that $3X = U$. That is, $\overline{3}$ partitions U into 3 congruent subsegments; $\overline{8}$ partitions a segment into 8 congruent subsegments. Hence $\overline{3}$ really shrinks U to what was described above as $\frac{1}{3}U$; $\overline{8}$ shrinks U to $\frac{1}{8}U$. Similarly $\overline{1}U$ leaves U exactly the same. Thus we see that the whole numbers operating on a segment act as stretchers (multipliers); the bar numbers operating on a segment act as shrinkers (divisors).

If we put both these operations into one unique operator, which we can indicate by writing the stretcher a above the shrinker $\overline{b}$ in the form $\frac{a}{b}$, we note that we have the fraction symbol. We shall say that $\frac{a}{b}$ operating on a segment (or unit) either:

a) stretches it by a and then shrinks the result by $\overline{b}$ or

b) shrinks it by $\overline{b}$ and then stretches the result by a.

The symbols $\frac{3}{5}\bullet\!\!-\!\!-\!\!\bullet$ mean stretch to $3U$ and then shrink by 5.

The symbol $\frac{3}{5}$ means shrink to $\overline{5}U$ and then multiply by 3.

These examples show that the order in which you apply the two parts of the fraction operation does not affect the result; that is, whether you stretch and then shrink or shrink and then stretch, you obtain the same partitioning. We can summarize all the above discussion by writing:

$$\frac{x}{y} = \frac{\text{numerator}}{\text{denominator}} = \frac{\text{multiplier}}{\text{divisor}} = \frac{\text{stretcher}}{\text{shrinker}}.$$

These relations, when operating on a unit (segment or element), mean

1. x of the y equal parts of a unit,

2. one of the y equal parts of x units,

3. the exact quotient $x \div y$.

(Later the fraction can also be conceived of as a ratio and as a name for a fractional or rational number.)

9-2 DEVELOPING THE FIRST CONCEPTS

The first concepts of fraction to be developed are those of one-half, one-fourth, and one-third, unit parts of *one* of something. When more than one of the somethings is under consideration, we must be sure that children use congruent elements, things that are just alike. Since for children in the early grades 'just alike' or 'same' mean the same as 'congruent', we can use the simpler words without any misconception arising.

An appreciable part of the difficulty we have been having in teaching the role of fractions in the computational algorisms may lie in our failure to recognize those situations in which the child is dealing with fractional numbers and those situations in which he is not. The fraction symbol has many uses, only one of which is naming a fractional number. The old-fashioned teacher who kept his questions specific and concrete was probably exhibiting more wisdom in this regard than some of the modern approaches we sometimes see. For instance, the confusion invited by an exercise like the following may be the result of the unfortunate formulation of the directions:

> Name the fractional number represented by the shaded portions of each of the figures in the margin.

The child who answers "correctly" that the first figure shows the fractional number $\frac{1}{2}$ and the second figure shows the fractional number $\frac{1}{3}$ may note that the shaded portions of the two figures are the same size. The obvious conclusion from this observation is that $\frac{1}{2} = \frac{1}{3}$. But do those diagrams show fractional numbers? *One-half of the first figure* is shaded; *one-third of the second figure* is shaded. It makes no sense to compare the shaded portions unless the appropriate wholes (units) are taken into account. An absolute comparison requires more information. Why? Because we are not dealing with numbers. The '$\frac{1}{2}$' and '$\frac{1}{3}$', if used at all, should be used as names for the relation of the shaded portion of each figure to its whole.

In none of the common learning aids—folding or cutting paper or flannel, playing with blocks or other counters, pouring sand from one container to another, *et al.*—does a child make any use of fractional numbers. Engaging in such activities may enable a child to discover some relationships which are analogous to relationships among fractional numbers, and this is both a blessing and a curse. Quite properly, a child spends a long time (at least two years) and performs many experiments folding, cutting, separating, or joining pieces of paper, cloth, wood, or plastic and discovers many relations which hold for fractional numbers as well as for the objects he has been using. It is well for him to do this before he ever sees a written symbol. It is a mistake to be too glib too soon. The child can discover "equivalence relations," "order relations," "addition facts," "subtraction facts," "multiplication facts," and "division facts," but he never has been working with fractional numbers. In the more complex of his discovery exercises, he has been working with concrete representations of composition of functions.

Usually we start out with the relation *one-half of*. We may use a sheet of paper, and folding it over on itself so as to match, we can cut it into 2 parts that are the same size and shape (because they fit). Children can usually tell us (and if they cannot, we tell them) that each of these parts is one-half of the sheet. At this stage, it is not wise to write the symbol '$\frac{1}{2}$'.

One   One-half   One-half

If two children have papers of different sizes which they partition in half, it is good to compare "one-half" of each paper. These halves are not the same, and the two halves do not make one sheet of paper. This helps the children to see that any two halves that produce one whole must be parts of the same unit. It shows, also, that these pieces of paper are not models for the number $\frac{1}{2}$. There is just one number $\frac{1}{2}$, and when we speak of numbers, it makes no sense to compare halves.

The same idea can then be achieved by folding a ribbon or piece of string, placing the two ends together, and cutting the material at the fold. Each is one-half of the given unit. Likewise

235

a circular disc can be folded over and cut in half, or an equilateral triangular region, and so on. By continued folding or bisection of the half of an element, the concept of one-fourth, one-eighth, and one-sixteenth can be developed.

For each of these fraction concepts, we should have activities similar to those shown below with either concrete objects or drawings on worksheets or both. We reinforce a concept of what something is by showing what it is not.

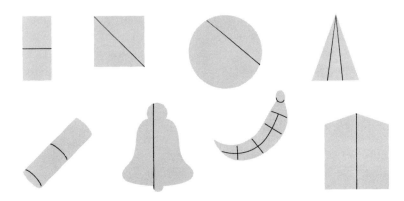

Halves

Not halves

Here is a sample worksheet. The directions to be given orally by the teacher are: "Draw a ring around pictures which show halves. Cross out those which do not."

Such activities are not complete until the class discusses how the children can distinguish halves from other pieces. Such discussions are helpful to everyone, including the teacher.

Using some sort of concrete aids, preferably cutouts which can be laid one on top of the other for purposes of comparison, the children should now compare the sizes of different unit fractions of the same object or of objects which are just alike. The question "which is more?" usually has more meaning for little children than the question "which is greater?"; surely with beginners the first of these questions is the better one to use from a pedagogical point of view. It is just as precise mathematically, too, since the children are not comparing numbers here.

When we wish to record the discoveries made in these exercises, a good notation to use for the time being is exemplified by:

1 half,   2 thirds,   5 eighths.

Now we may ask, "Which is more, 1 half or 1 fourth?" and record the result as:

$$1 \text{ half} > 1 \text{ fourth}$$

and read the ' $>$ ' as 'is more than'. (Sometimes children describe the inequality signs as being greedy; they always open their mouths toward the larger piece.) The children will make surprising discoveries if they have well-made cutouts to handle. They should be given a great many opportunities, with appropriate guidance, to make discoveries of these kinds. Here are some examples:

1. If you put 1 half and 2 fourths together you get 1 whole thing.

2. 3 eighths is more than 1 third. It is just a little bit more.

3. 3 sixths is just as much as 1 half.

4. 1 half and 1 fourth make the same amount as 3 quarters.

(It is interesting, and not really surprising, that children usually know the phrase '1 quarter' before they come to school and usually do not know the phrase '1 fourth'. 'One quarter' is correct, of course, but we wish to have the word 'fourth' to fit into the sequence 'third, fourth, fifth . . .' It is really too bad that halves are not called 'twoths'. 'Threeths' is hard to say, and 'thirds' is readily accepted as a substitute. We can talk about quarters at first, say that they are also called fourths, and get to the general use of 'fourths' gradually.)

5. So long as you start out with "same-size" things, the more parts you have, the smaller each part will be. We don't need any sevenths and ninths in order to know that 1 seventh is more than 1 ninth.

When we use the usual fraction notation, even bright second-graders have trouble with fractions in which the numerator is greater than 1 (sometimes called *multiple fractions*). They get along better if we speak initially of 2 of the 1 thirds, 5 of the 1 eighths, and so on, shortening these expressions a few days later to '2 thirds', '5 eighths', and so on. After the children understand the meaning of such expressions, and after they have had many experiences in comparing fractional parts and joining and separating them, we may introduce the common fraction notation as a shorter way of recording the same amounts.

Using a disc to represent a tart, we can partition it into three congruent sectors, and give a meaning to '$\frac{1}{3}$'. We learn that two-halves, written $\frac{2}{2}$, is equivalent to 1, and $\frac{3}{3}$ is also equivalent to 1. (In this early introduction to the meaning of a fraction, no distinction is made between equal and equivalent.) The children may say, "1 is the same as $\frac{2}{2}$ or $\frac{3}{3}$ or $\frac{4}{4}$." Later they say, "2 is the same as $\frac{4}{2}$ (four halves), or $\frac{6}{3}$," etc. Thus the use of whole numbers with fractions, such as in $2\frac{1}{2}$, becomes a natural way of associating number with a collection of objects and parts of objects.

The next step is to work with objects and fractional parts of these objects, so as to gain facility in thinking about them through the use of fractions. Objects to be used include discs (partitioned into halves, thirds, fourths, fifths, and so on), square regions, and finally a line segment on which, by proper partitioning, we can develop a ruler or number scale. First consider the collection of halves of grapefruit or oranges pictured below.

First we count the number of *halves*, saying and writing

$$\frac{1}{2}, \ \frac{2}{2}, \ \frac{3}{2}, \ \frac{4}{2}, \ \frac{5}{2}, \ \frac{6}{2}, \ \frac{7}{2}, \ \frac{8}{2}, \ \frac{9}{2}, \ \frac{10}{2}, \ \frac{11}{2}.$$

Then, noting that for every 2 halves we can say 1, we can now count the number of halves by using whole numbers and fractions, saying and writing

$$\frac{1}{2}, \ 1, \ 1\frac{1}{2}, \ 2, \ 2\frac{1}{2}, \ 3, \ 3\frac{1}{2}, \ 4, \ 4\frac{1}{2}, \ 5, \ 5\frac{1}{2}, \ \ldots$$

It must be pointed out that each of these numerals represents only one number. Thus '$3\frac{1}{2}$' is a numeral which represents a single number. [This number is a sum, to be sure $(3 + \frac{1}{2})$, just as 31 is a sum $(30 + 1)$, and there are other ways to think of each of them.] In everyday affairs, most people prefer the mixed form $3\frac{1}{2}$ rather than $\frac{7}{2}$, because it quickly tells us how much, while $\frac{7}{2}$ requires rethinking before they know how much it represents.

Of course, the same kind of counting can be done with halves of square regions, halves of triangular (isosceles) regions, or halves of strings, all of the same length. A pupil should never get the idea that fractions are used solely to tell about parts of circles, discs, or pies.

Now we can use the collection of grapefruit halves to discuss operations with fractions informally. Problems to be discussed are: (a) If we have 5 grapefruit and we use $1\frac{1}{2}$ grapefruit today, how much is left? We write this $5 - 1\frac{1}{2}$, which by observation or reasoning is readily established as $3\frac{1}{2}$. (b) If each day we use $1\frac{1}{2}$ grapefruit for breakfast, how many grapefruit will we need to last us 5 days? We write this $1\frac{1}{2} \times 5$ and the answer is reasoned to be $7\frac{1}{2}$; or we could say that we need 8 grapefruit (and $\frac{1}{2}$ grapefruit will remain). Similarly, problems in addition and division can be attacked. All this is to be done without any formal algorism. We just relate the arithmetic to a physical setup and use the number sentences as shorthand ways of keeping a record.

Having worked with one-half, we can extend the same activity to thirds of tarts, where we first write (and say)

$$\frac{1}{3}, \frac{2}{3}, \frac{3}{3}, \frac{4}{3}, \frac{5}{3}, \frac{6}{3}, \frac{7}{3}, \frac{8}{3}, \frac{9}{3}, \frac{10}{3},$$

and then we change to mixed form and write

$$\frac{1}{3}, \frac{2}{3}, 1, 1\frac{1}{3}, 1\frac{2}{3}, 2, 2\frac{1}{3}, 2\frac{2}{3}, 3, 3\frac{1}{3}, \ldots$$

Then we can informally tackle problems in the four operations with thirds. If the same process is repeated for fourths and fifths, this is sufficient preparation for the formal work that comes later.

To culminate this activity we resort to the partitioning of a segment. (Here we may use lined or ruled paper to advantage also.) We first draw a horizontal segment, $\overset{\bullet}{0} \quad \overset{\bullet}{1}$ which will be our unit. We place '0' at the start and '1' at the end of the segment. Next we discuss what it means to multiply this segment by 2, 3, 4, and so on, by extending the unit segment to contain 2, 3, 4, . . . units, all congruent to the segment taken as 1.

Then we divide each unit into halves (two congruent segments), noting the positions of bisection points. The problem is now posed as to what number we should assign to these bisection points. It is an easy matter, relating back to the grapefruit halves, to get the proper assignment. Next we can either bisect each half-unit segment, or partition each unit segment into four congruent segments. In the latter case we can readily see that we repeat some of the "half" points, but this should cause no trouble. When we name the new points, we find that we have constructed a ruler with *our own* unit. This ruler can be used to construct and to find the measure of segments such as

$$1\tfrac{1}{2} + 2\tfrac{3}{4}; \qquad 2\tfrac{1}{4} - 1\tfrac{1}{2}; \qquad 3 \times 1\tfrac{3}{4}; \qquad 6 \div 1\tfrac{1}{2},$$

where the children first decide what meaning is to be given to the operation signs in this context so that the problems will make sense. Further, we can use the ruler to show that the fractions

$$\tfrac{1}{1}, \ \tfrac{2}{2}, \ \tfrac{4}{4}, \qquad \text{or} \qquad \tfrac{2}{1}, \ \tfrac{4}{2}, \ \tfrac{8}{4}, \qquad \text{etc.}$$

in each case name the same measure of a segment. They are *equivalent measures.*

It is further instructive to build rulers that measure thirds and sixths, or fifths and tenths, and finally to relate the ruler of each child to the standard ruler for which the unit segment is an inch, and the subdivisions are either $\tfrac{1}{2}$, $\tfrac{1}{4}$, $\tfrac{1}{8}$, to $\tfrac{1}{16}$, or in tenths of an inch.

All this activity is necessary for thinking about and understanding fractions. It is also basic to the development of the concept of equivalent fractions.

Another way of thinking about fractions is to use the idea of an operator, that is, the stretcher-shrinker idea mentioned earlier. An excellent start for this purpose is to use a tape measure in an automatic winding case. Pull the tape out to the 1-inch mark and represent it on the board. Then ask for whole-number multipliers from the class. If a child says "3," we unwind the tape until the '3' mark appears.

Thus multiplying a 1-inch segment by 3 produces a 3-inch segment. Similarly,

Whole numbers, operating on a segment, transform the segment by stretching it.

To show how unit fractions operate on a segment, it is desirable to use a fairly large segment as a unit segment, for example, 1 foot. Suppose that we multiply this segment by $\frac{1}{2}$. It shrinks until it would require 2 of these segments to make the original. Thus

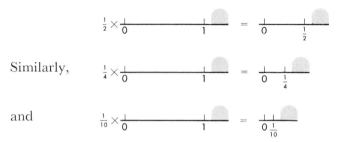

Similarly,

and

Now we combine the whole number and the unit fraction operators as an ordinary fraction, for example, $\frac{2}{3}$, and ask what effect it has on a unit segment. The 2 stretches it, as shown in the first diagram.

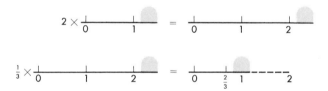

Then $\frac{1}{3}$ operates on the result and shrinks it. Suppose that the order of operations were reversed: shrinking first, stretching second. Would we get a different result? Experiments show that we get the same result (segment) either way.

In practical applications of this stretcher-shrinker notion, including its use in the standard algorism for multiplying fractions, it is usually desirable to do the shrinking first; we get smaller numbers to work with that way. A great deal of practice with this type of operation on segments, in which pupils can use rulers they constructed themselves, leads to the conclusion that:

a) $\frac{2}{3}$ of a segment is one of the *three* congruent parts of *two* segments;

b) $\frac{2}{3}$ of a segment is *two* of the *three* congruent parts of a segment.

Now the same idea for any fraction as an operator can be carried over to any type of object that can be partitioned appropriately and can be "stretched" or "shrunk." For example, amounts of money, quarts of milk, dozens of tangerines, even scores in games, may be discussed in this context.

With the foregoing practice in the use of fractions, and with other similar treatments that teachers can create or find in the literature, the child is prepared to study the equivalence of fractions. At this stage, when he is given the numerator and denominator, he should be able to represent any fraction and state what roles these two parts of a fraction play in describing the meaning to be attributed to the fraction.

9-3 EQUIVALENCE OF FRACTIONS

When we are teaching the equivalence of fractions, it is of no real value to distinguish between the logical difference of *equal* and *equivalent*. The teacher may refer to '$\frac{1}{2}$' and '$\frac{2}{4}$' as equal in that they represent the same number, or, in other contexts, the same relation. The only symbol needed is that of equality. The goal of the teaching is to have children recognize that an equivalence class of fractions can be used to name one value, which we shall then call a fractional number.*

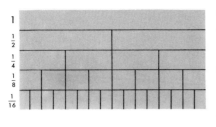

At the start, we use a unit segment or strip which is partitioned into congruent parts. In the study of these parts we look for two things, (a) a comparison of their sizes, that is, which are larger or smaller parts of a unit, and (b) how many of one kind of part are needed to cover another part. We compare size of parts and number of parts. Relating this to

---

* The words 'rational number' need not be used in elementary school unless negative integers and fractions are also taught. It is generally conceded that the study of rational numbers should be deferred until the seventh grade.

fractions, we study the denominators and numerators. Thus from the diagram the child sees many equivalences:

$$1 = \tfrac{2}{2} = \tfrac{4}{4} = \tfrac{8}{8}; \qquad \tfrac{1}{2} = \tfrac{2}{4} = \tfrac{4}{8} = \tfrac{8}{16}; \qquad \tfrac{12}{16} = \tfrac{6}{8} = \tfrac{3}{4}; \qquad \text{etc.}$$

After a brief study of this type of fraction strips, we can introduce others, for example, strips divided into thirds, sixths, and twelfths, from which children recognize the existence of equivalences such as the following:

$$1 = \tfrac{3}{3} = \tfrac{6}{6} = \tfrac{12}{12} = \tfrac{2}{2} = \tfrac{4}{4} = \cdots;$$

$$\tfrac{2}{3} = \tfrac{4}{6} = \tfrac{8}{12}; \qquad \tfrac{1}{2} = \tfrac{6}{12} = \tfrac{2}{4} = \tfrac{3}{6} = \tfrac{4}{8},$$

and so on. To extend the study, the children may be asked to discover what kind of fractional parts we can make from given parts. We stress the idea that the only shrinkers we have for use are $\overline{2}, \overline{3}, \overline{4}, \ldots$, so that we can divide any given segment into 2, 3, 4, 5, ... parts. Starting with a unit strip, we can divide it into halves, thirds, fourths, fifths, and so on. With a half-unit strip, we can subdivide it into fourths, sixths, and so on. Similarly, children learn that a third of a unit strip can be subdivided into sixths and ninths. Other fractional parts of a unit strip can be treated in the same way.

All this study yields the fact that

$$\tfrac{1}{2} = \tfrac{2}{4} = \tfrac{3}{6} = \tfrac{4}{8} = \cdots, \qquad \tfrac{1}{3} = \tfrac{2}{6} = \tfrac{3}{9} = \tfrac{4}{12} = \cdots$$

This is extended to any unit fraction; for example,

$$\tfrac{1}{9} = \tfrac{2}{18} = \tfrac{3}{27} = \tfrac{4}{36} = \cdots$$

For unit fractions, the pupil discovers the relation: the larger the denominator, the smaller the fraction.

Now pupils can represent a given fraction in terms of another fraction when either the denominator or the numerator is given. All that is needed is to refer to the relation of the size of the equal parts with respect to the number of them in a unit, and the number of such parts being considered. Thus we pose the problem

$$\tfrac{2}{3} = \tfrac{?}{9},$$

where the question mark is to be replaced by a numeral to give an equivalent fraction. The class first compares the denominators, saying

1. thirds are greater than ninths,
2. 1 third is equivalent to 3 ninths (why?),
3. then 2 thirds is equivalent to 2 · 3 ninths.

The answer is 6 ninths, and

$$\tfrac{2}{3} = \tfrac{6}{9}.$$

Many problems of this type should be solved, and then a reverse problem posed:

$$\tfrac{6}{9} = \tfrac{?}{3}.$$

Here the sequence is:

1. thirds are greater than ninths,
2. 3 ninths equal 1 third (why?),
3. then 6 ninths yield 2 thirds.

Problems can also be posed that have no answer, if it is understood that the question mark asks for a whole number. For example,

$$\tfrac{18}{25} = \tfrac{?}{5} \quad \text{(18 twenty-fifths equal how many fifths?)}$$

Since 5 twenty-fifths equal 1 fifth, 15 twenty-fifths equal 3 fifths, but there are not sufficient numbers of twenty-fifths to yield another fifth. Bright children may say

$$\tfrac{18}{25} = \tfrac{3}{5}, \quad \text{Rem.} \quad \tfrac{3}{25},$$

and this should not be discouraged. But an answer such as

$$\tfrac{18}{25} = \tfrac{3}{5} + \tfrac{3}{25}$$

is too sophisticated at this stage, unless addition of fractions has been discussed previously. Problems of the type $\tfrac{18}{24} = \tfrac{6}{?}$ should also be given. This merely reverses the order of the questions to be asked. If 18 parts are changed to 6 parts, each part is 3 times as large as the original. Then twenty-fourths must be changed to eighths because 1 eighth is 3 twenty-fourths.

Children should be encouraged to interpret each of the equivalent fractions in terms of the concepts developed with strips and number scales. They should see that all the members of a given family of equivalent fractions are assigned to the same point of a number scale, and all give (essentially) the same result when they operate on a quantity or serve as a measure. As a last step, the fundamental principle of fractions should be developed, namely:

> If both terms of a fraction are multiplied by or divided by the same number (not zero), the result is a fraction equal (equivalent) to the given fraction (or the fraction is transformed into an equivalent fraction).

This principle is abstracted from the process they have used in transforming fractions to equivalent fractions. It is suggested that the words 'reduce', 'reduction of fraction', 'reducing to lowest terms', be abandoned, and that in their place the word *transform* be used. This word is as simple as 'reduce' and is far more meaningful, since we have carried the fraction symbol into another form. We have not reduced or augmented the fraction, we have merely created an equivalent fraction. Eventually, everyone should see that this principle is a special case of the principle for multiplying by 1:

$$n \times 1 = n.$$

As a final mathematical goal, every child should see the relationship of fractions to points on a number line. Each pupil can select a unit segment and extend it to two or three units. He associates the points of division with the whole numbers, as on a ruler.

Then he divides each unit segment in half, each half in half, each new segment in half, and writes the fraction assigned to the points of division, as shown in the diagram.

Then any column of fractions is assigned to only one point on the line (ruler). We say that all these fractions have the same value, and we call this value a *fractional number*. Now we can say that, in a set of equivalent fractions, any one of them may be used to name the same value, or the same point of a number scale or ruler. Thus, transforming a fraction to higher or lower terms is merely finding another fraction in the equivalence class to represent the same value (value is taken as undefined). The important reason for developing this concept of a fractional number is its usefulness in solving problems; thus the practical aspects of partitioning of physical objects are of prime importance. The more abstract mathematical ideas of equality and equivalence should not be emphasized at this time.

9-4 COMPARING FRACTIONS

As soon as children learn the whole numbers, they can put them in order, according to the manyness each number represents. Thus the order

$$0, 1, 2, 3, 4, \ldots, n, \ldots$$

is meaningful and also useful. On a number scale, it is easy to see which of several fractions is the greater: the one that is the farthest to the right. But when we are given two fractions, for example, $\frac{3}{7}$ and $\frac{11}{27}$, it is very difficult to know which is the greater. We attempt to find a way of doing this.

First there should be a period of general discussion. For example, a boy is asked whether he prefers $\frac{4}{9}$ or $\frac{9}{17}$ of a bar of his favorite candy. After a little thinking he replies $\frac{9}{17}$, because this is more than half, while $\frac{4}{9}$ is less than half. In each fraction he has compared the numerator with its denominator. Another pupil, when asked which is more, $\frac{9}{11}$ or $\frac{7}{9}$, says $\frac{9}{11}$, because each fraction is 2 parts less than a whole (one); but ninths are larger parts than elevenths, and if 2 larger parts are removed from a whole, the part left is smaller than if 2 smaller parts are removed. However, when the teacher changes the question to "Which is greater, $\frac{7}{9}$ or $\frac{10}{13}$?" the class is unable to answer. This poses the real problem. How can you tell, for any two fractions, which is the greater?

First, when we have fractions with the *same denominators*, the ordering is easy; the *greater numerator* indicates the *greater fraction:*

$$\frac{17}{12} < \frac{21}{12}; \qquad \frac{2}{13} < \frac{5}{13}; \qquad \text{etc.}$$

Second, when we compare fractions with the *same numerators,* the ordering is easy; the *greater denominator* indicates the *smaller fraction:*

$$\frac{20}{18} < \frac{20}{15}; \qquad \frac{213}{5} < \frac{213}{4}; \qquad \text{etc.}$$

These two cases suggest the way to solve the problem when the numerators and denominators are different: Try to transform the fractions to equivalent fractions having the same denominators or the same numerators. With the best students both methods should be used. But for most students, the teacher should remember the work which lies ahead in adding and subtracting fractions, and concentrate on "same denominators." At first, it is best to resort to trial and error when we are finding a common denominator; it does not have to be the least or lowest common denominator. Thus, given the fractions $\frac{1}{2}$ and $\frac{1}{3}$, children note that halves can be transformed to sixths and so can thirds. So $\frac{1}{2} = \frac{3}{6}$ and $\frac{1}{3} = \frac{2}{6}$, and since $\frac{3}{6} > \frac{2}{6}$, then $\frac{1}{2} > \frac{1}{3}$.

Children must distinguish between the use of *same* and *like* in this study. Thus fractions with the same (equal) denominators are referred to as *like* fractions. But like fractions are not necessarily equal, for example, $\frac{3}{5}$ and $\frac{2}{5}$. Never use the word 'like' in referring to denominators only; use it to refer to fractions having the same denominators.

When we extend the work in fractions to larger denominators, the necessity for finding the lowest common denominator for several fractions becomes apparent. It simplifies the computation involved. Thus $\frac{7}{9}$ and $\frac{13}{24}$ can readily be transformed to

$$\frac{7 \cdot 24}{9 \cdot 24} \quad \text{and} \quad \frac{13 \cdot 9}{24 \cdot 9} \qquad \text{or} \qquad \frac{168}{216} \quad \text{and} \quad \frac{117}{216},$$

but if we transform each fraction to

$$\frac{7 \cdot 8}{9 \cdot 8} \quad \text{and} \quad \frac{13 \cdot 3}{24 \cdot 3} \qquad \text{or} \qquad \frac{56}{72} \quad \text{and} \quad \frac{39}{72},$$

the work is much simpler. Children should be asked to propose methods of finding the lowest common denominator. If there are only two fractions, or several fractions with small denominators, a workable method is to compare the largest denominator with the smaller ones to see if it is a multiple of the smaller denominators. If not, multiply it by 2, 3, 4, 5, and so on, in each case testing the new number as a multiple of the other denominators. Thus for $\frac{7}{9}$ and $\frac{13}{24}$, since 24 is not a multiple of 9, we try 2×24 or 48, and then 3×24 or 72; the latter will be a common denominator, and the least one. For $\frac{1}{3}$, $\frac{5}{6}$, and $\frac{9}{14}$, since 14 is not a multiple of 3 or 6, we try 2×14 or 28. This is not a multiple of 3 or 6. Then we try 3×14 or 42, and find that it is the lowest common denominator. Then

$$\frac{1}{3} = \frac{?}{42}, \qquad \frac{5}{6} = \frac{?}{42}, \qquad \frac{9}{14} = \frac{?}{42},$$

are all previously solved problems and we can compare the transformed fractions.

Later, as fractions have much larger denominators, the method of using prime factorization and finding the lowest common multiple of the denominators can be introduced (see Chapter 6). To compare $\frac{13}{60}$ and $\frac{19}{84}$, we first factor

$$60 = 2 \times 2 \times 3 \times 5 \qquad \text{and} \qquad 84 = 2 \times 2 \times 3 \times 7.$$

Comparing the prime factors, we note that the LCM $= 2 \times 2 \times 3 \times 5 \times 7$, or 420. This is the lowest common denominator: $420 \div 60 = 7$ and $420 \div 84 = 5$. Hence

$$\frac{13}{60} \times \frac{7}{7} = \frac{91}{420}, \qquad \frac{19}{84} \times \frac{5}{5} = \frac{95}{420}, \qquad \text{and} \qquad \frac{13}{60} < \frac{19}{84}.$$

When fractions have values greater than 1, that is, when the numerator is greater than the denominator, it is frequently convenient to write the numeral in mixed form. Thus

$$\frac{13}{8} \quad \text{is} \quad \frac{8+5}{8} \quad \text{or} \quad 1\frac{5}{8}, \qquad \frac{231}{13} \quad \text{is} \quad \frac{221+10}{13} \quad \text{or} \quad 17\frac{10}{13}.$$

The children learn to make this transformation by thinking of the fraction as an indicated quotient. Thus for $\frac{13}{8}$ the division

$$
\begin{array}{r}
1 \\
8\overline{)13} \\
8 \\
\hline
5
\end{array}
$$

$$
\begin{array}{r}
17 \\
13\overline{)231} \\
130 \\
\hline
101 \\
91 \\
\hline
10
\end{array}
$$

means that $\frac{13}{8}$ is 1 and $\frac{5}{8}$ or $1\frac{5}{8}$. Again, $\frac{231}{13}$ by division yields the arrangement shown in the margin, and means that $\frac{231}{13}$ is 17 and $\frac{10}{13}$ or $17\frac{10}{13}$. Now we can practice changing a mixed form to the fraction form and vice versa. Thus

$$2\frac{7}{8} \quad \text{means} \quad \frac{2 \times 8}{8} + \frac{7}{8} \quad \text{or} \quad \frac{23}{8} \, ;$$

$$17\frac{10}{13} \quad \text{means} \quad \frac{17 \times 13}{13} + \frac{10}{13} \quad \text{or} \quad \frac{231}{13} \, .$$

When we are comparing fractions there are times when we wish to represent the fraction in its simplest form. The simplest form is one in which the numerator and denominator have no common factor. To accomplish this we use the fundamental principle of fractions, namely that we may divide the numerator and denominator of a fraction by their greatest common factor, thus transforming the fraction to one in which numerator and denominator have no common factor. For example, in $\frac{60}{84}$ we note that 60 and 84 have a common factor. Since $60 = 2 \times 2 \times 3 \times 5$ and $84 = 2 \times 2 \times 3 \times 7$, the GCF is $2 \times 2 \times 3$ or 12. (See Chapter 6.) Then

$$\frac{60 \div 12}{84 \div 12} = \frac{5}{7} \, ,$$

which is the simplest form.*

9–5 ADDITION OF FRACTIONS

By the time pupils are ready to study operations on fractions, they will have had considerable experience in the meaning of an operation and the use of computational algorisms for finding the results of operations. The first step is to review the meaning of operations with whole numbers. One can pose to the class an ordered pair of whole numbers,

$$(673, 41),$$

and say "addition." How do you write this? What is the sum?

---

* Note that nowhere have we used the word 'cancel', and it is recommended that this word be dropped from its ordinary usage in elementary school arithmetic. It leads frequently to erroneous computation on the part of pupils. For example, pupils who know something about canceling, but not enough, may assert that $\frac{153}{397} = \frac{15}{97}$ because the threes cancel out.

Give a practical situation in which you can justify the operation. Use the same numbers and say in turn "subtraction," "multiplication," and "division." Pose the same three questions as for addition: the concept of an operation, its name, its components, and a practical application. This routine provides the basis for studying operations with fractions.

When we pose the ordered pair of fractions

$$(\tfrac{1}{2}, \tfrac{1}{3}),$$

and say "addition," what do we mean? And how do we find the sum? The children have a problem for discussion. If a child answers, "It's how much $\tfrac{1}{2}$ of something and $\tfrac{1}{3}$ of something is," it must be made clear that the word 'something' refers to a unit element and to the same unit in both cases. Then we can consider a square or a rectangular region or a circular disc as a unit and build a physical situation which is an analog for addition of fractions. Using the $\tfrac{1}{2}$ and $\tfrac{1}{3}$ as operators, we can write

Join

$$\tfrac{1}{2} \times \boxed{} = \boxed{}, \qquad \tfrac{1}{3} \times \boxed{} = \boxed{}, \qquad \boxed{}$$

and by $\tfrac{1}{2} + \tfrac{1}{3}$ we mean the fraction which tells what part the join of these two parts is of the unit region. If we divide the half of a region into thirds, and the third of a region into halves, the new parts are congruent sixths of the unit. Altogether the join has $\tfrac{5}{6} \times \boxed{}$. Thus we write

$$\tfrac{1}{2} + \tfrac{1}{3} = \tfrac{5}{6} \qquad \text{or} \qquad \begin{array}{r} \tfrac{1}{2} \\ + \tfrac{1}{3} \\ \hline \tfrac{5}{6} \end{array}$$

A study of the example shows that we transformed $\tfrac{1}{2}$ and $\tfrac{1}{3}$ to the like fractions $\tfrac{3}{6}$ and $\tfrac{2}{6}$. Hence the number of sixths was found by adding the numerators.

A study of a few similar analogs, using the number scale, discs, or rectangular regions will help to establish the *concept* of addition of fractions, and how the sum is to be interpreted. Thus if it is found, through the use of square or circular regions, that

$$\tfrac{1}{3} + \tfrac{1}{4} = \tfrac{7}{12},$$

the child could also be expected to say, "If a segment of 1 foot is divided into 3 equal parts, and then 4 equal parts, and 1 of each of these parts is joined to form a new segment, this segment will be 7 of the 12 equal parts. You can check this, using a foot ruler."

A productive pedagogical device which helps to minimize the occurrence of mistakes such as

$$\tfrac{2}{5} + \tfrac{1}{5} = \tfrac{3}{10}, \qquad \tfrac{1}{2} + \tfrac{1}{3} = \tfrac{2}{5}, \qquad \text{and} \qquad \tfrac{3}{4} + \tfrac{2}{3} = \tfrac{5}{7}$$

is the use of the write-the-denominator-as-a-word notation:

2 fifths	1 half	3 fourths
+ 1 fifth	+ 1 third	+ 2 thirds

"In the first example, what kinds of fractions are we adding?" "Fifths." "What will the answer be?" "A number of fifths. You have to get what you're adding." "How about the second example?" "You are adding different kinds of fractions. You can add them, but the answer is not 2 of something. If you don't know the answer, you have to transform the fractions so that they both can use the same word." "How do you do that?" "You think about like fractions which are equivalent to 1 half and 1 third. We could use 3 sixths and 2 sixths and then just add the same way we add 3 hundreds and 2 hundreds." "How about the third example?" "It's just like the second except that 3 fourths of something and 2 thirds of it will be more than 1 of the thing, and we may want to write the answer in a different way." (17 twelfths = 1 unit and 5 twelfths = $1\tfrac{5}{12}$.)

This last remark brings up an important feature of all problems and computation, that of *estimating the answer*. Estimates need not be close, in terms of relative size, to exact answers. A child who sees that $\tfrac{2}{3} + \tfrac{3}{4} > 1$ is not likely to give the incorrect answer $\tfrac{5}{7}$. When we are working with fractions, whatever operation is involved, it is usually sufficient to compare the predicted "sensible answer" with 1. $[\tfrac{1}{2} + \tfrac{1}{3} < 1, \tfrac{2}{3} \times \tfrac{6}{15} < 1, \tfrac{3}{7} \div \tfrac{3}{7} = 1$ (any number except 0 divided by itself . . .), $\tfrac{1}{6} \times \tfrac{19}{2} > 1$, etc.] In the case of subtraction, particularly, and sometimes with addition and the other operations, it may be desirable to compare the "sensible answer" with $\tfrac{1}{2}$.

It is not sufficient to have a concept and to be able to estimate answers. Skill in using a computational technique is also necessary.

This can be developed in several ways. The following is only a suggested procedure for developing skill in finding sums.

a) If the fractions to be added are like fractions, we can illustrate them by marking segments on a number scale. Thus to find $\frac{3}{5} + \frac{4}{5}$, we divide a unit segment of a number scale into 5 congruent segments. We mark the point $\frac{3}{5}$ and annex a segment of $\frac{4}{5}$ to it. The last point has the number $\frac{7}{5}$. Thus $\frac{3}{5} + \frac{4}{5} = \frac{7}{5}$. After a number of such examples, the child will generalize that when we add like fractions the numerator of the sum is the sum of the numerators and the denominator of the sum is the common denominator.

b) If the fractions to be added are unlike, then we transform them to fractions with a common denominator and the process is the same as in (a) above. Thus to find $\frac{1}{2} + \frac{1}{3}$, we transform the fractions to sixths. If the problem is to find $\frac{5}{6} + \frac{7}{15}$, we find the lowest common denominator to be 2×15 or 30. The problem becomes $\frac{25}{30} + \frac{14}{30} = \frac{39}{30}$. In mixed notation, the answer can be written $1\frac{9}{30}$. The simplest form of $\frac{9}{30}$ is $\frac{3}{10}$, so that the answer can also be written as $1\frac{3}{10}$. Of course, it is possible to transform

$$\frac{39}{30} \quad \text{to} \quad \frac{13 \times 3}{10 \times 3} \quad \text{or} \quad \frac{13}{10}$$

and then write the answer as $1\frac{3}{10}$. All these possibilities should be explored. There is *no one way* in which the process *must* be done.

If the explanation of addition of fractions follows the above procedure it is evident at once that addition is commutative, that is, the order in which two fractions are added does not alter the sum. However, if the problem is to combine three fractions by addition, for example,

$$\frac{1}{2} + \frac{2}{3} + \frac{3}{4}, \qquad \begin{array}{r} \frac{1}{2} \\ \frac{2}{3} \\ + \frac{3}{4} \end{array} \Rightarrow \begin{array}{r} \frac{6}{12} \\ \frac{8}{12} \\ + \frac{9}{12} \\ \hline \frac{23}{12} = 1\frac{11}{12} \end{array}$$

then the associative law must be tacitly assumed. In this case, the LCD is 3 × 4, or 12, so that the problem becomes

$$\tfrac{6}{12} + \tfrac{8}{12} + \tfrac{9}{12} = \tfrac{23}{12} \quad \text{or} \quad 1\tfrac{11}{12}.$$

If the problem is given in columnar form (bottom of page 252) we rewrite the problem in terms of the common denominator, as shown. The '⇒' merely connects two forms of the same problem.

When the numbers are given in mixed form, the addition should be compared with the algorism for whole numbers. In the example shown in the margin, there is a units column, a tens column, and a column with fourths and fifths in it called a *fraction column*. If this column contained only fourths, it would be a simple matter to add the fourths and exchange four of them for one unit. A similar thing could be said if it were a column containing any like fractions. So we transform the problem into one in which the fraction column does contain only like fractions, i.e., twentieths:

$$\begin{array}{r} 12\tfrac{3}{4} \\ +\ 49\tfrac{3}{5} \\ \hline \end{array}$$

	Tens	Units	Twentieths		
$12\tfrac{3}{4}$	1	2	15		$12\tfrac{15}{20}$
$49\tfrac{3}{5} \Rightarrow$	4	9	12	$\Rightarrow$	$49\tfrac{12}{20}$
	5	11	27		
	6	2	7		$62\tfrac{7}{20}$

When the children progress from the second item of the display above to the third item, they should see that the regrouping (exchange) involving fractions differs from that with whole numbers only in that they cannot "go by tens" unless the fractions happen to be tenths. They have to think about what they are doing. If they are dealing with fourths, they exchange 4 fourths for 1 unit, and the exchange can be made either way. They should be able to explain this. For an analogous reason they exchange 20 twentieths for 1 unit, 12 twelfths for 1 unit, 33 thirty-thirds for 1 unit, and so on.

Once the children understand the algorism, the teacher must provide an abundance of drill and applications to practical problems. In the problems, the children should picture or dramatize what happens to the physical entities involved and then represent a model of the physical situation by numbers and operations on the numbers. Some examples in which fractional numbers occur are hours of baby-sitting, yardage of lace, weights of goods, recipes for cooking, and share of earnings or profits.

9–6 SUBTRACTION OF FRACTIONS

After the children have studied addition, subtraction of fractions should cause no trouble. The operation can be related back to addition of fractions in the same way that subtraction of whole numbers was related to addition of whole numbers. The same techniques used to teach subtraction of whole numbers may be used with fractions. Again a physical analog involves taking away a part of material from a given amount of the material. Thus

$$\tfrac{2}{3} - \tfrac{1}{4}$$

can be interpreted to mean that '$\tfrac{2}{3}$' refers to $\tfrac{2}{3}$ of a pie and '$\tfrac{1}{4}$' refers to $\tfrac{1}{4}$ of the same pie, and the '−' means to slash away $\tfrac{1}{4}$ of the pie from the $\tfrac{2}{3}$ of a pie and find what part of the pie remains.

 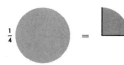

It is evident that if we change the divisions of the pie to twelfths, then $\tfrac{2}{3} = \tfrac{8}{12}$, $\tfrac{1}{4} = \tfrac{3}{12}$, and

$$\tfrac{8}{12} - \tfrac{3}{12} = \tfrac{5}{12},$$

which is the part of the pie that remains. The number $\tfrac{5}{12}$ is called the *difference* when $\tfrac{3}{12}$ is subtracted from $\tfrac{8}{12}$ or $\tfrac{1}{4}$ from $\tfrac{2}{3}$.

Here again it is important for children to recognize that in practical situations the subtrahend refers to a part of the same thing that the minuend refers to, and in both cases the same unit is implied. So, in elementary school, since we cannot remove $\tfrac{2}{3}$ of a pie from $\tfrac{1}{4}$ of the pie, we say that it is impossible to subtract a greater fraction from a smaller fraction. Thus

$$\tfrac{1}{4} - \tfrac{2}{3} \qquad \text{is not possible.}$$

If the fractions are like fractions, no trouble arises. Thus

$$\frac{11}{13} - \frac{7}{13} = \frac{11 - 7}{13} \quad \text{or} \quad \frac{4}{13},$$

$$\frac{13}{5} - \frac{8}{5} = \frac{13 - 8}{5} \quad \text{or} \quad \frac{5}{5} \quad \text{or} \quad 1,$$

$$\frac{23}{7} - \frac{6}{7} = \frac{23 - 6}{7} \quad \text{or} \quad \frac{17}{7} \quad \text{or} \quad 2\frac{3}{7}.$$

These problems should also be given in columnar form. If the fractions are unlike, they can be transformed to like fractions. Thus $\frac{7}{15} - \frac{1}{6}$ becomes

$$\frac{14}{30} - \frac{5}{30} = \frac{9}{30} \quad \text{or} \quad \frac{3}{10}$$

$$\begin{array}{r} \frac{7}{15} \\ - \frac{1}{6} \\ \hline \end{array} \Rightarrow \begin{array}{r} \frac{14}{30} \\ - \frac{5}{30} \\ \hline \frac{9}{30} \quad \text{or} \quad \frac{3}{10} \end{array}$$

If the numbers are given in mixed form, we follow the same procedure we would follow in subtracting whole numbers, merely transforming the fractional column to like fractions. The pupil should review the rationale of subtracting whole numbers by working out examples of the following type, explaining any exchange or regrouping that he made in carrying out the algorism:

$$\begin{array}{r} 64 \\ - 37 \\ \hline \end{array} \qquad \begin{array}{r} 60 \\ - 37 \\ \hline \end{array} \qquad \begin{array}{r} 40 \\ 8 \\ \hline \end{array} \qquad \begin{array}{r} 204 \\ - 19 \\ \hline \end{array}$$

Then, confronted with the problem shown in the margin and referring to algorisms with whole numbers, he can think of 5 as $4\frac{4}{4}$ (by exchanging a unit for 4 fourths). If he can do the exchange mentally, there is no need to rewrite the example. The pupil merely thinks $\frac{4}{4} - \frac{3}{4}$ is $\frac{1}{4}$ and $4 - 2$ is 2.

$$\begin{array}{r} 5 \\ - 2\frac{3}{4} \\ \hline \end{array} \Rightarrow \begin{array}{r} 4\frac{4}{4} \\ - 2\frac{3}{4} \\ \hline 2\frac{1}{4} \end{array}$$

$$\begin{array}{r} 12\frac{2}{3} \\ - 3\frac{1}{4} \\ \hline \end{array} \Rightarrow \begin{array}{r} 12\frac{8}{12} \\ - 3\frac{3}{12} \\ \hline 9\frac{5}{12} \end{array}$$

A problem of the type shown above is at first rewritten so as to contain a like-fraction column of twelfths. The following writing is incorrect mathematically and should be avoided.

$$\begin{array}{r} 12\frac{2}{3} = \frac{8}{12} \\ - 3\frac{1}{4} = \frac{3}{12} \\ \hline 9 \quad \frac{5}{12} \end{array}$$ ($12\frac{2}{3}$ does not equal $\frac{8}{12}$, and we do not subtract equations to get an answer.)

Similarly, writing

$$\begin{array}{r} 12\frac{\cancel{2}}{\cancel{3}} \quad \frac{8}{12} \\ 3\frac{\cancel{1}}{\cancel{4}} \quad \frac{3}{12} \\ \hline 9 \quad \frac{5}{12} \end{array}$$ is messy, to say the least.

Finally, speed algorisms such as indicated in the margin are unnecessary, and they fail to show the inherent concepts needed to understand the algorism.

$$\begin{array}{r|r} & 12 \\ 12\frac{2}{3} & 8 \\ - 3\frac{1}{4} & 3 \\ \hline 9 & \frac{5}{12} \end{array}$$

At times both an exchange and rewriting of the example will be necessary for most pupils. The following worked example of finding the difference is self-explanatory when we compare it with whole-number computational procedures.

$$
\begin{array}{ccc}
214\frac{1}{3} & 214\frac{5}{15} & 213\frac{20}{15} \\
-\quad 25\frac{4}{5} & \Rightarrow \quad -\quad 25\frac{12}{15} & \Rightarrow \quad -\quad 25\frac{12}{15}
\end{array}
$$

Hundreds	Tens	Units	Fifteenths
2	1	4	5
−	2	5	12
		⇓	
1	10	13	20
−	2	5	12
1	8	8	8

Note: $214\frac{1}{3}$ was regrouped to 1 hundred, 10 tens, 13 units, and 20 fifteenths.

If the children understand the principles involved, then they can carry out the operations on fractions with any denominator, no matter how large. To restrict denominators to those of one digit, or of two digits (only 12 and 16) because these fractions are in common use is to use a mechanistic rote philosophy of learning arithmetic, and not a philosophy which leads to learning the meaning and structure of the subject. Thus a child who understands the theory will have no more difficulty adding or subtracting $185\frac{3}{23}$ and $21\frac{7}{17}$ than he does with $\frac{5}{8}$ and $\frac{2}{9}$. All he has to do is to perform a little more computation.

To summarize: In teaching fractions, we first develop the concept of a fraction as a mathematical entity that can be used in working with a number of congruent parts of a unit of physical or geometrical magnitude. After this is understood, we can extend the idea of $\frac{a}{b}$, where a and b are whole numbers, $b \neq 0$, to mean a of the b equal parts of 1 or 1 of the b equal parts of a units, again starting with physical or geometrical models and abstracting this fraction concept. A third step is to develop the fraction as an operator, one that stretches the unit and then shrinks the result (or vice versa), as a multiplier and divisor, or as a numerator and denominator, all of which tie the previous ideas into one.

Next, when we consider fractions as operators, there are many fractions that yield the same result, and we study these equivalent fractions as classes, any one of which represents a unique point on a number scale. The number scale is calibrated with these unique points, and any fraction assigned to a given point can be used to represent the number which we call a fractional number. Although fractions are used to name this number, we do not at this stage stress the distinction between a fractional number and its name.

When we have assigned numbers to points on a line, it is easy to tell which of two points is associated with the greater number: the point that is rightmost. But when we are given two numbers, $\frac{a}{b}$ and $\frac{c}{d}$, it is not always easy to tell which is the greater. We resort to the equivalence of fractions and use those fractions having a common denominator to tell which is the greater. This requires us to teach the process of finding the LCD of a given set of fractions.

Now that the children understand fractions fairly well, we can teach operations on fractions. Although we could teach multiplication and division of fractions before addition and subtraction of fractions, we chose to teach the latter operations first because of the usual school procedure, and because these operations make use of the order and equivalence properties of fractions. Each operation is referred to a physical or geometrical model from which the arithmetical structure of operations on fractions can be abstracted. Once the operations are understood, the algorisms are developed by relating them to similar operational algorisms on whole numbers. Practice and application to problems then completes this introductory study.

EXERCISES

1. Distinguish among the terms (a) fraction, (b) fractional number, (c) ordered pair of whole numbers, (d) rational number. Describe the way you would develop the concept of a fractional number.

2. List at least three physical or geometrical materials which can be used to illustrate the meanings to be given to a fraction. Select a geometrical model that can be used on a flannel board and illustrate how you would teach the meaning of

$$\frac{a}{b}, \qquad b = \{1, 2, 3, 4, 5\}, \qquad \text{as } a \text{ of the } b \text{ equal parts of 1.}$$

3. Select an issue of a good daily newspaper and search it for uses of fractions. State the concept of fraction needed to interpret each use.

4. Sometimes the word 'whole' is used instead of 'one'. Give arguments for and/or against the use of the word 'whole' in connection with teaching a meaning of a fraction.

5. In teaching fractions the words 'congruent parts' and not 'equal parts' were used when referring to a line or region. Justify the use of the word 'congruent' in place of 'equal'.

6. The numbers 0, 1, 2, and so on, are whole numbers. The numbers $\frac{0}{1}, \frac{0}{2}, \ldots, \frac{1}{1}, \frac{2}{2}, \frac{3}{3}, \ldots, \frac{2}{1}, \frac{4}{2}, \frac{6}{3}, \ldots$, are fractional numbers.

   a) What distinction, if any, would you make between the whole number 1 and the fractional number represented by $\frac{1}{1}, \frac{2}{2}, \frac{3}{3}, \ldots$?

   b) In writing $2\frac{2}{3}$, would you teach this symbol as representing 2 units and $\frac{2}{3}$ of a unit or as representing $\frac{8}{3}$ units or as one way of representing any of the following units: $\frac{8}{3}, \frac{16}{6}, \frac{24}{9}, \ldots$?

   c) Look up the concept of isomorphism and tell the difference and the likeness of the set $\{0, 1, 2, \ldots, n, \ldots\}$ and the set

$$\left\{ \left\{ \frac{0}{1}, \frac{0}{2}, \ldots \right\}, \left\{ \frac{1}{1}, \frac{2}{2}, \frac{3}{3}, \ldots \right\}, \left\{ \frac{2}{1}, \frac{4}{2}, \frac{6}{3}, \ldots \right\}, \ldots, \left\{ \frac{n}{1}, \frac{2n}{2}, \frac{3n}{3}, \ldots \right\}, \ldots \right\}.$$

7. Some teachers prefer to order fractions by the rule

$$\frac{a}{b} < \frac{c}{d} \qquad \text{if and only if} \qquad ad < bc.$$

   Thus $\frac{2}{3} < \frac{6}{8}$ because $2 \times 8 < 3 \times 6$.

   a) Show that this rule is really one of transforming the fraction to the same denominator.

   b) Show that the rule:

$$\text{If } \frac{a}{b} < \frac{c}{d} \qquad \text{then} \qquad ad < bc$$

   is also validated by transforming the fractions to the same numerator and comparing the denominators.

8. Pick three specific examples to show addition of fractions and three to show subtraction of fractions. Describe the discussion about estimating answers you would anticipate if these were used in a classroom.

9. Starting with a unit line segment U, $\vdash\!\!\overset{\textstyle U}{\rule{3cm}{0.4pt}}\!\!\dashv$ explain what you would do to operate on this segment to explain each of the following:

   a) $\frac{2}{3}U$ b) $\frac{1}{4}U$ c) $\frac{2}{3}U + \frac{1}{4}U$ d) $\frac{2}{3}U = \frac{8}{12}U$

   e) $\frac{1}{4}U = \frac{3}{12}U$ f) $\frac{2}{3}U + \frac{1}{4}U = \frac{11}{12}U$ g) $\frac{2}{3} + \frac{1}{4} = \frac{11}{12}$

10. Using Exercise 9 as an illustration, explain how you would study the meaning of $\frac{2}{3} - \frac{1}{4}$, starting with a unit segment U.

11. Show how the derivation of the words 'numerator' and 'denominator' suggest their meaning and use with fractions.

12. List the set of mathematical goals implied in the study of this chapter. For each goal list a set of activities that you feel will be sufficient to achieve the desired goals.

REFERENCES

GUNDERSON, A. G., "Arithmetic for Today's Six- and Seven-Year-Olds," *The Arithmetic Teacher* **2,** 5, November 1965

HARTUNG, M. L., "Fractions and Related Symbolism in Elementary School Instruction," *Elementary School Journal* **58,** April 1958, pages 377–384

NATIONAL COUNCIL OF TEACHERS OF MATHEMATICS, *The Growth of Mathematical Ideas, Grades K–12.* Twenty-Fourth Yearbook, 1959, Chapter 2

OSBORNE, R., M. V. DEVAULT, C. C. BOYD, and W. R. HOUSTON, *Extending Mathematics Understanding.* Columbus, Ohio: Charles E. Merrill Books, Inc., 1961, Chapter 5

PHILLIPS, J. M., *Seeing the Use of Numbers, Sets III–VII* (filmstrips), Eye Gate Productions, Jamaica, N. Y.

SCANDURA, J. M., "Fractions—Names and Numbers," *The Arithmetic Teacher* **11,** November 1964, page 468

multiplication
and division
of fractions

The teaching of fractions begins in the earliest grades, in which the primitive notions of one-half, one-third, and one-fourth are used. As children advance through the grades, they learn to deepen and broaden their concept of fractions, and to integrate it with other mathematical ideas. Eventually they come to recognize a class of equivalent fractions in which any member represents the same value, or point on a number line. This sophisticated idea leads to the concept of arithmetical rational numbers, also referred to as fractional numbers.

10-1 MULTIPLICATION OF FRACTIONS

The operation of multiplication of fractions can be taught either as an operation independent of any other operation on fractions, or it can be taught as an operation in which meaning is achieved by relating it to addition. At present, the latter is the more common way of introducing the operation of multiplication of fractions, but since relating it to addition seems far-fetched when the multiplier is not a whole number, there is a growing movement toward using the more generally applicable way of treating it as an independent operation. We shall present both ways here, because each method can give insight into the operation by relating it to the other method. Let us start with the independent-operation idea.

Suppose that a child is confronted with a situation such as

$$\tfrac{2}{3} \times \tfrac{4}{5} = ?$$

The first step is to obtain some meaning that can be given to the problem. The usual interpretation of '$\times$' in this situation is 'of'. That is, the child says, "It means $\tfrac{2}{3}$ *of* [$\tfrac{4}{5}$ (of something)]." Since this is the typical idea of an operator, that is, $\tfrac{4}{5}$ operating on something followed by $\tfrac{2}{3}$ operating on the result, it can be referred to many practical situations; for example, parts of a journey (on a line), changing recipes (measuring devices), areas (a rectangle or square). Thus the first step in teaching the operation is to see what happens when this meaning is ascribed to the problem.

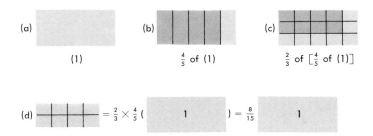

Suppose that we have a rectangular region which we take as a unit, or 1 [see part (a) of the diagram]. Then

means that we must shrink the region to a part $\tfrac{1}{5}$ and stretch this to 4 of these parts [see part (b)]. Now we must operate on the result by $\tfrac{2}{3}$; that is, we must shrink the shaded region to $\tfrac{1}{3}$ and stretch the result to 2 of these parts [see part (c)]. Now the result must be related to the original region 1 with which we began our operation. It is easy to see that the original region has been divided into 15 congruent regions and that our result has 8 of these regions. Hence

$$(\tfrac{2}{3} \times \tfrac{4}{5}) \text{ of a region is } \tfrac{8}{15} \text{ of the region.}$$

When the result has been achieved, it should be studied until the class understands how the rectangle was divided into 5 regions, then each of these into 3 regions, giving 15 congruent subregions. Next the child should recognize that only 4 of the 5 regions were used, followed by using only 2 of the second subdivision of the rectangle, giving 8 of the 15 congruent subregions. This relates the result back to the numbers in the problem. In this way, the child comes to see that, by definition, or by the meaning we give the problem,

$$(\tfrac{2}{3} \times \tfrac{4}{5})(\boxed{}) \quad \begin{cases} \text{is} \\ \text{or} \\ \text{means} \end{cases} \quad \tfrac{2}{3} \times (\tfrac{4}{5} \times \boxed{}),$$

and since the right-hand member is found to be $\tfrac{8}{15}(\boxed{})$, we agree to drop the regions and write:

$$\frac{2}{3} \times \frac{4}{5} = \frac{2 \times 4}{3 \times 5} = \frac{8}{15}.$$

In the above presentation it is assumed that the child has already been introduced to area (see Chapter 8) and to congruent geometric figures (Chapter 7). In any learning situation, not only do we, as good teachers, bring in a physical or geometrical situation, but we also ask the child to dip into the reservoir of facts and concepts he has already learned and bring them to the problem at hand, so as to discover a new idea or define a new operation. Thus the idea of a fraction as an operator, the concept of subdividing an area into congruent subregions, and the multiplication of cardinal numbers are brought into a new idea of multiplication of fractions. Now the pupil must take other similar examples and generalize, until he has abstracted the general rule.

The same problem can be illustrated on a number line.

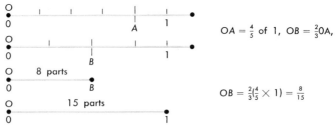

$OA = \tfrac{4}{5}$ of 1, $OB = \tfrac{2}{3}OA$,

$OB = \tfrac{2}{3}(\tfrac{4}{5} \times 1) = \tfrac{8}{15}$

First the segment O to 1 is operated on by $\tfrac{4}{5}$, locating point A.

Then the segment OA is operated on by $\frac{2}{3}$. The easy way to do this is to *divide each fifth into 3 equal parts*. Thus $\overline{OA}$ has 4×3 or 12 of these small parts; $\frac{1}{3}$ of these is 4, and $\frac{2}{3}$ of them is 8. This locates point B, which could be labeled '$\frac{8}{15}$'. Again the class studies the example until they notice that the unit (1) was divided into 5 congruent parts, and then each part into 3 smaller congruent parts, giving 15 congruent parts in the segment. Next we found 4 of the fifths, and then, having divided each fifth into 3 parts, we used only 2 of the 3 congruent parts of $\overline{OA}$.

    After many problems have been solved with two fractions, each less than 1, the process can be extended to the product of fractions equal to, or greater than, 1. For example, the problem $3 \times \frac{4}{5}$ on a number line becomes one of finding a segment of length $\frac{4}{5}$ and then stretching the result to 3 times its size.

This yields

$$3 \times \left(\frac{4}{5}\right) = \frac{3 \times 4}{5} = \frac{12}{5} = 2\frac{2}{5}.$$

If a rectangular strip is used as the unit, we have a similar diagram:

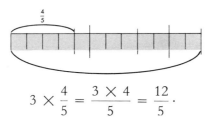

$$3 \times \frac{4}{5} = \frac{3 \times 4}{5} = \frac{12}{5}.$$

In cases like this, there seems little to be gained by writing 3 as $\frac{3}{1}$, since the denominator 1 as a shrinker leaves the result unchanged. Thus

$$3 \times \tfrac{4}{5} \qquad \text{is preferred to} \qquad \tfrac{3}{1} \times \tfrac{4}{5}.$$

The latter form was derived from the old rote learning method which we do not advocate. Now it is sometimes presented in developments which are based on an isomorphism between the cardinal numbers and a subset of the rationals. This requires a level of mathematical sophistication which is hard to achieve with elementary school pupils.

If, finally, we multiply $\frac{7}{3} \times \frac{5}{2}$ (or $2\frac{1}{3} \times 2\frac{1}{2}$, the terms of which can easily be converted into the fractional form), the picture becomes as shown.

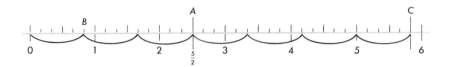

First we locate $\frac{5}{2}$ on the number line. Then, to find $\frac{7}{3}$ of the segment OA, we divide each part (a half) into three congruent parts, forming 15 small units in $\frac{5}{2}$. If $\overline{OA}$ is shrunk to $\frac{1}{3}$ of its length, there will be 5 small units in $\overline{OB}$. Then 7 of $\overline{OB}$ is 7×5, or 35, of the small units so that $\overline{OC} = 7 \times \frac{5}{6} = \frac{35}{6}$ or $5\frac{5}{6}$.

With these and similar examples, the children are led to the formula that, for any two fractions,

$$\frac{a}{b} \times \frac{c}{d} = \frac{a \times c}{b \times d}.$$

The product of two fractions is a fraction whose numerator is the product of the numerators and whose denominator is the product of the denominators.

Thus $8\frac{5}{7} \times 4\frac{2}{9}$ is merely $\frac{61}{7} \times \frac{38}{9}$ and $8 \times 2\frac{5}{13}$ is $8 \times \frac{31}{13}$, and we have learned the entire process of multiplication of fractions in fraction form or mixed-numeral form.

A necessary part of the learning is to establish commutativity. In the case of fractions it is not as easy to comprehend that

$$\frac{2}{3} \text{ of } \frac{4}{5} \qquad \text{is the same as} \qquad \frac{4}{5} \text{ of } \frac{2}{3}$$

as it was to grasp the fact that $2 \times 4 = 4 \times 2$. The diagrams below show how children can be led to predict that multiplication

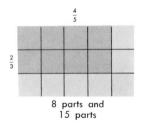

8 parts and
15 parts

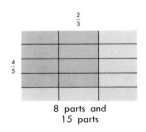

8 parts and
15 parts

of fractions has this property. Similar diagrams can be made on a number line.

Finally we should extend the multiplication to expressions with three or more fractions and establish the associative principle. To do this, we make use of all that we have learned previously. The teacher confronts the pupil with

$$\tfrac{2}{3} \times \tfrac{4}{5} \times \tfrac{6}{7}$$

and asks, "What can this mean?" Various replies may be obtained; for example:

a) $\tfrac{2}{3}$ of ($\tfrac{4}{5}$ of $\tfrac{6}{7}$), that is, $\tfrac{2}{3} \times (\tfrac{4}{5} \times \tfrac{6}{7})$.

b) ($\tfrac{2}{3}$ of $\tfrac{4}{5}$) of $\tfrac{6}{7}$, that is, ($\tfrac{2}{3} \times \tfrac{4}{5}$) $\times \tfrac{6}{7}$.

c) It ought to work the same as whole numbers.

Children will multiply the fractions in parentheses, and then the result by the other fraction, always obtaining the same answer in either way.

If the children are encouraged merely to indicate the multiplication, they can get a verification of their conclusions. Thus we might suggest that pupils write

$$\frac{2}{3} \times \left(\frac{4}{5} \times \frac{6}{7}\right) = \frac{2}{3} \times \left(\frac{4 \times 6}{5 \times 7}\right) = \frac{2 \times 4 \times 6}{3 \times 5 \times 7}$$

and

$$\left(\frac{2}{3} \times \frac{4}{5}\right) \times \frac{6}{7} = \left(\frac{2 \times 4}{3 \times 5}\right) \times \frac{6}{7} = \frac{2 \times 4 \times 6}{3 \times 5 \times 7}.$$

The better students can generalize the result and write:

$$\frac{a}{b} \times \frac{c}{d} \times \frac{e}{f} = \frac{a}{b} \times \left(\frac{c}{d} \times \frac{e}{f}\right) = \left(\frac{a}{b} \times \frac{c}{d}\right) \times \frac{e}{f} = \frac{a \times c \times e}{b \times d \times f}.$$

More useful in applications than the associative principle by itself is a general rearrangement or "any-order" principle which combines the commutative and associative principles to allow any changes of order and grouping of fractions. An example of this principle in action is

$$\tfrac{2}{3} \times \tfrac{7}{8} \times \tfrac{9}{2} = \tfrac{2}{3} \times \tfrac{9}{2} \times \tfrac{7}{8} = (\tfrac{2}{3} \times \tfrac{9}{2}) \times \tfrac{7}{8} = 3 \times \tfrac{7}{8}.$$

10–2 RELATING MULTIPLICATION TO ADDITION

If a teacher wishes to relate the multiplication process to addition, it is a good procedure to start with the product of a fraction and a whole number. Thus, if we write "one-fourth multiplied by three" as

$$\tfrac{1}{4} \times 3, \qquad \text{it means} \qquad \tfrac{1}{4} + \tfrac{1}{4} + \tfrac{1}{4} \quad \text{or} \quad \tfrac{3}{4}.$$

The denominator tells the relative *size* of each part (compared with the same unit); the numerator tells the number of parts. Hence, to multiply by 3, we multiply the numerator by 3, and use the same denominator, since we did not change the size of our parts. Similarly,

$$\frac{2}{3} \times 4 \qquad \text{means} \qquad \frac{2}{3} + \frac{2}{3} + \frac{2}{3} + \frac{2}{3} \quad \text{or} \quad \frac{2 \times 4}{3} = \frac{8}{3} \left(\text{or } 2\frac{2}{3} \right).$$

We could assume that the commutative principle holds, and thus could accept $\tfrac{2}{3} \times 4$ as equal to $4 \times \tfrac{2}{3}$. However, as mentioned earlier, children do not readily believe this and some justification is needed. Hence it is necessary to start with some practical situation in which the operation can be given a meaning. For example, suppose that we want to find one-half of a group of 6 people. How do we express this situation in numbers? The answer, of course, is $\tfrac{1}{2}$ of 6 or $6 \times \tfrac{1}{2}$, which the pupil knows is 3. Does $\tfrac{1}{2} \times 6$ produce the same result? After a few examples with unit fractions, we can pose a problem like $12 \times \tfrac{2}{3}$, or two-thirds of a dozen; how do you find that? A common interpretation is very similar to the operator idea; that is, find one-third and then double the answer. Thus

$$\tfrac{2}{3} \times 12 \qquad \text{means shrink 12 to } \tfrac{1}{3} \text{ of itself to obtain 4.}$$
$$\text{Double the answer to yield 8.}$$

That is,

$$\tfrac{2}{3} \times 12 = 2 \times (\tfrac{1}{3} \times 12) = 2 \times 4 = 8.$$

This leads to the question, "Can we multiply 12 by 2 and then divide by 3?" Repeated trial shows that in all cases

$$N \times \frac{a}{b} = \frac{a \times N}{b} = a \times \frac{N}{b}.$$

As a last problem of this type, consider the case in which b is not a divisor of N, for example, $\frac{5}{7} \times 11$. A meaning is $5 \times (\frac{1}{7} \times 11)$ and pupils know that $\frac{1}{7} \times 11$ can be written $\frac{11}{7}$. Then the problem becomes $5 \times \frac{11}{7}$, which they already know how to do, namely $\frac{5 \times 11}{7}$. The commutative law works and the formula is:

$$N \times \frac{a}{b} = \frac{a}{b} \times N = \frac{a \times N}{b}.$$

Now that we have solved cases involving a fraction and a whole number, consider the case of two fractions,

$$\tfrac{2}{3} \times \tfrac{4}{5}.$$

This can be explained by the operator technique described in the previous section. Another meaning that can be given is clearly

$\frac{4}{5}$ of something (one) means use a $\overline{5}$-shrinker and a 4-stretcher.

Consider one of the fifths and use a $\overline{3}$-shrinker on it. Then there are 15 small parts in one thing. But if we take 2 of these parts for each fifth $[2 \times (\frac{1}{3} \times \frac{1}{5})]$ and have 4 of these fifths to consider, we shall have:

$$4 \times 2 \times \left(\frac{1}{3} \times \frac{1}{5}\right) = \frac{4 \times 2}{3 \times 5} = \frac{8}{15}.$$

By diagram and reasoning the pupil argues: the product of the denominators gives you the size of the new parts, the denominator of the product; the product of the numerators gives the number of these parts, the numerator of the product. Thus,

$$\frac{a}{b} \times \frac{c}{d} = \frac{a \times c}{b \times d}.$$

When a product involves fractions represented in mixed form, for example, $3 \times 2\frac{2}{5}$, we can change the problem to $3 \times \frac{12}{5}$. It is a good idea, however, in everyday affairs, in later study, and in seeking common algorisms, to solve the problem by using the distributive law. Thus, since $2\frac{2}{5}$ means $2 + \frac{2}{5}$, we can write

$$3 \times 2\tfrac{2}{5} = 3 \times (2 + \tfrac{2}{5}) = (3 \times 2) + (3 \times \tfrac{2}{5})$$
$$= 6 + \tfrac{6}{5} = 7\tfrac{1}{5}.$$

This can also be written in vertical form and related to the algorism of multiplication for whole numbers.

$$2\tfrac{2}{5}$$
$$\times\ 3$$
$$\overline{7\tfrac{1}{5}}$$

Think: $3 \times \tfrac{2}{5}$ is $\tfrac{6}{5}$ or $1\tfrac{1}{5}$.
Write $\tfrac{1}{5}$ in the fraction place and retain 1.
Then $3 \times 2 = 6;$ $\quad 6 + 1 = 7.$
Answer: $7\tfrac{1}{5}$.

$$7$$
$$\times\ 3\tfrac{2}{3}$$
$$\overline{25\tfrac{2}{3}}$$

Similarly, $3\tfrac{2}{3} \times 7$ means $(3 + \tfrac{2}{3}) \times 7 = (3 \times 7) + (\tfrac{2}{3} \times 7),$ which is $21 + 4\tfrac{2}{3} = 25\tfrac{2}{3}$. Vertically (see margin), we think of the problem as $\tfrac{2}{3} \times 7$, which is $\tfrac{14}{3}$ or $4\tfrac{2}{3}$. We write $\tfrac{2}{3}$ and retain 4 in our mind. $7 \times 3 = 21$, plus 4 is 25. Answer: $25\tfrac{2}{3}$.

For each of these products, a geometric or number-line illustration can be given. This is left as an exercise for the reader.

A problem more difficult to solve except by converting to common-fraction form is one of the type $2\tfrac{2}{5} \times 3\tfrac{1}{2}$. Although we may use the distributive law and expanded notation, the simplest procedure is to compare it with the product of a two-place number and a two-place number. Thus, just as

$$
\begin{array}{c}
27 \\
35 \\
\hline
135 \\
810 \\
\hline
945 \Leftarrow \text{Product}
\end{array}
\Rightarrow
\begin{array}{r}
7 \\
\times\ 5 \\
\hline
35
\end{array}
\quad
\begin{array}{r}
20 \\
\times\ 5 \\
\hline
100 \\
135
\end{array}
\quad
\begin{array}{r}
7 \\
\times\ 30 \\
\hline
210
\end{array}
\quad
\begin{array}{r}
20 \\
\times\ 30 \\
\hline
600 \\
810
\end{array}
$$

or

$$(20 + 7) \times 5 + (20 + 7) \times 30,$$

so we also have

$$
\begin{array}{c}
2\tfrac{2}{5} \\
\times\ 3\tfrac{1}{2} \\
\hline
1\tfrac{1}{5} \\
7\tfrac{1}{5} \\
\hline
8\tfrac{2}{5} \Leftarrow \text{Product}
\end{array}
\quad
\begin{array}{r}
\tfrac{2}{5} \\
\times\ \tfrac{1}{2} \\
\hline
\tfrac{1}{5}
\end{array}
\quad
\begin{array}{r}
2 \\
\times\ \tfrac{1}{2} \\
\hline
1
\end{array}
\quad
\begin{array}{r}
\tfrac{2}{5} \\
\times\ 3 \\
\hline
1\tfrac{1}{5}
\end{array}
\quad
\begin{array}{r}
2 \\
\times\ 3 \\
\hline
6
\end{array}
$$

Of course, the problem can also be changed to

$$\tfrac{12}{5} \times \tfrac{7}{2} = \tfrac{84}{10} = 8\tfrac{4}{10} = 8\tfrac{2}{5}.$$

One objective of teaching the algorisms for multiplication is to obtain an efficient process to find the product. However, another important objective is to obtain a comprehension of the underlying theory of the operations on number that make the algorism possible. Thus a study of several acceptable algorisms gives a better mathematical education than a study of only one procedure. Essentially, all the above explanations are related to the *operator* concept of a fraction. This idea serves as a unifying element in understanding and recalling the computational algorisms for fractions.

10-3 SIMPLIFICATION OF THE OPERATION

In contemporary mathematics there are two cancellation laws, one for addition and one for multiplication, which are used in simplifying equalities and inequalities. These are illustrated by the statements:

$$\text{If } 5 + 8 = x + 8, \text{ then } 5 = x.$$
$$\text{If } 5 \cdot 8 = x \cdot 8, \text{ then } 5 = x.$$

The word 'cancel', however, has had a completely different meaning in elementary school arithmetic, and a lack of understanding of its meaning has led to many errors on the part of the pupils. The use of the word is unnecessary, and we recommend that it be discarded, but the *principle* involved is important and should be learned by all students.

For this purpose the pupil must be able to distinguish between a *factor* and an *addend*: Thus in $2 \times 4 = 8$, the 2 and 4 are *factors*, but in $2 + 4 = 6$, the 2 and 4 are addends. In $(3 \times 4) + 5$, 3 and 4 are factors of the first term, but (3×4) and 5 are addends. In $4 + 6 + 8$, the numbers are addends, but in $4 \times 6 \times 8$, they are factors. All children should practice recognizing factors and addends in given numerical expressions.

A second concept to be clearly understood is the relation between division of whole numbers and multiplication of a whole number by a fraction. Thus $17 \div 3$ is a division with quotient ·5 and remainder 2. If we now permit fractions in quotients, we can transform the problem to one having an exact quotient. The division is illustrated below. While the remainder 2 permits no whole-number quotient greater than 5, we can divide

2 by 3 to obtain the fraction $\frac{2}{3}$. Then the *exact* quotient is $5\frac{2}{3}$. Check: $5\frac{2}{3} \times 3 = 17$.

$$
\begin{array}{r}
5\frac{2}{3} \\
\hline
3)\overline{17} \\
\end{array}
$$

$$
\left.\begin{array}{l}
15 \leftarrow 5 \times 3 \\
\overline{2} \\
2 \leftarrow \frac{2}{3} \times 3 \\
\hline
0 \leftarrow \text{Rem.}
\end{array}\right\} \Rightarrow
\begin{array}{c}
3 \times (5 + \frac{2}{3}) \\
\text{or} \\
3 \times 5\frac{2}{3}
\end{array}
$$

Thus fractions, and multiplication of fractions, permit us to find an exact quotient for every division of whole numbers. Practice in this type of division not only reviews the division process, but it makes use of the multiplication of fractions by a whole number. Best of all, it refines the concept of exact division which will be necessary in the study of division of fractions. Thus $17 \div 3 = 5\frac{2}{3} = \frac{17}{3}$. From now on, every indicated division of two whole numbers can be considered a fraction, and every fraction can be considered an indicated division.

Now $17 \times \frac{1}{3} = 17 \div 3$. We see that, while two different operations are involved, the results are the same. We say that the product of 17 multiplied by $\frac{1}{3}$ is equal to the exact quotient of 17 divided by 3. Similarly, $2184 \div 29$ is equal to $\frac{1}{29} \times 2184$ or the fraction $\frac{2184}{29}$. We also say that these two *operations* are *equivalent*.

A third concept, useful in simplifying computation, is the fact that if a number is given in factored form, dividing a factor of the number by a given second number divides the entire number by this second number. Thus $30 = 2 \times 3 \times 5$. If 30, or $2 \times 3 \times 5$, is divided by 5, we know that the quotient is 6. In the factored form, if we divide the factor 5 by 5, the quotient is 1, and $2 \times 3 \times 1 = 6$. This is written

$$
30 \div 5 = \frac{2 \times 3 \times \cancel{5}^{1}}{\cancel{5}_{1}} = 2 \times 3 = 6,
$$

where the numerator and denominator were each divided by 5, as indicated by the (/) stroke through the numeral and the quotient indicated above and below the factor.

This third concept is not easy for children to acquire. It should be developed in progressive degrees of complexity (begin with two factors and study the effect on their product of doubling one factor, halving one factor, doubling both, halving both, etc.) over a period of at least two years before the children can be expected to use it in algorisms for multiplying two or more fractions.

On the other hand, $5 + 10 + 15 = 30$, but here 5, 10, and 15 are addends. If we divide 30 by 5, the result is 6. But in the form

$$\frac{{}^1\cancel{5} + {}^2\cancel{10} + {}^3\cancel{15}}{\cancel{5}_1} = 6,$$

note that each addend must be divided by 5, and the sum of the quotients is the quotient of $30 \div 5$. This is sometimes expressed by saying that division is *distributive* over a sum. It is better, however, at first learning to think of $(5 + 10 + 15) \div 5$ as $\frac{1}{5}(5 + 10 + 15)$, and here the distributive law for multiplication holds. Thus

$$\frac{5 + 10 + 15}{5} = \tfrac{1}{5}(5 + 10 + 15) = \tfrac{1}{5} \times 5 + \tfrac{1}{5} \times 10 + \tfrac{1}{5} \times 15$$

$$= 1 + 2 + 3 = 6$$

but

$$\frac{2 \times 3 \times 5}{5} = \tfrac{1}{5}(2 \times 3 \times 5) = (2 \times 3) \times (5 \times \tfrac{1}{5})$$

$$= 2 \times 3 \times 1 = 2 \times 3 = 6.$$

Practice should be given on many problems in which the pupils can check. For example:

$$\frac{8 \times 15}{5} = 8 \times \frac{\cancel{15}^3}{\cancel{5}_1} = 24. \qquad\qquad \text{Check } \frac{120}{5} = 24.$$

$$\frac{9 \times 16}{24} = \frac{{}^3\cancel{9} \times 16}{\cancel{24}_8} = \frac{3 \times \cancel{16}^2}{\cancel{8}_1} = 6. \qquad \text{Check } \frac{9 \times 16}{24} = \frac{144}{24} = 6.$$

$$\frac{4248}{24} = ?$$

Finally, children should express in some verbal way the principle that: If the terms of a fraction are in factored form, dividing a factor of both numerator and denominator by a common factor does not change the fractional value. If a sum is to be divided by a given number, each addend of the sum must be divided by the given number, and the sum of the quotients is the quotient of the sum divided by the given number. In formulas:

$$\frac{a \times b \times c}{r} = a \times b \times \frac{c}{r} \; ; \qquad \frac{a + b + c}{r} = \frac{a}{r} + \frac{b}{r} + \frac{c}{r}.$$

Thus

$$\frac{4}{14} \times \frac{7}{12} = \frac{4 \times 7}{14 \times 12} = \frac{1 \times 7}{14 \times 3} = \frac{1 \times 1}{2 \times 3} = \frac{1}{6}$$

By definition   ÷ 4   ÷ 7   multiply

It is our hope, possibly optimistic, that by the end of fifth grade the children will be able to write

a) $$\frac{{}^1\cancel{4}}{{}_2\cancel{14}} \times \frac{\cancel{7}{}^1}{\cancel{12}{}_3} = \frac{1}{6} \qquad \text{or} \qquad \frac{{}^1\cancel{2}\cancel{4}}{{}_1{}^7\cancel{14}} \times \frac{\cancel{7}{}^1}{\cancel{12}{}_6} = \frac{1}{6}$$

and understand that this is a handy way to record the mechanics of a truly complicated procedure.

Almost all children, given the kind of experiential background we have been advocating, accept as a matter of course that multiplying or dividing both terms of a fraction by the same number changes the appearance of the fraction but leaves its value unchanged. They transform a single fraction to higher or lower terms correctly and with understanding. Some of them get all mixed up when they try to apply the same principle to an indicated product of two or more fractions. Possibly a part of their trouble is that they do not recognize this product as equivalent to a single fraction. One way to help them acquire this idea is to teach them, at first, to write all such examples like this:

b) $$\frac{4}{14} \times \frac{7}{12} = \frac{4 \times 7}{14 \times 12} = \cdots$$

Then, if it helps them, they may use the "any-order" principle (or just commutativity, in this case) to rearrange the factors so that the display looks better to them:

c) $$\frac{4}{14} \times \frac{7}{12} = \frac{4 \times 7}{14 \times 12} = \frac{7 \times 4}{14 \times 12} = \cdots$$

They must understand that dividing one factor by a given number divides the entire product by that number, as was discussed previously. They should cross out the numerals they have used and record the results of each division:

c') $$\cdots = \frac{{}^1\cancel{7} \times \cancel{4}^1}{\cancel{14}_2 \times \cancel{12}_3} = \frac{1}{6}.$$

Never permit them to omit the '1's, unless you wish to get a great many papers with mistakes like this:

d) $$\frac{\cancel{4}}{{}_2\cancel{14}} \times \frac{\cancel{7}}{\cancel{12}_3} = \frac{0}{6} = 0.$$

When the child himself sees that he can shorten the computation to the form shown in (a), he should then do his examples that way. If he never sees this himself, there is no harm in not telling him.

All the above development should be accompanied by problems of a practical nature, which children can collect, invent, or find in the books they use. These problems include measures such as $2\frac{2}{3}$ hr, $1\frac{5}{8}$ lb, $2\frac{1}{3}$ yd, $2\frac{3}{8}$ points (in stock transactions), $\frac{2}{7}$ of a share, and so on. It is the child's recognition of fractions and the required operations on them in practical situations that will enable him to use fractions correctly during the years to come.

10-4 DIVISION OF FRACTIONS

The division of fractions introduces no new division concept. Thus, $N \div \frac{a}{b}$ can mean: (a) How many pieces of size $\frac{a}{b}$ can one obtain from one piece of size N? or (b) How much is a thing if $\frac{a}{b}$ of it is N? Thus

      30 gallons of liquid distributed in $\frac{2}{3}$-gallon containers

implies that there are $30 \div \frac{2}{3}$ or 45 containers. Check. Similarly,

$$30 \text{ gallons is } \tfrac{2}{3} \text{ of an amount of water}$$

implies that $30 \div \frac{2}{3}$ is the amount of water.

In teaching the algorism, we first develop the meaning of division by relating it to the exact division. We know that $24 \div 6 = 4$ because $4 \times 6 = 24$. Similarly, $17 \div 3 = 5\frac{2}{3}$ because $5\frac{2}{3} \times 3 = 17$. In exactly the same way, we shall try to find the quotients of, for example,

$$\tfrac{2}{3} \div \tfrac{1}{9}.$$

Here it is easy to discover that $6 \times \frac{1}{9} = \frac{2}{3}$ and hence

$$\tfrac{2}{3} \div \tfrac{1}{9} = 6 \qquad \text{because} \qquad 6 \times \tfrac{1}{9} = \tfrac{2}{3}.$$

However, if the problem $\frac{2}{3} \div \frac{1}{7}$ is given, the trial-and-error discovery of the quotient is more difficult. A first suggestion may be to change the fractions to like fractions, obtaining

$$\tfrac{14}{21} \div \tfrac{3}{21}.$$

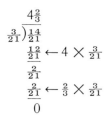

Now the problem can be stated, "How many parts, each measuring $\frac{3}{21}$, can be obtained from $\frac{14}{21}$?" The diagram shows 4 parts and $\frac{2}{21}$ remaining. We also note that the $\frac{2}{21}$ is $\frac{2}{3}$ of another part, so that we can express our answer (see margin) as:

1) A total quotient of 4 and a remainder of $\frac{2}{21}$.

2) An exact quotient of $4\frac{2}{3}$.

After the children have experimented with this type of division —both total quotient and remainder and exact quotients—and have a feeling for the physical situation related to such division, they can move on to a more mathematical study of the problem.

a) *The reciprocal of a number.* With only whole numbers to work with, we are limited in division, for most answers are total quotients with remainders. Exact quotients are not nearly so common. However, now that we have fractions at our command, every division of whole numbers has an exact quotient. With fractions we also gain a solution to another type of problem. This can be posed to the children in this way:

Given a first number, find a second number such that their product is 1.

If we were limited to whole numbers, there would be only one solution: $1 \times 1 = 1$.

Now if we open the numbers to include fractions we can ask, in symbolic form, $\frac{4}{7} \times ? = 1$. When children recall the work in multiplication, and are given the hint that for a whole-number answer the products of the numerators and the denominators must be the same (why?), children will soon try $\frac{7}{4}$ and say $\frac{4}{7} \times \frac{7}{4} = \frac{28}{28}$. Repeat the same type of problem with other fractions, $\frac{2}{3} \times \underline{\hspace{1cm}} = 1; \frac{8}{3} \times \underline{\hspace{1cm}} = 1; 4 \times \underline{\hspace{1cm}} = 1; \frac{1}{5} \times \underline{\hspace{1cm}} = 1$. Children are then told that if the product of two numbers is 1, each number is called the *reciprocal* of the other. Another name for reciprocal is *multiplicative inverse*, but this phrase need not be used. We may obtain the numeral for the reciprocal of a given number by interchanging the numerator and denominator of the fractional numeral for the number.

Then the pupils should be asked to find a reciprocal of $\frac{0}{5}$ or $\frac{0}{3}$ or $\frac{0}{n}$. When they fail, they should be able to explain why there is no reciprocal for 0. This occurs for two reasons: one, the product of any number multiplied by 0 is 0 and could never be 1, and two, if a fraction is $\frac{0}{3}$, to write the reciprocal as $\frac{3}{0}$ would be prohibited; we may never divide by 0 in arithmetic. Thus 0 has no reciprocal and it follows that $\frac{0}{n}$, $n \neq 0$ is the only fraction that has no reciprocal. Pupils should practice until they can automatically give the reciprocal of any number.

b) *The uniqueness of multiplication.* The product of a given first number by a given second number is a unique third number. A statement such as '$2 + 3 = 5$' is true if and only if '$2 + 3$' and '5' name the same number. Thus, since $2 + 3 = 5$, $6(2 + 3) = 6 \times 5$ (verify this). Pupils will accept this rule, but they should check. For example, if $\frac{1}{2} + \frac{1}{3} = \frac{5}{6}$, are we sure that $\frac{12}{5}(\frac{1}{2} + \frac{1}{3}) = \frac{12}{5} \times \frac{5}{6}$? Yes, because

$$\frac{12}{5} \times \frac{1}{2} + \frac{12}{5} \times \frac{1}{3} = \frac{6}{5} + \frac{4}{5} = 2 \quad \text{and} \quad \frac{\overset{2}{\cancel{12}}}{\underset{1}{\cancel{5}}} \times \frac{\overset{1}{\cancel{5}}}{\underset{1}{\cancel{6}}} = 2$$

also. This same procedure should be extended to the use of equations or inequalities containing frames. For example, if $3 + 4 = \square$ is made into a true sentence, does the same substitution make $5(3 + 4) = 5 \cdot \square$ true? Check by substituting the same number in the first expression and in the second. Is it true that if $3 \cdot \square = 12$, then $\frac{1}{3}(3 \cdot \square) = \frac{1}{3} \times 12$? Check in the same way as in the first example.

c) *Finding the quotient.* First we recall what exact division means for whole numbers. Thus $24 \div 6$ is the number which, multiplied by 6, yields 24. This number is 4, the quotient. Thus

$$24 \div 6 = 4 \qquad \text{because} \qquad 24 = 4 \times 6.$$

A few more examples of this type should lead to the generalization

$$a \div b = x \qquad \text{because} \qquad a = x \cdot b.$$

Now, by analogy, the pupils should be able to tell what is meant by exact division of two fractions. Thus

$$\frac{4}{3} \div \frac{2}{9} \qquad \text{means find a fraction } \frac{\square}{\triangle} \text{ such that} \qquad \frac{\square}{\triangle} \cdot \frac{2}{9} = \frac{4}{3}.$$

By trial and error, the pupils can supply the numerals. Some will reason: If I use 36 for the $\square$, 9 will divide into it to give 4. Then I must use a 6 for the $\triangle$ and 2 will divide into it to give 3. Thus the answer is $\frac{36}{6}$, or 6. Looking at the original problem, children may see the 4 and 9, the 2 and 3, and see how these numbers relate to $\frac{36}{6}$. The children should check that $\frac{4}{3} \div \frac{2}{9} = \frac{36}{6}$ because $\frac{36}{6} \times \frac{2}{9} = \frac{4}{3}$.

After a number of these discoveries, or even only a trial-and-error method of finding two replacements that give the quotient, a more mathematical study should be made. Here we let the children argue (by directed activity) in the following manner. First, they know that

$$\frac{5}{3} \div \frac{2}{11} = \frac{\square}{\triangle} \Rightarrow \frac{5}{3} = \frac{\square}{\triangle} \times \frac{2}{11}.$$

The directed questions are (a) What are we attempting to find? Answer: the number we can use for '$\frac{\square}{\triangle}$' to make the sentence true.

(b) What part of this number do we know? Answer: $\frac{2}{11}$ of it because this is $\frac{5}{3}$. (c) If you have $\frac{2}{11}$, what must you multiply it by to obtain 1? Do you recall reciprocals? Answer: $\frac{11}{2}$. (d) What can we do if we have $\frac{2}{11}$ of $\frac{\square}{\triangle}$ to find $\frac{\square}{\triangle}$? Answer: multiply it by the reciprocal of $\frac{2}{11}$ or $\frac{11}{2}$. (e) Look back at our problem. If we do this multiplication and write an equation, what must be done to $\frac{5}{3}$? Answer: multiply it by $\frac{11}{2}$ also. (Have this explained.) Then we have

$$\frac{5}{3} \times \frac{11}{2} = \left(\frac{\square}{\triangle} \times \frac{2}{11}\right)\frac{11}{2} = \frac{\square}{\triangle}.$$

What can we use for the frames $\frac{\square}{\triangle}$? Answer: $\dfrac{5 \times 11}{3 \times 2}$.

Now we relate this to the original problem and write

$$\frac{5}{3} \div \frac{2}{11} = \frac{5}{3} \times \frac{11}{2} = \frac{5 \times 11}{3 \times 2} = \frac{55}{6} \text{ or } 9\frac{1}{6}.$$

This first example is restudied until every step is understood.

Now we repeat with several examples. Pupils should not generalize from one example. Thus $\frac{8}{5} \div \frac{3}{13} = \frac{\square}{\triangle}$ becomes $\frac{8}{5} = \frac{\square}{\triangle} \times \frac{3}{13}$, and, multiplying each number by $\frac{13}{3}$, we have:

$$\frac{8}{5} \times \frac{13}{3} = \frac{\square}{\triangle} \times \frac{\overset{1}{\cancel{3}}}{\underset{1}{\cancel{13}}} \times \frac{\overset{1}{\cancel{13}}}{\underset{1}{\cancel{3}}}, \qquad \text{so} \qquad \frac{8}{5} \div \frac{3}{13} = \frac{8}{5} \times \frac{13}{3}.$$

After three or four examples, pupils who do not see a pattern should be encouraged to look for one. Finally, we have the formula

$$\frac{a}{b} \div \frac{c}{d} = \frac{a}{b} \times \frac{d}{c}.$$

To find the quotient of two fractions, multiply the dividend by the reciprocal of the divisor.

It should be stressed that this rule gives an exact quotient and not a total quotient with a remainder. It should also be stressed that the divisor may not be zero.

There are many other suggested procedures for developing this algorism, and some are listed in the bibliography at the end

of this chapter. We shall now illustrate a few of these other procedures. We have already mentioned, as a first approach, changing
each fraction to the same denominator. This method also has
some difficulties. Thus $\frac{2}{3} \div \frac{1}{7}$ becomes $\frac{14}{21} \div \frac{3}{21}$. If these fractions
are related to twenty-firsts (parts) of a segment on a number line,
the children recognize that the problem is now really one of

$$14 \div 3,$$

which is 4 and a remainder of 2. The remainder bothers pupils.
Of course, it is not 2, but 2 twenty-firsts, and this can be seen
geometrically. The answer is that there are 4 groups, each con-
sisting of $\frac{3}{21}$, and $\frac{2}{21}$ remaining (see page 274). If the problem is
done by the usual multiplication by the reciprocal of the divisor,
the answer is

$$\frac{2}{3} \times \frac{7}{1} = \frac{14}{3} \qquad \text{or} \qquad 4\frac{2}{3},$$

and now the $\frac{2}{3}$ is a part of the exact quotient, while the $\frac{2}{21}$ was a
remainder. The children must be shown that the $\frac{2}{21}$ is really
$\frac{2}{3}$ of $\frac{3}{21}$, and thus $4\frac{2}{3}$ is exact; 4 and $\frac{2}{21}$ remaining is a total quotient
with a remainder. A diagrammatic representation on the number
line aids in the interpretation.

Another bothersome element in this method is the elimination
of the denominators. Thus $\frac{14}{21} \div \frac{3}{21}$ is obtained by $14 \div 3$; but,
pupils ask, what happened to the 21? Of course, it is just a name
of the part or thing with which we are concerned, and by con-
sidering $\frac{14}{5} \div \frac{3}{5}$, $\frac{14}{7} \div \frac{3}{7}$, etc., we note that the exact division is
$4\frac{2}{3}$ in every case. The answer is not all dependent on the size of
the parts, only on the number of them in both the dividend and
the divisor.

There is value in this method of studying division, since it
does require discrimination between exact division and total
quotients and remainders. If the teacher desires to develop from
it the usual rule, he can extend it as follows:

$$\frac{2}{3} \div \frac{1}{7} = \frac{2 \times 7}{3 \times 7} \div \frac{1 \times 3}{7 \times 3} \qquad \text{(changing to a common denominator)}$$

$$= \frac{2 \times 7}{3 \times 1} = \frac{2}{3} \times \frac{7}{1} \qquad \text{(dividing the numerators)}$$

$$= \text{dividend} \times \text{reciprocal of divisor (by observation)}.$$

For less mathematically inclined pupils, a method of induction may be used. This method usually involves three stages: (1) dividing by a unit fraction, that is, $\frac{1}{2}$, $\frac{1}{3}$, $\frac{1}{4}$, and so on; (2) considering how a quotient decreases as the divisor increases, the dividend remaining the same; and (3) applying the results of (1) and (2) to a fraction other than a unit fraction.

1. We start by thinking of division as finding the quotient of a whole number divided by a unit fraction. For example, we begin:

Question: What does $1 \div \frac{1}{2}$ mean?
Answer: How many halves there are in 1.
Question: How many halves are there in 1?
Answer: 2.
Question: How many halves are there in 2?
Answer: Twice as many as in 1, or $2 \div \frac{1}{2} = 2 \times 2$ (the last
                '2' shows the number of halves in 1).
Question: How many halves are there in 4?
Answer: Four times as many as in 1, or $4 \div \frac{1}{2} = 4 \times 2$.

And finally, how many halves are there in any number? Answer: that number times the number of halves in 1, so $n \div \frac{1}{2} = n \times 2$. The process is now repeated with the divisor $\frac{1}{3}$, leading to $n \div \frac{1}{3} = n \times 3$. Then it is extended to $\frac{1}{4}$, $\frac{1}{5}$, and finally to $\frac{1}{c}$ where c is any cardinal number (not zero) and $n \div \frac{1}{c} = n \times c$.

The general conclusion is: When a number is divided by a unit fraction, the quotient is the product of that number and the denominator of the fraction (which shows how many of these unit fractions are in 1).

2. Consider, with the pupils, a dividend with a large number of divisors, for example, 60. Then study the relation of the divisors to the quotient, as the divisor increases. The table shows the quotients.

$$
\begin{array}{ll}
2 = 2 \times 1 \left[\begin{array}{l} 60 \div 1 \;\; = 60 \\ 60 \div 2 \;\; = 30 \end{array} \right. & \left. \begin{array}{l} \\ \end{array} \right] 30 = \tfrac{1}{2} \times 60 \\[2ex]
4 = 2 \times 2 \left| \begin{array}{l} 60 \div 3 \;\; = 20 \\ 60 \div 4 \;\; = 15 \end{array} \right. & \left| \begin{array}{l} 15 = \tfrac{1}{2} \times 30 \end{array} \right. \\[2ex]
10 = 2 \times 5 \left| \begin{array}{l} 60 \div 5 \;\; = 12 \\ 60 \div 6 \;\; = 10 \end{array} \right. & \left. \begin{array}{l} \\ \end{array} \right] 6 = \tfrac{1}{2} \times 12 \\[2ex]
30 = 3 \times 10 \left| \begin{array}{l} 60 \div 10 = 6 \\ 60 \div 12 = 5 \\ 60 \div 15 = 4 \\ 60 \div 30 = 2 \end{array} \right. & \left| \begin{array}{l} 2 = \tfrac{1}{3} \times 6 \end{array} \right. \\[2ex]
& 60 \div 60 = 1
\end{array}
$$

Questions of the following type are discussed: If the divisor is multiplied by 2, what will the effect be on the quotient? Answer: It will be $\frac{1}{2}$ the original quotient. If a divisor is multiplied by 3, what will be the effect on the quotient? Answer: It will be $\frac{1}{3}$ of the original quotient. (Compare quotients 2 and 6, or 5 and 15.) Further study leads to the induction that, if a divisor is multiplied by a number n, the original quotient is divided by n. Teachers may reason: If $N \div a = c$, then $N = c \times a$. Since $\frac{n}{n}$ is 1,

$$N = \frac{n}{n} \cdot c \cdot a = a \cdot n \cdot \frac{c}{n} \qquad \text{so} \qquad N \div an = \frac{c}{n}.$$

This same reasoning can be strengthened if we consider dividends of 180, 360, 100, or 200. Children say that if you divide by twice as much, your answer is only half as much. A good analog is to imagine having a certain amount of ice cream for a party and consider the portions as the number of guests increases.

3. Now return to $4 \div \frac{1}{3}$. The answer is 4×3. Suppose we double the divisor and write $4 \div \frac{2}{3}$. Since the divisor is multiplied by 2, the quotient is divided by 2 and the answer is

$$\frac{4 \times 3}{2} \qquad \text{or} \qquad 4 \times \frac{3}{2}.$$

These conclusions were reached in (2) above for whole numbers and assumed to hold for fractions. Similarly,

$$8 \div \tfrac{1}{5} = 8 \times 5.$$

Then

$$8 \div \frac{2}{5} = \frac{8 \times 5}{2} = 8 \times \frac{5}{2}; \qquad 8 \div \frac{3}{5} = 8 \times \frac{5}{3}, \text{ etc.}$$

After many examples, children generalize that to divide a whole number by a fraction, we multiply it by the reciprocal of the fraction and then generally agree that it holds even if the dividend is itself a fraction. That is,

$$\frac{a}{b} \div \frac{c}{d} = \frac{a}{b} \times \frac{d}{c}.$$

Another common procedure is to write a fraction in which the numerator and denominator are fractions. This results in a complicated expression to place before children, and when three fraction bars appear, one on top of the other, care must be taken in writing them so that the "main one" looks different from the rest. The operation also depends on the property that the quotient of any number divided by 1 is that number, so it can be written without the denominator 1. Thus

$$\frac{2}{3} \div \frac{5}{6} = \frac{\frac{2}{3}}{\frac{5}{6}} = \frac{\frac{2}{3} \times \frac{6}{5}}{\frac{5}{6} \times \frac{6}{5}} = \frac{\frac{2}{3} \times \frac{6}{5}}{1} = \frac{2}{3} \times \frac{6}{5}.$$

Now we see that we can get rid of this "double-decker" fraction if we make the denominator of the main fraction 1. To do this we multiply $\frac{5}{6}$ by its reciprocal $\frac{6}{5}$, but then, by the fundamental principle of equivalent fractions, we must also multiply the main fraction numerator by $\frac{6}{5}$. Since $\frac{5}{6} \times \frac{6}{5} = 1$, and since the quotient of any number divided by 1 is that number, we can eventually omit this step and thus obtain the quotient by using the numerator of the transformed complex fraction. There is much formalism in this procedure that makes it undesirable as a first approach. It should be used at some later stage, though, when children have enough background to understand it. When they learn it at such a stage of understanding, and do not just learn it by rote, it really clarifies the standard division-of-fractions algorism. It helps, also, to answer one question, "How can a problem in division of fractions become a multiplication problem?" The answer, of course, is, "It doesn't. It becomes a division problem in which the divisor is 1, and since $n \div 1 = n$, we usually shorten our work by omitting this step."

In all the above illustrations we have considered division of fractions given in common form, $\frac{a}{b}$. If fractions are given in mixed form, we first transform them to the common form and proceed in the usual way. Thus

$$12\frac{3}{4} \div 1\frac{7}{8}$$

becomes

$$\frac{51}{4} \div \frac{15}{8} = \frac{\overset{17}{\cancel{51}}}{\underset{1}{\cancel{4}}} \times \frac{\overset{2}{\cancel{8}}}{\underset{5}{\cancel{15}}} \quad \text{or} \quad \frac{34}{5} = 6\frac{4}{5}.$$

10-5 THE FRACTION AS AN
INDICATED DIVISION OF ANY TWO NUMBERS

The first concept of a fraction as a new number (that is, a number other than a whole number) is an *ordered pair of whole numbers*. The members of this pair suggest different relations, but it is the combined result that yields what we call a fraction. Thus a child thinks of $\frac{2}{3}$ as 1 of 3 equal parts of 2 or 2 of 3 equal parts of 1, both of which lead to the ideas of numerator-denominator or multiplier-divisor or stretcher-shrinker. As the child proceeds in his study of mathematics, he must broaden this concept and also extend it to include the rational-number idea. For the ordinary numbers of arithmetic, the rational number is frequently called a fractional number. The teacher should give the children some experiences in this extension of the fraction concept as soon as they have learned the fundamental operations and have attained skill in computing with fractions.

A first and fundamental idea—one which has been stressed earlier in this chapter—is that a fraction is "a pair of numbers associated with the idea of division." The teacher can stress this by considering at first a problem in division of whole numbers, but allowing the use of fractions to obtain an answer. Thus the problem is placed before the children as:

$$2 \div 3 = \square.$$

By the definition of multiplication, the pupils should say

$$2 \div 3 = \square \Rightarrow 2 = \square \times 3.$$

The pupils find that $\frac{2}{3}$ can be written in place of the '$\square$', to give a true statement, and since $2 \div 3 = \frac{2}{3}$, they accept calmly the definition that $2 \div 3$ means the same as '$\frac{2}{3}$'. The fraction bar acts like the '$\div$' sign.

The question can now be raised: "Can the indicated quotient of two fractions also be considered as a fraction?" Of course, we can think of a fraction this way, if we broaden or enlarge our concept of fraction to give meaning to it. Thus we can ask the same question we did with whole numbers: What is the meaning of $\frac{2}{3} \div \frac{5}{7}$? If this division behaves in the same way as $2 \div 3$, we can write

$$\frac{2}{3} \div \frac{5}{7} \quad \text{means} \quad \frac{\frac{2}{3}}{\frac{5}{7}},$$

where the heavy fraction bar takes the place of the '÷' sign. If we allow the principle of fractions of multiplying numerator and denominator by the same nonzero fraction (as we did with whole numbers) we can make a fraction with denominator $\frac{1}{1}$:

$$\frac{2}{3} \div \frac{5}{7} = \frac{\frac{2}{3} \times \frac{7}{5}}{\frac{5}{7} \times \frac{7}{5}} = \frac{\frac{2 \times 7}{3 \times 5}}{\frac{1}{1}}.$$

Now, since the fraction $\frac{1}{1}$ is an identity fraction, the result can be written

$$\frac{2}{3} \div \frac{5}{7} = \frac{\frac{2}{3}}{\frac{5}{7}} = \frac{2 \times 3}{3 \times 5},$$

and the child's knowledge has been extended to conceive of a fraction (sometimes, but unnecessarily, called a complex fraction) as a number divided by another number. The simplification of such a fraction, when the numerator and denominator are themselves fractions, is already inherent in the algorism for dividing fractions.

Such simplifications are not always possible in later work, when we shall meet fractions of the form

$$\frac{\sqrt{3}}{2}, \quad \frac{\pi}{3}, \quad \frac{2}{\sqrt{2}}, \quad \text{etc.}$$

But the above treatment prepares the way for considering means of relating fractions to rational numbers, and rational approximations to real numbers.

A first step toward the rational-number concept can also be taken if the teacher stresses the manner in which each of a whole class of fractions behaves like a single whole number. Thus

$$\left\{ \frac{2}{1}, \frac{4}{2}, \frac{6}{3}, \frac{8}{4}, \cdots, \frac{2a}{a}, \cdots \right\}$$

is a set of many fractions, each of which behaves like the whole number 2. Since

$$2\tfrac{1}{2} = \tfrac{4}{2} + \tfrac{1}{2} = \tfrac{5}{2}, \qquad 2\tfrac{1}{5} = \tfrac{10}{5} + \tfrac{1}{5} = \tfrac{11}{5},$$

and so on, we note that any element of this set suggests a *name* for a number which behaves like the whole number 2.

Similarly, the set

$$\left\{ \frac{2}{3}, \frac{4}{6}, \frac{6}{9}, \ldots, \frac{2a}{3a}, \ldots \right\}$$

as a set of operators all produce the same result. In this sense, they act as different names for a same *value;* they are measures of the same distance $0 < d < 1$ on a number scale. This value which any of the fractions (the members of the set) represent is called a *rational number*. Although we do not suggest that the teacher carry out operations on rationals (classes of equivalent fractions), study of equivalence classes of fractions provides the experiential background for the subsequent study of rationals. Teachers, in this case, must recognize that when we say that $\tfrac{2}{3}$ is equivalent to $\tfrac{4}{6}$, or write '$\tfrac{2}{3} \sim \tfrac{4}{6}$', we are referring to the numerals; when we say that $\tfrac{2}{3}$ equals $\tfrac{4}{6}$ or write '$\tfrac{2}{3} = \tfrac{4}{6}$', we are using fractions as names for the same rational number. When we are teaching fractions to elementary school children, we must handle this subtle (for them) distinction carefully, if we make it at all. There is no harm in using the '$=$' sign for equivalence when we are first developing fractions and operations with fractions.

10–6 HIERARCHY OF LEARNING

Although in the past most pupils have had little trouble in understanding and using whole numbers, fractions have usually been difficult for pupils both to understand and to manipulate. One source of this difficulty has been the lack of a meaningful and useful concept which can aid retention of the knowledge of how fractions operate. Thus the phrase "a part of a whole" mitigates against thinking of a fraction as greater than one, and indeed, confuses the whole of a thing with the number 1. Another source of difficulty has been rote teaching of the operation—the how-to-do-it —because of the belief that rationalization with fractions would be too difficult for children.

The newer programs in teaching mathematics are attempting to stress meaning, concept formation, discovery of operational meanings, and genuine applications. For this purpose, the fraction concept is abstracted from concrete physical situations, and developed from simple ideas to those of a more mature and complex nature, all leading gradually to the idea of rational number. This hierarchy in presentation may follow many sequences, and as educators learn more about concept formation, new sequences may be in order. At present, the following sequence is a workable one and should be studied carefully in light of the expositions in this and the preceding chapter. Grade placements are based on pupils of average and above-average ability and can be adjusted to the rate at which pupils can advance confidently in their study.

In Grades 1 and 2, children learn to say and use the concepts of one-half, one-third, one-fourth, as they occur in everyday experiences. Without pointing it out, teachers use the operator idea, in which 'of' plays a role similar to 'times'. Children learn one-half of *one* sheet of paper (not a whole paper); that one-fifth of a group is one *of* the five equal subgroups of *one* group; etc. In the second and third grade they learn how to write the symbol for one-half, one-third, etc., since they see it in everyday print.

In Grade 3, this concept is extended to the use of other simple fractions, that is, a number (numerator) of equal-sized parts (denominator) of *one* thing or *one* group of things. In this grade the teacher undertakes *representations* of the result of operating on a thing, that is, finding $\frac{1}{4}$ *of* a region, or $\frac{2}{3}$ *of* a circular disk (pie). At this stage it is plain to see that

represents a region and that $\frac{1}{2}$ is a fraction; we *do not* write

$$\frac{1}{2} = \quad ,$$

because a number is not a region. We may illustrate a part of a region, and write

$$\frac{1}{2} \text{ of} \quad = \quad .$$

In Grade 4 we develop the several ideas that fractions can convey, along with the symbolic representation of fractions. There are several uses for the fraction symbol. Here we must present the use of geometric regions and the extension to a number line (or scale), as well as explicit use of the operator idea of a fraction. The essential development at this stage is that of comparison of fractions, leading to the idea of equivalent fractions (called equal at this time) and of transforming fractions to equivalent fractions. We establish the fact that $\frac{1}{1}$ is a fraction equivalent to the whole number 1, and hence that fractions may be less than, equal to, or greater than 1. The representation of a fraction greater than 1 as a mixed numeral and informal intuitive operations on fractions complete this study.

In Grade 5, the children study formal operations on fractions. Either addition or multiplication can be introduced first, followed respectively by subtraction and division, using the idea of inverse operation. If multiplication is introduced first, it should be through the use of the operator idea of fractions. In any case, the teacher should present the idea of the commutativity and associativity of the two major operations, without necessarily using or referring to these words. For practical purposes, the commutative and associative principles are combined into a general rearrangement, or "any-order" principle: You can add (or multiply) in any order you please as long as you use each addend (or factor) exactly one time. The distributive property should be used first with fractions greater than 1. For example, $\frac{3}{4} \times 2\frac{2}{3}$ can be examined as $\frac{3}{4}(2 + \frac{2}{3})$ or $\frac{3}{4}(\frac{4}{2} + \frac{2}{3})$. Of course, these operations will be reviewed in Grade 6 when the children study decimal representation of rational numbers. At the end of Grade 5, most pupils should understand fractions, give several meanings to a fraction, including that of division of two numbers, and be able to apply the concepts and operations to genuine problems in which fractions occur in social, business, and elementary science situations.

EXERCISES

1. Show how multiplication of fractions may be presented entirely independently of any previous knowledge of addition of fractions; discuss the pros and cons of presenting multiplication first when you are introducing operations on fractions.

2. Write each of the following as common fractions: $4\frac{1}{2}, 1\frac{1}{3}, 1\frac{1}{4}, 1\frac{3}{5}, 1\frac{7}{8}$. In each case, what meaning was given to the symbol for 1? Using

your answer to the first two examples, explain how to teach the meaning of 1 as a whole number, and the symbols $\frac{2}{2}$, $\frac{3}{3}$, $\frac{4}{4}$, ... as fractions equivalent to the whole number 1.

3. Explain how to teach that the order of multiplying two fractions does not change the product. Use both a geometric region and a line segment to illustrate this property of multiplication.

4. The terms 'proper fraction', 'improper fraction', 'cancel', and 'invert' are now considered unnecessary in the teaching of fractions. Give arguments for and against using these words. State and defend your own position.

5. The idea of an inverse element for any given element with respect to a given operation is an important property in mathematical study. Discuss this property with respect to fractions for multiplication and its identity element. How and when would you teach this idea?

6. If a and b are whole numbers each greater than one, then $ab > a$ and $ab > b$. Discuss this same inequality for fractions, considering a a fixed number and $b < \frac{1}{1}$, $b = \frac{1}{1}$, and $b > \frac{1}{1}$. Explain how you would teach this property and stress it in contrast to the rule for whole numbers.

7. State the difference between exact division and total quotient with a remainder, illustrating with $28 \div 7$ and $28 \div 5$. Do the same for fractions, illustrating with $\frac{5}{6} \div \frac{2}{11}$ in both cases. How would you clinch the idea that $\frac{5}{6} \div \frac{2}{11}$ is $\frac{55}{12}$ (exactly) but that $\frac{5}{6} \div \frac{2}{11}$ is $\frac{48}{12}$ and $\frac{7}{66}$ remaining? Give a practical situation in which (a) the exact quotient would be desirable; (b) the total quotient and remainder would be desirable.

8. Give illustrations to show that the operator (stretcher-shrinker) concept of a fraction is applicable to all the various interpretations given to a fraction in the last two chapters.

9. a) To divide $\frac{a}{b}$ by $\frac{c}{d}$ and to multiply $\frac{a}{b}$ by $\frac{d}{c}$ are two distinct and different operations. In what way are they related?

   b) If
   $$\frac{a}{b} \div \frac{c}{d} = \frac{e}{f} \qquad \text{then} \qquad \frac{a}{b} = \frac{e}{f} \cdot \frac{c}{d}.$$

   In what way are these two operations related?

   c) What is an inverse of a given multiplication? Of a given division?

10. Explain how you would teach fifth- and sixth-graders the idea that fractions can calibrate a scale to greater refinement than whole numbers. If measurement to the nearest eighth of an inch is closer to a true length than measurement to the nearest quarter of an inch, what distinction would you make between $\frac{3}{4}$ and $\frac{6}{8}$?

Multiplication and division of fractions

11. Outline a sequence of lessons to use for convincing students that, for all a, b, and c, excluding 0 divisors, the following is true:

$$(a \times b \times c) \div c = (a \times b) \times (c \div c) = a \times b,$$
$$(a \times b \times c) \div b = a \times (b \div b) \times c = a \times c,$$
$$(a \times b \times c) \div a = (a \div a) \times b \times c = b \times c.$$

REFERENCES

HOFFMAN, H. W., "Meaning for Multiplication of Fractions," *The Arithmetic Teacher* **5,** March 1958, pages 89–90

JOHNSON, H. C., "Division with Fractions: Levels of Meaning," *The Arithmetic Teacher* **12,** May 1965, pages 362–368

KOLESNIK, T. S., "Illustrating Multiplication and Division of Common Fractions," *The Arithmetic Teacher* **10,** May 1963, pages 268–271

PHILLIPS, J. M., and H. VAUGHAN, "Fractions," *UICSM Newsletter*, No. 12, Oct. 21, 1963, pages 1–20

VAN ENGEN, H., "Rate Pairs, Fractions, and Rational Numbers," *The Arithmetic Teacher* **7,** December 1960, pages 389–399

teaching
rational numbers and
decimal notation

In the past, and even today, one frequently reads of decimals as though they represent numbers less than 1, always in the form 0.12, and so on. A numeral such as '21.46' is then called a mixed decimal. This only adds to the confusion, as the word *decimal* refers only to a system of notation and not to numbers. Thus 248, 26, 0.41, and 4.31 are all decimal numerals. It is the use of decimal notation for fractions that gives greater insight into the nature of rational (or fractional) numbers. The extension of the decimal representation of whole numbers to fractions (greater than, equal to, or less than 1) then forms the basis for a better understanding of the operations on rational numbers, which, in turn, may be used to give even deeper understanding of rational numbers. Teaching should proceed in this spiral order.

11-1 EXTENDING DECIMAL NOTATION

Children, by the time they reach the fifth grade, are quite familiar with decimal notation for cardinal numbers. They are also aware that every whole number corresponds to a fraction with the denominator 1, that is, 2 corresponds to $\frac{2}{1}$ (and of course, many other equivalent fractions), and 268 corresponds to $\frac{268}{1}$. Also *place value* in the decimal system is well understood. A natural first step in extending this knowledge is to study the place value of a column to the right of the ones column. What would be the value of this place *if* the same pattern (decimal notation) of place values of any two adjoining places continued to hold?

The answer involves recognizing that 10 units in this column to the right of the ones column must equal 1, hence each unit in this right-hand column would be $\frac{1}{10}$, or one tenth. Geometrically, this is illustrated by a square which represents 1, divided into 10 strips, each of which represents a unit in the column to the right of the ones column. (See illustration in margin.) Coordinated or ruled paper can be used quite successfully in displaying this and further extensions of decimal notation.

1

We can now represent numbers of tenths from 0 to 99 in two ways, using the common fraction notation:

(a) $\frac{0}{10}, \frac{1}{10}, \frac{2}{10}, \frac{3}{10}, \ldots, \frac{10}{10}, \frac{11}{10}, \ldots, \frac{98}{10}, \frac{99}{10}$

(b) $0, \frac{1}{10}, \frac{2}{10}, \ldots, \frac{9}{10}, 1, 1\frac{1}{10}, 1\frac{2}{10}, \ldots, 8\frac{9}{10}, 9, 9\frac{1}{10}, \ldots, 9\frac{9}{10}$

When we attempt to list all these numbers (without using the ellipsis dots), we begin to wish we had a way to avoid writing all those monotonous denominators. Most children who have arrived at the maturity level at which decimal fraction notation may be taught have noticed that a cyclometer and the odometer on a car count by tenths, and that the manufacturers of these instruments avoid having to write denominators by printing the figures for less than 10 tenths on a background of a different color from that used for multiples of 10 tenths (whole numbers). This is one scheme we could use, but it would be as much trouble as writing those denominators. We could get the same effect by just using two colors of ink, or pencils, but that would be unhandy. We could think of all sorts of typographical schemes, all of which would accomplish the central purpose of distinguishing (separating) the whole-number part of the numeral from the proper-fraction part. (A treatise on the history of mathematics informs us that what we call the decimal point used to be called the *separatrix*.)

All children above the primary level are familiar with the way we write numbers which refer to amounts of money. They know that we write the number of whole dollars, then a dot which is called a decimal point in this context, then the number of cents. They know that the first figure to the right of the decimal point may be interpreted as naming a number of dimes and that 10 dimes may be exchanged for 1 dollar. They know that the second figure to the right of the decimal point may be interpreted as naming a number of pennies, that 10 pennies may be exchanged for 1 dime, and that 100 pennies may be exchanged for 1 dollar. The teacher should recognize this understanding, and should capitalize on it now, referring to dimes as tenths of a dollar and to pennies as hundredths of a dollar.

The children have probably seen newspaper headlines carrying something like ". . . $1.5 million." What could that mean? Well, what might $1.5 mean? It could mean 1 dollar and 5 dimes, which is 1 dollar and 5 tenths of a dollar, and this is worth a dollar and a half, of course. Then $1.5 million must be a shortcut for writing 1 million dollars and 5 tenths (or 1 half) of another million dollars.

Since we are so familiar with the simple device for separating whole dollars from parts of dollars in the way we write amounts of money, we can agree to use the same scheme (write a little dot, called a decimal point, after the ones digit) to separate the whole numbers and the proper fractions in the way we write amounts of anything. Thus, we can look at '2.3' and know that the '3' refers to the number of tenths. With this agreement, we can write numerals for rational numbers such as 0.0, 0.1, 0.2, . . . , 0.9, 1.0, 1.1, . . . , 2.0, 2.1, . . . , 9.9, 10.0, and so on.

Children should practice reading the numerals; for example, '3.4' is "three and four-tenths," where we use "and" only to designate the decimal point. Thus 248.7 is read "two hundred forty-eight and seven tenths." Conversely, when a numeral is read, the children must be able to write it symbolically in decimal notation. The children may observe that when the teacher is reading something written on a piece of paper and says "three and eight tenths," for example, they cannot tell whether what was written on that paper was '3.8' or '$3\frac{8}{10}$'. Some children like to say that decimal fractions have unwritten denominators: the place-value name of the rightmost place tells what denominator you write if you wish to use the common-fraction form. When the decimal fraction is less than 1, it is sometimes called a *proper decimal fraction*. In this case it is customary to write a digit 0 in the ones place to indicate that the fraction represented is a value less than 1. Thus we write '0.4' instead of '.4'.

After the children have made the first step to the right, the next step is important, since if they understand it, they will be able to continue the extension on their own by generalization. Suppose that there is another place to the right of the tenths: "What would it represent?" (The *ths* at the end of the word tenths must be stressed, for otherwise pupils may think of it as another tens column.) Some pupils may find it difficult to think of a number (fraction) which multiplied by ten equals one-tenth, but referring back to decimal parts of a dollar, dimes as tenths and pennies as hundredths may help. Also, the problem can be reversed. Each place in the decimal system of notation has a place value which is one-tenth of the place value at its left, and $\frac{1}{10} \times \frac{1}{10}$ is readily seen to be $\frac{1}{100}$. Conversely, $10 \times \frac{1}{100} = \frac{1}{10}$. So it must be a hundred*ths* column.

Our diagram is now extended to illustrate hundredths, as shown in the margin. Now 2.46 would be read "two and four tenths six hundredths." (Children who say "two and forty-six hundredths" should be asked to explain how they arrive at 'forty-six hundredths'.) Since for every tenth there are 10 hundredths, then 4 tenths are 4 × 10 or 40 hundredths. This added to the 6 hundredths gives 46 hundredths. After a few examples children should be able to read and write rational numbers to hundredths:

0.00, 0.01, 0.02, . . . , 0.10, 0.11, . . . , 0.90, 0.91, . . . , 0.99, 1, 1.01,

and so on. A diagrammatic representation for 2.46 on graph paper, using a 10 × 10 square region for 1 unit, is as follows:

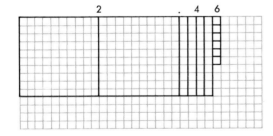

The extension to thousandths, ten-thousandths, . . . , millionths, and so on, is now an easy generalization. The following diagram is quite common in all the textbooks, and can be used in reading and writing fractions:

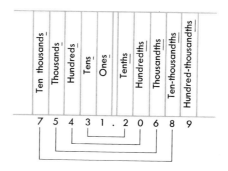

Everyone should note that the place-value names are (almost) symmetrical around the ones place, not around the decimal point.

The teacher should give the pupils practice in reading decimal fractions in various ways. In this practice, the pupil can write the decimal fraction in common form, and give diagrammatic explanations of each of his interpretations. Thus the fraction 2.34 may be read:

a) *Two and thirty-four hundredths.*   Here the integral and the proper-fractional part (i.e., the part less than 1) of the decimal fraction are separated by the word 'and'.

b) *Two hundred thirty-four hundredths.* Note the absence of the word 'and'. The 2 is thought of as "two hundred hundredths" and this combined with the usual reading of 0.34 gives the total response. The pupils can also think of this as

$$2 + 0.34 = \tfrac{200}{100} + \tfrac{34}{100} = \tfrac{234}{100}.$$

A geometric interpretation, if a square has the value of 1, is:

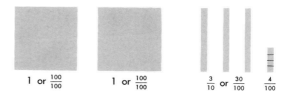

1 or $\frac{100}{100}$ 1 or $\frac{100}{100}$ $\frac{3}{10}$ or $\frac{30}{100}$ $\frac{4}{100}$

The number is expressed in terms of the whole number of units of the rightmost place. The above are the important interpretations. However, others are:

c) *Two and three tenths, four hundredths*
d) *Twenty-three tenths, four hundredths*
e) *Twenty-three and four-tenths tenths*

Children may suggest other correct interpretations. Pupils come to understand the decimal system of notation only by looking at all possible correct ways of interpreting a decimal. Thus 13.496 may be expressed in terms of thousandths, hundredths, tenths, ones, or even tens; then there are 1.3496 tens (not tenths).

11-2 THE NUMBER LINE AND RATIONAL NUMBERS

Children see that in the decimal system of notation there is *only one finite numeral*, only one way, that represents the value expressed previously by a whole set of equivalent fractions. When we are relating these numbers to points on the number scale, it is valuable to use the decimal notation. This should be done in two ways: (1) for a given decimal fraction, locate the corresponding point on a calibrated scale (or ray), and (2) for a selected point on the scale, attempt to find the decimal representation for the associated number. The second activity will lead to the discovery that not all points on the number line can be represented as decimal fractions. The fact is that there are rational numbers that have no finite decimal representation, and there are nonrational numbers that have no finite decimal representation, yet both types of number can be associated with points on the number line.

In this study it is wise to use a decimally divided scale, such as a foot rule divided decimally and each tenth subdivided decimally. Better still is a meter stick which may be used as the unit segment for calibrating a ray drawn on the chalkboard.

First, the teacher asks a pupil to locate the point corresponding to a given numeral on the line: for example, 0.47.

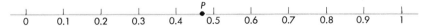

The pupil first locates the point for 0.4 and then the seventh division mark in the interval from this point to that for 0.5. This point *P* corresponds to 0.47. After a few examples of this type, the teacher can extend the exercise to locating 0.673. On a meter stick, where millimeters are indicated, the child will find the sixth large major division, then the seventh smaller division mark in the interval 0.6 to 0.7 and finally the third division mark of the interval 0.67 to 0.68.

As a last type of example, children may be asked to find the point corresponding to 0.3427, in which the position of 0.0007 must be estimated. If several children are asked to make this last estimate, they will never agree exactly, and in this way they get an introduction to the approximateness of reading points on a scale. They can never be sure of the exact position of the point if the rightmost figure they locate must be estimated. This exercise will prove of value in the subsequent study of a slide rule.

Next the children should reverse the process; that is, they should select a point on the number scale and give the decimal numeral for the corresponding number. At first they select a mark on the scale and read its number as in the figure, where A corresponds to 0.542.

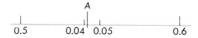

When they do this, it is helpful if the teacher draws an enlargement of the segment 0.04 to 0.05 on the board.

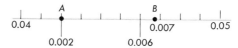

Now the point can be changed to a position such as B, and the pupils are asked to estimate the ten-thousandths point. Here again, approximateness of estimation will enter in, and children may say that B corresponds to 0.5467 or 0.5468. All the above work strengthens the concept that for each point there is only one number and for each rational number there is exactly one point.

Suppose that an attempt is made to locate the point corresponding to $\frac{1}{3}$ on a scale divided decimally. Certainly we can find the point corresponding to $\frac{1}{3}$ by dividing the segment 0 to 1 into three congruent parts. First we find that $\frac{1}{3} > \frac{3}{10}$ but $\frac{1}{3} < \frac{4}{10}$, so that the beginning of the decimal representation is 0.3. To find the next decimal place we find that $\frac{1}{3} < \frac{34}{100}$ but $\frac{1}{3} > \frac{33}{100}$, so that the extended representation is 0.33. Further testing shows that we always get the same situation; that is, the point $\frac{1}{3}$ lies between the third and fourth division point of each smaller interval, so that $\frac{1}{3}$ becomes approximately 0.3333, and we could get closer and closer to $\frac{1}{3}$ by writing more and more threes. (It is the rare elementary school pupil who really understands that we have an exact numeral for $\frac{1}{3}$ when the succession of threes goes on forever.) Thus there is no finite decimal to represent the point which is one-third of the distance from the zero-point to the one-point, even though the point can be readily constructed. Similar experiences with fractions such as $\frac{3}{11} \approx 0.2727$ gives the conclusion that not all rational numbers have finite decimal representations.

As a final study of this part of the rational numbers, it is of value to know which rationals do and which do not have finite decimal representation. An examination of finite decimals of the type 0.15, 0.47, 0.265, 0.4343 when written in common form $\frac{15}{100}, \frac{47}{100}, \frac{265}{1000}, \frac{4343}{10000}$, gives the clue: If the denominators of decimal fractions are written in factored form and *in simplest form*, they contain only the prime factors 2 and 5. Thus

$$\frac{3}{20} = \frac{15}{100} \quad \text{and} \quad \frac{3}{20} = \frac{3}{2^2 \cdot 5}; \quad \text{even} \quad \frac{143}{325} = \frac{143}{5^2 \cdot 13},$$

although it appears to have 13 as a factor in the denominator, when changed into its simplest form becomes $\frac{11}{25}$:

$$\frac{143}{325} = \frac{11 \times 13}{25 \times 13},$$

and since the denominator of $\frac{11}{25}$ in factored form is 5^2, the fraction can be represented decimally $\rightarrow \frac{11}{25} = \frac{44}{100} = 0.44$. Thus children discover the following principle.

If a rational number, given in its simplest fraction form, has only the prime factors 2 and 5 in the denominator, it has a finite decimal numeral.

If any other prime factor appears in the denominator, it has no finite decimal representation, only an approximate one.

11-3 PRECISION AND LINEAR MEASURE

By the time children study rational numbers, they have had considerable study of linear measures using units such as inch, foot,
yard, meter, centimeter, and so on (see Chapter 8). Now, with
elementary notions of the number line at their disposal, they can
learn the meaning of precision and estimation in making linear
measurements. As a start, several differently scaled rulers should
be used: one in inches only, another in quarter-inches, another in
eighths or sixteenths of an inch, and another in tenths of an inch.
On worksheets we draw a number of segments which the children
are asked to measure using the differently scaled rulers. Some of
the answers using the above suggested scales for the segment shown
might be as follows. The measure of $\overline{AB}$ is: A ——————————————— B

Scale	Measure
Inch	About $1\frac{1}{2}$ inches
Half-inch	A little more than $1\frac{1}{2}$ inch
Quarter-inch	About $6\frac{1}{4}$ quarter inches
Eighth-inch	Almost $1\frac{5}{8}$ inches
Sixteenth-inch	Nearly $1\frac{10}{16}$ inches
Tenth of an inch	About (a little more than) 1.6 inches

Further comparison of the smallest calibrated unit of measure
in each scale would lead to $1 > \frac{1}{2} > \frac{1}{4} > \frac{1}{8} > \frac{1}{10} > \frac{1}{16}$, and the
most precise of all these measures is the one with the smallest unit:
$\frac{1}{16}$ of an inch. Precision, then, is refinement of measure, and the
smaller unit gives a more precise measure, because it has a smaller
interval between successive calibration marks on the scale. With
this knowledge, children can easily determine which is a more
precise measure, one given to $\frac{1}{100}$ or to $\frac{1}{32}$ of a unit; or to $\frac{1}{20}$ or $\frac{1}{16}$
of a unit. At this time no mention need be made of accuracy,
which is an entirely different concept and involves not only the
precision of measure, but the size of the quantity which is being
measured.

An excellent activity is estimating the final digit of a measure,
a process which is quite similar to estimating the decimal representation of a point on the number scale when each subunit is
divided into tenths. Referring again to the differently scaled rulers,

the children discover the following:

a) If inches only are marked, you can *estimate* within half an inch, perhaps closer still if you mentally subdivide the unit.

b) If half-inches only are marked, you can estimate within a quarter of an inch, or a little better if you mentally subdivide.

c) If quarter-inches only are marked, since this unit is much smaller, you can probably estimate only to the nearest eighth of an inch.

d) For scales marked in tenths of an inch, probably the best you can do is estimate to a twentieth of an inch, that is, one-half of the smallest calibrated segment.

e) For scales marked in sixteenths of an inch, you can estimate only to the nearest thirty-second of an inch.

Now the children should make measures using a rule divided into binary units ($\frac{1}{2}$, $\frac{1}{4}$, $\frac{1}{8}$, etc.) and decimal units (0.1 and 0.01). A teacher who has at hand a very precise ruler with fine division points can demonstrate, by using a magnifying lens, how more precise measures and estimates may be made.

11–4 COMPUTATIONAL ALGORISMS WITH DECIMAL FRACTIONS

As shown in the preceding section, decimal fractions can be given to any desired precision. In any real situation, however, such as the use of instruments to measure lengths, it is safe to assume that all measures will be given to the same degree of precision. Thus, if lengths are measured to the nearest thousandth of an inch, and we want to find the sum of these measures, we will probably encounter an example of the type 1.042 + 2.964 + 0.978 + 1.765, or in column form as shown in the margin. Similarly a sum of money might be required to the nearest dollar (as in some tax return forms) or to the nearest cent, for example:

$$1.042$$
$$2.964$$
$$0.978$$
$$+\ 1.765$$

9.62 + 27.43 + 5.50 + 95.00 + 6.78 (as in a series of bank checks).

Finding the sum of a series of rational numbers all expressed to the same degree of precision presents no new problem, for, beginning with the rightmost column, we consider each ten-set of this column a one-set of the column (or place) next to the left. This is merely the definition and meaning that we ascribe to this column. For example, for the problem of linear measures listed above, the process is shown below, where the vertical line indicates that the operation is completed.

$$
\begin{array}{cccc}
1 & 21 & 2\ 21 & 2\ 21 \\
1.042 & 1.042 & 1.042 & 1.042 \\
2.964 \Rightarrow & 2.964 \Rightarrow & 2.964 \Rightarrow & 2.964 \\
0.978 & 0.978 & 0.978 & 0.978 \\
1.765 & 1.765 & 1.765 & 1.765 \\
\hline
9 & 49 & 749 & 6.749
\end{array}
$$

Of course, in practice, the problem is done in one writing, and the strokes are never drawn. The numbers carried to the next column may be retained mentally, or written above the relevant column as shown. When we are dealing with a long column, it is usually a good practice to make a note of the number carried.

The sum can also be worked out in a horizontal form. Here it is a more difficult process to add numbers with the same place values, since the eye must select this digit from each numeral, whereas in the columnar arrangement, the numerals all appear directly under each other. Thus $2.04 + 3.96 + 7.82 + 24.57$ is done by thinking 4, 10, 12, 19 $(4 + 6 + 2 + 7)$, write '9' and carry '1'. 1, 1, 10, 18, 23 $(1 + 0 + 9 + 8 + 5)$, write '3' and carry '2'. Place the decimal point '.'. Then think 2, 4, 7, 14, 18 $(2 + 2 + 3 + 7 + 4)$, write '8' and carry '1'. $1 + 2$ is 3. Write 3. The sum is 38.39.

Similarly, there is no new algorism to be learned for subtraction. If like values of the minuend and subtrahend are in the same column, the decimal points are in a column and the subtraction procedure is exactly the same as for whole numbers. In any practical situation each of the two given numbers will have the same degree of precision, and examples given to children for practice should observe this.

$$
\begin{array}{r}
34.184 \\
- \ 9.726 \\
\hline
24.458
\end{array}
\Rightarrow
\begin{array}{r}
20{,}000 + 13{,}000 + 1{,}100 + 70 + 14 \text{ (thousandths)} \\
- \qquad\qquad\quad 9{,}000 + \quad\ 700 + 20 + \ 6 \text{ (thousandths)} \\
\hline
20{,}000 + \ 4{,}000 + \quad 400 + 50 + \ 8 \text{ (thousandths)}
\end{array}
$$

Although the expansion at the right above illustrates the work that is done mentally, the child does the problem with the skill and efficiency of the algorism used with whole numbers. The decimal point in the numeral for the difference is placed directly below the decimal point of the given numerals.

12.341
236.
1.72
24.3
————

Examples such as this should be avoided in measurement contexts.

Frequently, in textbooks, the teacher will find examples similar to the one in the margin. These decimals are referred to as "ragged." In practical applications, these examples should not occur, since they usually indicate measurements with different degrees of precision. To fill in the missing places with zeros is to give a spurious precision. The best that can be done is to round off each number to that place given by the least precise measurement and then add. Thus the example shown should be written $12 + 236 + 2 + 24$.

11-5 MULTIPLICATION WITH DECIMAL FRACTIONS

Multiplication with decimal fractions can be related to the algorism for multiplying whole numbers; hence there is no new computational skill to be learned. The only *new* idea to learn is the location of the decimal point in the product. There are several good pedagogical procedures for teaching the location of the decimal point: one can use estimation, or an analogy to the multiplication with equivalent common fractions. A good procedure is to allow children to estimate first, and then, by reasoning, to discover a rule for locating the decimal point in the product.

The teacher confronts the pupil with an example such as '5 × 0.3', and asks, "About how much is this product?" If the child thinks $\frac{3}{10}$ for 0.3 and then $5 \times \frac{3}{10}$, he knows that the answer is $\frac{15}{10}$ or $1\frac{5}{10}$. He can easily see that this can be expressed as '1.5'. After a few examples of this type, some children will generalize by saying that they multiply the 5 and 3 and the answer is in tenths, i.e., 15 tenths or 1.5. The class can be challenged to find the product of 0.5 × 0.3. Again, if the child does not immediately sense the way to get an answer, he can be asked to tell another way of thinking of 0.5, perhaps as a common fraction. Then $\frac{1}{2}$ of 0.3 is $1\frac{1}{2}$ tenths or $\frac{1}{2}$ of $\frac{3}{10}$ is $\frac{3}{20}$ which is $\frac{15}{100}$ or 0.15. A few examples of this type will lead pupils to think of the decimal numbers as whole numbers, perform the multiplication, and, since the answer is in hundredths, place the decimal point accordingly.

If pupils have difficulty, try using graph paper and relating the multiplication to finding the area of a rectangle drawn to scale. Choose some convenient region, preferably a 10 × 10 square, as a unit. To show that

$$0.5 \times 0.3 = 0.15,$$

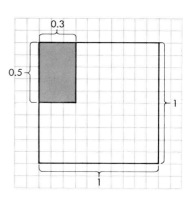

make a diagram similar to the one shown here. We see that the shaded portion occupies 15 small squares, and each of these small squares is $\frac{1}{100}$, or 0.01, of the unit square. Then 15 small squares represent 0.15 of a unit. This graphic device helps to clear the hurdle many children encounter in realizing that the product of 0.5 (which is $\frac{1}{2}$) by 0.3 (which is nearly $\frac{1}{3}$) is much smaller than either of its factors. Other products, including those greater than 1 and less than 0.01, can be illustrated in this way.

After several extensions of this type of multiplication, children should be urged to seek a general rule for obtaining the product. As a first step, they should be encouraged to relate the problem to something they already know: how to multiply numbers expressed in common-fraction form. Thus

$$2.43 \times 0.8 \quad \text{becomes} \quad \tfrac{243}{100} \times \tfrac{8}{10};$$
$$0.034 \times 2.8 \quad \text{becomes} \quad \tfrac{34}{1000} \times \tfrac{28}{10}.$$

The second step is to study the common-fraction form in relation to the decimal form. In every problem, the children note that the sequence of digits in the product is found by multiplying the numerators of the two common fractions.

To discover how to place the decimal point, without making an estimation, we introduce the term *decimal places*. By this we mean "the number of places in the decimal numeral *to the right* of the decimal point." This is the common use of 'decimal places'. Thus

hundredths have two decimal places,	$2.43 = \frac{243}{100},$
tenths have one decimal place,	$0.8 = \frac{8}{10},$
ten-thousandths have four decimal places,	$1.4168 = \frac{14,168}{10,000},$
a whole number has no decimal places,	$13 = \frac{13}{1},$

and so on. Then in simple steps the pupils generalize as follows:

If tenths are multiplied by tenths⎫ tells us ⎧1 place × 1 place
the result is in hundredths   ⎭   ⎩   ⇒ 2 places

$$0.3 \times 0.2 = \tfrac{3}{10} \times \tfrac{2}{10} = \tfrac{6}{100} \qquad \text{so} \qquad 0.3 \times 0.2 = 0.06$$

If tenths are multiplied by⎫   ⎧1 place × 2 places
hundredths the result is in⎬ tells us   ⎨   ⇒ 3 places
thousandths   ⎭   ⎩

$$0.8 \times 3.14 = \tfrac{8}{10} \times \tfrac{314}{100} = \tfrac{2512}{1000} \qquad \text{so} \qquad 0.8 \times 3.14 = 2.512$$

and so forth. The number of decimal places in the product is the sum of the decimal places in the factors of the product.

As practice, it is a good procedure to give the products of two given factors with a decimal point missing in the product, or in one of the factors, and ask the pupils to insert the decimal point correctly and check. As examples, consider:

$$0.24 \times 34.1 = 8_{\wedge}184 \qquad \text{requires a decimal point as shown by } _{\wedge}.$$
$$024_{\wedge} \times 3.41 = 81.84 \qquad \text{requires a decimal point as shown by } _{\wedge}.$$
$$02_{\wedge}4 \times 0.341 = 0.8184 \qquad \text{requires a decimal point as shown by } _{\wedge}.$$

A difficulty occurs when it is necessary to insert zeros in empty tenths, hundredths, or smaller-valued places. For example, 0.2×0.004 involves $2 \times 4 = 8$. Since there must be four places in the answer and the digit '8' holds one of these places, we must write *three* zeros between the decimal point and the '8' to obtain 0.0008 as the product. This situation occurs, for example, when 20 sheets of gold leaf, each sheet 0.0015 of an inch in thickness, are in a package with sheets of tissue paper 0.002 inch thick between each two leaves. How thick is the package, given that a tissue is on the top and on the bottom of the leaves? (That is, there are 21 tissues.) Here $20 \times 0.0015 = 0.030$ and $21 \times 0.002 = 0.042$ and the sum is 0.072.

11–6 DIVISION WITH DECIMAL FRACTIONS

There are two common approaches to teaching the algorism for division with decimal fractions, one using a division as an inverse of a multiplication and the other using the fundamental principle of fractions. Since the latter method is more prevalent, we shall consider it first.

The children already know how to divide with whole numbers to obtain a total quotient with a remainder or to express the answer exactly as a rational number in common-fraction form. This process should be reviewed briefly before considering division with decimal fractions. Then the process is extended to dividing an appropriate number (one having a numeral with decimal places) by a whole number, for example, $8.43 \div 3$; $56.4 \div 8$; or $258.46 \div 14$. In every case, we can estimate the quotient in the same way we do in the case of division with whole numbers. We can also relate each problem to division of whole numbers by transforming the exercise to division with common fractions. Thus

$$8.43 \div 3 = \tfrac{843}{100} \div 3 \text{ which is } \tfrac{1}{100} \text{ as much as } 843 \div 3, \text{ or } \frac{843 \div 3}{100},$$

so the answer is in hundredths;

$$56.4 \div 8 = \tfrac{564}{10} \div 8 \text{ which is } \tfrac{1}{10} \text{ as much as } 564 \div 8, \text{ or } \frac{564 \div 8}{10},$$

so the answer is in tenths;

$$258.46 \div 14 = \frac{25,846}{100} \div 14 = \frac{25,846 \div 14}{100},$$

and thus the answer is in hundredths. The algorisms are:

$$
\begin{array}{llll}
\begin{array}{r} 281 \\ \hline 3)843 \\ 600 \\ \hline 243 \\ 240 \\ \hline 3 \end{array}
&\Rightarrow&
\begin{array}{r} 2.81 \\ \hline 3)8.43 \\ 6\ 00 \\ \hline 2\ 43 \\ 2\ 40 \\ \hline 3 \end{array}
&
\begin{array}{r} 7.0 \\ \hline 8)56.4 \\ 56\ 0 \\ \hline 4 \end{array}
\end{array}
$$

$$
\begin{array}{r}
18.46 \\ \hline
14)258.46 \\
140\ 00 \\ \hline
118\ 46 \\
112\ 00 \\ \hline
6\ 46 \\
5\ 60 \\ \hline
86 \\
84 \\ \hline
2
\end{array}
$$

In this manner we evolve a rule for placing the decimal point properly in the quotient, namely: if a decimal fraction is divided by a whole number, there are as many decimal places in the quotient as there are in the dividend.

The next step is to transform a division involving a decimal divisor into an equivalent division with a whole-number divisor. For this purpose we use the fact that every division may be looked on as a fraction, and apply the fundamental principle of fractions to transform the denominator to a whole number. If children are to have a genuine feeling for the reason this method works, as opposed to an intellectual acceptance of the application of the principle for fractions in this seemingly different situation, they should have much preliminary experience in experimenting with sets of examples like those which follow:

$$\text{(a)}\quad 4\overline{)8}\qquad 12\overline{)24}\qquad 20\overline{)40}\qquad 40\overline{)80}\qquad 400\overline{)800}$$

$$\text{(b)}\quad \tfrac{1}{2}\overline{)3}\qquad 1\overline{)6}\qquad 4\overline{)24}\qquad 5\overline{)30}\qquad 50\overline{)300}$$

For each set, they should be asked not only to compare quotients, but also to study the way each example is related to each other example in the set. They should do enough such exercises to "feel in their bones" that multiplying both the dividend and divisor of a division example by the same nonzero number (any same number, not just a power of 10) leaves the quotient unchanged. Then the children may be asked for advice about how to contend with a division example in which the dividend involves a decimal fraction. They are prepared to reason as follows: "If the divisor were a whole number, I could work the example. The divisor is not a whole number, but I know a way to fix that. Let's see. What is an easy number I can multiply by to change the divisor to a whole number? Now I must multiply the dividend by the same number so that my new example will have the same quotient as my original example. . . . See? The quotient checks for the original example." The children soon find out that "an easy number to multiply by" which works out well for all examples (but is not necessarily the best in certain specific examples) is a power of 10. Then simple examples are studied, such as:

$$\frac{2}{0.4} = \frac{2\times 10}{0.4\times 10} = \frac{20}{4} = 5 \Rightarrow 0.4\overline{)2.0}$$
$$\qquad\qquad\qquad\qquad\qquad\quad \begin{array}{r} 5 \\ \hline 2\ 0 \end{array}$$

$$\frac{0.2}{0.04} = \frac{0.2\times 100}{0.04\times 100} = \frac{20}{4} = 5;\qquad \frac{3.1}{0.5} = \frac{31.0}{5} \Rightarrow 5\overline{)31.0}$$
$$\qquad\qquad\qquad\qquad\qquad\qquad\qquad\qquad\qquad\qquad\qquad\qquad\begin{array}{r} 6.2 \\ \hline 30\ 0 \\ \hline 1\ 0 \\ 1\ 0 \\ \hline \end{array}$$

In the last example the '0' annexed to the 31 to read 31.0 must be explained, namely, $10 \times 3.1 = 31.0$. After several examples of this type, the pupils should generalize the result for all similar division problems in which the quotient is equal to or greater than 1. Thus

$$268.4 \div 0.31 = 26840 \div 31.$$

Two difficulties arise in using the preceding process: The first is how to properly place the decimal point in the quotient when it is less than 1; the second is how to interpret the remainder. Children should be led to discover what happens to a remainder when the dividend and quotient are each multiplied by the same number (usually a power of ten).

$$\frac{20}{6} = 3, \text{ Rem. } 2; \qquad \frac{200}{60} = 3, \text{ Rem. } 20;$$

$$\frac{2000}{600} = 3, \text{ Rem. } 200; \qquad \frac{2.0}{0.6} = 3, \text{ Rem. } 0.2.$$

Similar examples show that although under the transformation to an equal fraction, as a division, the total quotient remains the same, the remainder is multiplied by the same number as the dividend and divisor. Teachers should see this as:

$$\text{If } N = d \cdot q + r, \quad \text{then} \quad 10^k N = (10^k \cdot d)q + 10^k r,$$

and q is the same in both divisions; the remainder is not (it is r in the first equation and $10^k r$ in the second). As an example, consider how many washers, each 0.24 inch thick, can be cut from a cylindrical pipe 2.6 inches long:

$$
\begin{array}{r}
18.0 \\
\hline
0.24)\overline{2.600} \\
2.400 \\
\hline
.200 \\
.192 \\
\hline
.008 \text{ Rem.}
\end{array}
\qquad\qquad
\begin{array}{r}
18.0 \\
\hline
24)\overline{260.0} \\
240.0 \\
\hline
20.0 \\
19.2 \\
\hline
.8 \text{ Rem.}
\end{array}
$$

The division with the given numbers yields a remainder of 0.008 inch, but the division with the transformed problem yields a remainder of 0.8, which is surely not 0.8 inch. If it were, we could cut 3 more washers!

The other difficulty arises when the dividend is less than the divisor. Consider 3.4 ÷ 5. Here it is easy to estimate that the answer lies between $\frac{3}{5}$ and $\frac{4}{5}$ or between 0.6 and 0.8. But a problem of the type 0.24 ÷ 56.12 gives more difficulty. Again, pupils who understand can estimate that 4 × 0.24 is about 1 and hence the answer is about

$$\frac{1}{56 \times 4} \qquad \text{or} \qquad \frac{1}{224}.$$

The actual division process, however, calls for further explanation. To make division possible as a whole-number process, the dividend must be as large as or larger than the divisor. Hence, to have the division analogous to division of whole numbers, it is necessary to annex zeros after the decimal point of the quotient, at least three of them:

$$
\begin{array}{r}
.004 \\
5612\overline{)24.000} \\
22\ 448 \\
\hline
1\ 552
\end{array}
$$

Thus the quotient would be 4 if the dividend were 24,000. But since the dividend is only one thousandth of this or 24.000, it is observed that the quotient is also $\frac{1}{1000}$ of 4, or 0.004. There are as many decimal places in the quotient as there are in the dividend, if the divisor is a whole number.

A final step in most division problems is to decide the degree of precision required in the quotient. This is discussed at the end of the next section.

11–7 DIVISION AS AN INVERSE OF MULTIPLICATION

Since multiplying with decimal fractions entails the same steps as multiplying with whole numbers, except for the location of the decimal point in the product, there should be a way of reversing the procedure. There is. To learn this process we define division in terms of the quotient and remainder:

$N \div d \Rightarrow (q, r)$ such that $N = dq + r,$ $0 \le r < d,$
$80 \div 7 \Rightarrow (11, 3)$ because $80 = 7 \times 11 + 3,$ $0 \le 3 < 7.$

First consider the multiplication and its check by division.

$$
\begin{array}{r}
8.96 \\
2.4 \\
\hline
3584 \\
1792 \\
\hline
21.504
\end{array}
\quad\Rightarrow\quad
\begin{array}{r}
8.960 \\
2.4\overline{)21.504} \\
19\ 200 \\
\hline
2\ 304 \\
2\ 160 \\
\hline
144 \\
144 \\
\hline
\end{array}
$$

In the division the decimal points are ignored until the computation is complete. There must be two decimal places in the quotient. Children note that $\boxed{2 + 1 = 3}$ shows the number of decimal places in the product. Hence $\boxed{3 - 1 = 2}$ gives the number of decimal places in the quotient. Note also that if we had performed $21.504 \div 8.96$, the quotient would have been 2.4 because $\boxed{3 - 2 = 1}$ tells us there is one decimal place in the quotient. Generally, the number of decimal places in the dividend minus the number of decimal places in the divisor equals the number of decimal places in the quotient.

    Children should do a number of multiplications and check, as above, before they discover or learn the rule for placing the decimal point in the quotient. After they have gained confidence, they can practice on placing the decimal point in examples such as the following:

$$
\begin{array}{ll}
2.0 \div 4 = {}_{\wedge}5; & 7.000 \div 8 = {}_{\wedge}875; \\
3.000 \div 40 = {}_{\wedge}075; & 15.838 \div 2.4 = 6{}_{\wedge}59; \qquad \text{etc.}
\end{array}
$$

Finally, the children should learn to find quotients which are not exact, only approximate. For this purpose, at first, we *always* make sure that there are as many (or more) decimal places in the dividend as (than) there are in the divisor. Thus

$$
6.3\overline{)15} \quad \text{is altered to} \quad 6.3\overline{)15.0} \quad \text{or to} \quad 6.3\overline{)15.000},
$$

$$
0.23\overline{)18.1} \quad \text{is altered to} \quad 0.23\overline{)18.10} \quad \text{or to} \quad 0.23\overline{)18.100}, \quad \text{etc.}
$$

This leads to the question: "How many places should be established in the dividend?" The answer lies in the degree of precision that is expected, or seems reasonable, in the quotient. Here the rounding off of numbers comes into play. If we desire a quotient correct to the nearest hundredth, how far should the quotient be extended? Only to hundredths? No, because if the thousandths place is 5 or more, we increase the hundredth place by 1. So a quotient is always "carried," or worked, out to one more decimal place than the required number of decimal places in the quotient, and then rounded off to the required answer:

(6.62)

or

6.621

$$0.37\overline{)2.45\,000}$$
$$\underline{2\,22\,000}$$
$$\overline{23\,000}$$
$$\underline{22\,200}$$
$$\overline{800}$$
$$\underline{740}$$
$$\overline{60}$$
$$\underline{37}$$
$$\overline{23}$$

Example: Find the quotient, to the nearest hundredth, of the example shown in the margin, 2.45 ÷ 0.37.

Solution: There are 2 decimal places in the divisor. The quotient must have 3 places. Hence the dividend must have *5 places.* Annex three '0's (see margin).

Since the above method of teaching division is simple, relates multiplication to its inverse, and gives a quick way of handling the precision of the quotient, it is recommended as preferable to other methods.

11–8 DECIMAL APPROXIMATION TO RATIONAL NUMBERS

Before the pupils began their study of operations with decimal fractions, they studied decimal fractions as ways of representing common fractions. In particular, they discovered that the decimal representation is a unique way of representing a whole class of equivalent fractions, all of which are associated with one point on the number line. For example, 0.5 is a numeral for the number which is the same as that represented by elements of the class $\{\frac{1}{2}, \frac{2}{4}, \frac{3}{6}, \ldots\}$ and all these are associated with the same point on the number scale.

The associated point is called a *rational point*, and the single value associated with this point is called *a rational number*. With the use of the operations with decimal fractions at hand, a deeper understanding of rational numbers can be established. One of the most important ideas is that of the *density* of the rational numbers; namely, for any point on the number line, there is a rational point as close to it as we care to have it. Some of these rational points have an exact decimal representation; others have an approximate decimal representation.

The students have already learned which fractions have an exact decimal representation: those in which the simplest fractional form contains only the factors 2 and 5 in the denominator. Some of the most commonly occurring fractions of this nature can be studied and committed to memory.

For example:
$$\begin{array}{r} 0.5 \\ 2\overline{)1.0} \\ 1.0 \\ \hline 0 \end{array}$$
$\frac{1}{2} = 0.5$.

Hence $\frac{2}{4}, \frac{3}{6}, \frac{4}{8}, \ldots, \frac{13}{26}, \ldots$ can all be replaced by 0.5.

By the same reasoning, $\frac{1}{4} = 0.25$ (see margin).
Hence $\frac{2}{8}, \frac{3}{12}, \ldots, \frac{7}{28}, \ldots$ can all be replaced by 0.25.

Then $\frac{3}{4}$ is $3 \times \frac{1}{4}$ or 0.75.

$$\begin{array}{r} 0.25 \\ 4\overline{)1.00} \\ 80 \\ \hline 20 \\ 20 \\ \hline 0 \end{array}$$

Similarly, the following equivalents can be *discovered* by the pupil:

$\frac{1}{5} = 0.2$;   and $\frac{2}{5} = 0.4, \frac{3}{5} = 0.6, \frac{4}{5} = 0.8$.

$\frac{1}{8} = 0.125$;   and $\frac{3}{8} = 0.375, \frac{5}{8} = 0.625, \frac{7}{8} = 0.875$.

Pupils can also find the decimal-fraction notation for sixteenth, twentieth, twenty-fifth, etc., but these should be stressed as practice on conversion and not as important facts to be recalled.

Pupils are now ready to study those fractions with approximate decimal representation. Here the greater the precision, the closer is the approximation to the given rational number. A study of a few of these rationals will lead pupils to discover the general method for getting approximations. A good start is to study the fraction $\frac{1}{3}$ or any of its equivalent fractions, $\frac{2}{6}, \frac{3}{9}, \ldots, \frac{11}{33}$. If the division process is carried out on any of these fractions, the result is an unending process, but always the same sequence of digits, 0.3, 0.33, 0.333. . . .

$$\begin{array}{r} 0.333 \\ 3\overline{)1.000} \end{array} \qquad \begin{array}{r} 0.333 \\ 6\overline{)2.000} \end{array} \qquad \begin{array}{r} 0.333 \\ 33\overline{)11.000} \end{array}.$$

Each of these quotients is a *decimal fraction* close to the fraction $\frac{1}{3}$, and the more precise the division, the closer the quotient is to $\frac{1}{3}$. However, no matter to how many decimal places the quotient is extended, the result will only be close to $\frac{1}{3}$. There are decimal fractions as close to $\frac{1}{3}$ as we care to make them, but there is no finite decimal fraction equal to $\frac{1}{3}$. We write

$$0.33 \approx \tfrac{1}{3} \quad \text{or} \quad 0.333 \approx \tfrac{1}{3},$$

where the symbol ' $\approx$ ' is read "is approximately equal to."

In some books, there is an attempt to express $\frac{1}{3}$ in a mixed form of decimal and common fraction. Thus we find

$$\tfrac{1}{3} = 0.33\tfrac{1}{3}.$$

Although the expression may be used, the '$\frac{1}{3}$' occurring in the two different places denote different values: the first is $\frac{1}{3}$ of a unit; the second is $\frac{1}{3}$ of one-hundredth (not *one-thousandth*, even though it occupies the thousandth place). In ordinary usage, '$\frac{1}{3}$' would always replace '$0.33\frac{1}{3}$'. However, in approximate computation, and in computer computation, the approximations 0.33 or 0.333, etc., would be used. On a meter stick used as a unit, it is a good practice to have children locate 0.3, then 0.33, then 0.333, and then estimate 0.3333 to see how each of these decimal fractions approaches $\frac{1}{3}$ but never exceeds $\frac{1}{3}$; in fact, none ever reach it.

Similar study can be made with such fractions as $\frac{2}{3}, \frac{1}{6}, \frac{5}{6}, \frac{1}{7}$, and so on. In each case, the pupil is asked to show:

1. How to locate the exact point on the number scale.

2. How to divide to get decimal fraction approximations.

3. How the points for decimal approximations, with increasing precision, get closer and closer to the exact point.

In summary, the pupil should comprehend the following ideas:

1. For each fraction, including those equivalent to whole numbers, there is a point on the number ray.

2. The numbers assigned to these points are called arithmetic rational numbers.

3. Some of these points (for example, $\frac{3}{4}$) can be named by finite decimal numerals.

4. Other rational points (for example, $\frac{2}{3}$) can be only approximated by finite decimal numerals.

5. Any finite set of rational numbers can be ordered, but between any two rational numbers there are many others. There is no next rational number. *The rational numbers are dense*, compared with whole numbers, where each number has an immediate successor (for example, 3 is *the* successor of 2).

6. The question should be raised, "Do the rational numbers account for all the points on the number ray, or are some points not associated with any rational number?" This question can be answered at this stage by a statement of fact, illustrated by a few examples. It is not intuitively obvious, but *there are points which are not associated with any rational number*.

11–9 SQUARE ROOTS OF A NUMBER

As a final look at numbers on the number ray (or line), the teacher can introduce children to numbers which are not rational, by seeking the square roots of numbers. Finding the square root of a number is a unary operation, since to a given number, say 16, we assign the number 4, because $4^2 = 16$. We say that 4 is the square root of 16 and write $\sqrt{16} = 4$. Generally, we define in symbols

$$\sqrt{a} = b \Rightarrow b^2 = a,$$

or, in words, "The square root of a given number is a second number such that the square of the second number is equal to the given number."

To teach this we first consider a few numbers that have whole-number square roots, for example, 36, and write the two factor representations of it. Since $6 \times 6 = 36$, 6 is a square root of 36. Neither 4 nor 9, nor 3 nor 12, are square roots. Why? Because 4^2, 9^2, 3^2, and 12^2 do not yield 36.

Average

36	$= 1 \times 36$	$\frac{37}{2} = 18.5$
	$= 2 \times 18$	$\frac{20}{2} = 10$
	$= 3 \times 12$	$\frac{15}{2} = 7\frac{1}{2}$
	$= 4 \times 9$	$\frac{13}{2} = 6.5$
	$= 6 \times 6$	$\frac{12}{2} = 6$

At the same time, these other factored forms should be studied, for they indicate that one factor is less than the square root, and the other is greater than the square root. In all these cases, note how the average of the two factors gets closer to the square root, the closer the two factors are to the square root. This study should be repeated with other "perfect-square" numbers, that is, numbers that have a whole-number square root.

$$64 = 1 \times 64 = 2 \times 32 = 4 \times 16 = 8 \times 8; \quad \sqrt{64} = 8.$$

Note also that $64 \div 8 = 8$.

$$81 = 1 \times 81 = 3 \times 27 = 9 \times 9; \quad \sqrt{81} = 9.$$

Note also that $81 \div 9 = 9$.

$$225 = 1 \times 225 = 3 \times 75 = 5 \times 45 = 9 \times 25 = 15 \times 15;$$
$$\sqrt{225} = 15.$$

Note also that $225 \div 15 = 15$.

If a square is divided by its square root, the quotient is its square root. However, if a square is divided by:

a) a number greater than the square root, the quotient is less than the square root;

b) a number less than the square root, the quotient is greater than the square root.

In both cases, the average of the dividend and quotient is a better approximation than either one to the value of the square root. Pupils can also find rational square roots of perfect-square rationals:

$$\frac{16}{9} = \frac{4 \times 4}{3 \times 3} = \frac{4}{3} \times \frac{4}{3}, \quad \sqrt{\frac{16}{9}} = \frac{4}{3},$$

$$\frac{144}{400} = \frac{12 \times 12}{20 \times 20} = \frac{12}{20} \times \frac{12}{20}, \quad \sqrt{\frac{144}{400}} = \frac{12}{20}.$$

Such examples lead gradually to the rule

$$\sqrt{\frac{a^2}{b^2}} = \frac{\sqrt{a^2}}{\sqrt{b^2}} = \frac{a}{b}.$$

The next step is to consider the square root of 2. Since $1^2 = 1$ and $2^2 = 4$, then $\sqrt{2}$ would have to be some number between 1 and 2. Since $1 \times 2 = 2$, we use the average of 1 and 2 as an approximation, namely $(1 + 2) \div 2 = 1.5$. If 1.5 were a square root, then $2 \div 1.5$ would give 1.5 as a quotient. But the quotient is 1.3 (see margin). Hence the average

$$\frac{1.3 + 1.5}{2} = 1.4$$

is a better approximation to $\sqrt{2}$. In fact,

$$1.4^2 = 1.4 \times 1.4 = 1.96, \text{ while } 1.3^2 = 1.69 \text{ and } 1.5^2 = 2.25.$$

How can we get a closer approximation? Let us use 1.4 as a value and divide. The average

$$\frac{1.4 + 1.428}{2} = 1.414$$

is a better approximation (see margin), and in fact

$$1.414^2 = 1.999396.$$

Thus $\sqrt{2} \approx 1.414$. This is as good an approximation as is demanded in most everyday cases. There is a question, however: If we continue, will we find an exact (finite) decimal fraction for the square root of 2? The answer must be taken on faith by most children at this stage. It is: "No, there is no decimal fraction, in fact, no fraction, that represents the square root of 2 exactly. The square root of 2, written $\sqrt{2}$, is a new number, not rational, and hence called *irrational*. In fact, all whole numbers that are not perfect squares have irrational square roots. We can find only rational approximations to these values."

Study a few more examples, such as $\sqrt{3} = ?$; try 1.5:

$$\frac{2.0}{1.5)\overline{3.0}} = \frac{2.0 + 1.5}{2} = 1.75.$$
$$\underline{3\ 0}$$

Now use 1.75 as a divisor:

$$\frac{1.750 + 1.714}{2} = 1.732; \qquad \sqrt{3} \approx 1.732.$$

Margin computations:

$$\begin{array}{r} 1.3 \\ 1.5)\overline{2.00} \\ 1\ 50 \\ \hline 50 \\ 45 \\ \hline 5 \end{array}$$

$$\begin{array}{r} 1.428 \\ 1.4)\overline{2.0000} \\ 1\ 4000 \\ \hline 6000 \\ 5600 \\ \hline 400 \\ 280 \\ \hline 120 \\ 112 \\ \hline 8 \end{array}$$

$$\begin{array}{r} 1.714 \\ 1.75)\overline{3.000} \\ 1\ 750 \\ \hline 1\ 250 \\ 1\ 225 \\ \hline 250 \\ 175 \\ \hline 750 \\ 700 \\ \hline \end{array}$$

The process can be extended to finding the square root of any number. Thus, to solve $\sqrt{750}$, a child thinks of 25×30, or perhaps $20^2 = 400$, $30^2 = 900$. Since 750 is nearer 900 than 400, the square root of 750 is probably about 27 or 28. The process then is:

$$\begin{array}{r} 28 \\ \hline 27)\overline{750} \\ 540 \\ \hline 210 \\ 216 \text{ (too much)} \\ \hline \end{array} \qquad \frac{28 + 27}{2} = 27.5 \qquad \begin{array}{r} 27.27 \\ \hline 27.5)\overline{750.000} \\ 550 \\ \hline 2000 \\ 1925 \\ \hline 750 \end{array}$$

$$\frac{27.5 + 27.27}{2} = 27.39; \qquad \sqrt{750} \approx 27.39.$$

By the time the pupil studies this topic, he will already have been introduced to finding the area of a square region (see Chapter 8). Here he has the formula $s^2 = A$. Hence, if we know a desired area of a square, we can find the approximate (or exact) length of the side of a square by finding the square root of the area. Similarly, if the distance traveled by a body falling from rest at an elapsed time t seconds later is given by a formula $d/16 = t^2$ and d is 1600, then $t^2 = 100$ and $\sqrt{100} = 10$ is the time it has been falling (from rest). We could cite a number of other situations in which it is useful to find square roots of numbers, and this is left as an exercise.

11–10 HIERARCHY OF LEARNING

When children learn how to write numbers which refer to amounts of money, in one sense they have their first introduction to decimal notation for rational numbers. However, here the decimal point merely separates the number of whole dollars from the number of hundredths of dollars, or cents. A start can be made by showing that the first number to the right of the decimal point tells the number of dimes, and ten dimes make one dollar. This should be accomplished in Grades 2 and 3.

In Grade 4, as children are introduced to fractions, care should be taken to include work with fractions with denominators of 10 and 100. A ruler graduated in tenths of an inch, or a meter stick graduated in centimeters, are excellent tools for studying tenths, hundredths, and thousandths.

In Grade 5, the decimal system is extended to the right of the ones place, and children learn to read and to write numerals to tenths, then hundredths and thousandths. They learn the operations of addition and subtraction, using these numerals and applying them to practical measurement problems. The year's work should end with a discussion of precision expressed by various numerals, in decimal or in common-fraction form. At this time, the pupils should be making linear measurements with a ruler divided into tenths of an inch and calibrated into centimeters also.

Using a meter stick graduated into millimeters as a unit segment is highly recommended, since it serves as a model for teaching precision of decimal-fraction representation, as well as readiness work for slide-rule reading in the years to follow. It is the best device to use as a model for decimal calibration of the real-number line.

In Grade 6, the decimal notation is extended rightward to include millionths, and the nature of a rational number as attached to points on the number scale, represented exactly or approximately by (finite) decimal fraction notation is strengthened and stressed. The operations of multiplication and division are extended to the use of decimal fractions. The pupils also learn rules for multiplying and dividing by powers of 10. The decimal equivalents of certain frequently used common fractions are derived and committed to memory. The nature of repeated cycles of digits in the decimal expansion of nondecimal fractions is noted. This leads to the density property of the rationals, to approximation by decimal fractions, to rounding off results of operations to desired precision, and to the important fact that there is no next rational point to any given point on the line.

As an enriched final study in the elementary school, the children study square root of a number, and recognize that there are nonrepeating (no-cycle) decimal fractions. These also represent points on the number line; the associated number is called irrational. The children accept the statement that all points on the line are either rational or irrational and thus close their elementary study with a first introduction to the arithmetic real numbers and number line (or better, ray). They can then apply real numbers to problems of measurement, science, and percent.

EXERCISES

1. Using the expanded notation in powers of ten, explain how the decimal system could be expanded to the right of the ones place, using $\frac{26,943}{1,000}$ as an example. Defend this procedure as being preferable to that given in the text, or give reasons why it would not be preferable.

2. a) There is more than one way to read a decimal fraction. Write out the two important ways to read 24.68 in interpreting this number as a fraction.

   b) The symbol '24.68' is sometimes called a mixed decimal. What meaning is to be given to the word "mixed" in this case?

   c) Distinguish among rational number, decimal numeral, and fraction.

3. A ray is a geometric entity. The arithmetic rational numbers are a set of abstract mathematical beings. Describe what you think would be meant by *the rational number ray*.

4. Distinguish among (a) decimal fraction, (b) nondecimal fraction, (c) decimal numeral, (d) approximate decimal numeral, giving an illustration of each.

5. Explain the method you would use to develop the division algorism with decimal numerals. Include in your description the way you would introduce the operation, develop the procedure for locating the decimal point in the quotient, and obtain the quotient to a desired precision.

6. Some textbooks are now introducing infinite decimals in the study of rational numbers. Make a study of this from a current textbook on mathematics, and state whether or not you would recommend teaching this in sixth-grade classes.

7. Square roots of numbers are found by algorisms other than that given in the text. One of these is called the *Euclidean algorism*, illustrated in

$$
\begin{array}{r}
4 \,.\, 6\ 3 \\
\overline{21.4620} \\
16 \\
\hline
5\ 46 \\
5\ 16 \\
\hline
3020 \\
2769 \\
\hline
251
\end{array}
$$

(2 × 4) | 86   4

(2 × 46) | 923

the example shown. Find an explanation for this procedure and explain whether or not, and why, this method should be taught in sixth grade.

8. Explain how an abacus with 9 or 10 beads to a string can be used to introduce decimals denoting values less than 1. Do the same for a number line (or ray). Do the same, using a number-pocket device. Compare these methods with that in the text with respect to concreteness and abstractness of presenting rational numbers.

9. Explain various methods of using graph paper to develop the concept of decimal representation of fractions. In particular, show how $\frac{1}{2}, \frac{2}{4}, \frac{3}{6}, \ldots$, all yield the same decimal representations, but $\frac{1}{3}$ has no finite decimal representation. Show also how to indicate that the area of a rectangle 2.4 in. $\times$ 3.7 in. is 8 sq. in. $+$ 0.8 sq. in. $+$ 0.08 sq. in.

10. Tell how, and which, equivalent decimal forms of common fractions the children should discover and memorize. Explain how you would justify $\frac{1}{3} = 0.33\frac{1}{3}$, or $\frac{5}{8} = 0.62\frac{1}{2}$ rather than 0.625. In particular, tell how you would give meaning to, and use, the symbol '$\approx$'.

REFERENCES

AMSTUTZ, M. G., "Let's 'Place' the Decimal Point, Not 'Move' It," *The Arithmetic Teacher* **10,** April 1963, pages 205–207

FEHR, H. F., and T. J. IIILL, *Contemporary Mathematics for Elementary Teachers,* Boston: D. C. Heath, 1966, Chapter 14

JOHNSON, J. T., "The Use of a Ruler in Teaching Place Value in Numbers," *The Mathematics Teacher* **46,** April 1962, pages 264–266

MUELLER, F. J., "The Neglected Role of the Decimal Point," *The Arithmetic Teacher* **5,** March 1958, pages 87–88

PHILLIPS, J. M., "Finding Square Roots," filmstrip E in *Seeing the Use of Numbers, Set VII,* Eye Gate Productions, Jamaica, N.Y.

teaching ratio,
proportion,
and percent

In general, ratio, proportion, and percent are ways of interpreting and using fractions in practical or applied situations. If pupils have a well-developed concept of a fraction, and of equivalence of fractions, they do not need to learn any new mathematical ideas. However, there is a new vocabulary, and a host of applications involving the vocabulary pertaining to each separate application, that make ratio, percent, and proportion each a special mathematical study. The goal in teaching these topics is to develop (a) meaningful concepts in relation to the fraction concept, and (b) the ability to apply these concepts to problems involving comparisons of magnitudes of the same kind.

12–1 RATIO

An idea which is prevalent in all human activities is that of comparison of quantities or qualities of like magnitudes. This is usually, but not always, accomplished by assigning numbers (measures of some kind) to the magnitudes, and subjecting these numbers to mathematical relations or operations. One of these relations of comparison is *order*, in which we use the special symbols ' $<$ ' or 'is less than', ' $=$ ' or 'is equal to', and ' $>$ ' or 'is greater than'. But in certain comparisons, people are not satisfied with the relations expressed by ' $<$ ' or ' $>$ '; they also want to know how much less (or more) one thing is than the other. For this purpose, we make use of the operation subtraction. Children use this method of comparison as soon as they know how to count. This is the starting point for leading to the study of ratio, a new way of making comparisons.

The pupils should be shown two collections of like kinds of objects, and then given the numbers of each of these collections, or told to find these numbers, and *compare* them. A number of different expressions of comparison may result. For example, if the sets number 10 and 8, respectively, then the following statements hold:

a) Set A is more than set B.

b) Set A is 2 more than set B (found by subtraction).

c) Set B is less than set A.

d) Set B is 2 less than set A.

e) Set A compares to set B as 10 compares to 8.

f) Set B compares to set A as 8 compares to 10.

An investigation of statements (e) and (f) may lead back to statements (a) through (d). However, pupils should be asked in the case of (b) and (d) how the number of one set can be found if we know the number in the other set and the difference. (Answer: We find it by either adding or subtracting the difference.) Finally, the pupils should be challenged to find another way of finding the number of one set from the number of the other, this time using either multiplication or division.

This should lead, with some investigation, to the fact that 8 is $\frac{8}{10} \times 10$ and 10 is $\frac{10}{8} \times 8$. Then a similar problem may be given concerning the ages of Bob (12 years) and his father (36 years). This should evoke the following comparisons:

a) Bob is 24 years younger than his father.

b) Bob's father is 24 years older than Bob.

If we *subtract* the difference from the larger age, we find the smaller age. If we *add* the difference to the smaller age, we find the larger age. This is the way a difference is used in making a comparison.

c) Bob's age is $\frac{12}{36}$ or $\frac{1}{3}$ of his father's age. His father's age is $\frac{36}{12}$ or $\frac{3}{1}$ times Bob's age.

If we multiply the larger age by the fraction less than 1, we find the smaller age. If we multiply the smaller age by the fraction greater than 1, we find the larger age. This is the way a fraction is used in making a comparison.

After discussing several similar examples, the teacher tells the child that when two numbers are compared by making a fraction, the fraction is called a *ratio*. We must investigate the nature of this ratio to see *how* and *why* it works. First we compare one number, the numerator, with the other number, the denominator. We always compare one thing with *another thing*, and it is the latter that is the basis (or *base*) for our comparison. The order is important. Thus, given two measures (numbers) we can always find two ratios of comparison, since either number can be used as the base of the comparison and the other number compared to it. Comparing a larger number to a smaller number always gives a ratio greater than 1; if the smaller is compared to the greater, the ratio is less than 1. If a number is compared to itself, the ratio equals 1.

As soon as the child comprehends the nature of a ratio as a fraction, he should practice forming and interpreting ratios. In all the initial work the ratio must represent a comparison of like magnitudes; that is, the numbers should represent measures, both of which are given in the same unit of measure. At first all the numbers should be whole numbers, but after a few days, the numbers to be compared should include fractions.

Occasionally, the method of comparison by subtraction should be compared with a comparison using ratio, to determine the *kinds* of insight each gives to a practical situation. Thus, when Bob was born, his father was 24 years of age, and this difference remains constant so long as both are alive. But using ratios, we note that, as they grow older, the ratio of Bob's age to his father's age grows larger year by year.

Father	Son	$\dfrac{\text{Son}}{\text{Father}}$
24	0	0
26	2	$\frac{1}{13}$
28	4	$\frac{1}{7}$
32	8	$\frac{1}{4}$
36	12	$\frac{1}{3}$
48	24	$\frac{1}{2}$

Similarly, a comparison of a new road, 350 miles, with the old road, 360 miles, brings out a striking distinction between the use of difference and the use of ratio for purposes of comparison. The comparison of a salary of $100 a week with one of $125, and a weekly salary of $1000 with one of $1025, again shows how the two methods of comparison yield quite different insights.

Instead of using the fraction method of representing a ratio, some books write it in the form

$$a:b; \quad \text{for example, } 3:7,$$

which is read

$$a \text{ is to } b; \quad \text{for example, } 3 \text{ is to } 7.$$

This method, although not very useful for computational work, does emphasize the *numbers* and the *order* of the comparison. It came from the ancient Greeks, to whom the only kind of number was a whole number, and the comparison was a division of whole numbers. The symbol ':' or 'is to' is really an abbreviation for the division symbol '÷'. If the 'is to' language and ':' symbol are introduced, they should be replaced as quickly as possible by the fraction, and then ways of using the fraction should be studied.

As an example, consider the case in which 5000 persons attended an event and 2000 of these received free admission. We can write this as follows: The number of free admissions is to the number of all admissions as

$$2000:5000.$$

But the ratio expressed as a fraction is $\frac{2000}{5000}$ or $\frac{2}{5}$.

A study of the situation reveals all the following ideas:

1. There were 3000 more admitted than those who were admitted free.
2. $\frac{2}{5}$ of all the admissions is the number of free admissions.
3. $\frac{5}{2}$ of the free admissions is the total number of admissions.
4. If these same ratios were to hold when 8000 persons were present, then $\frac{2}{5} \times 8000$ (or 3200) would be admitted free, $\frac{5}{2} \times 3200$ (or 8000) would be the total admission.
5. In either case, 5000 or 8000 attending, the ratio of free to paid admission is $\frac{2}{3}$, that is, $\frac{2000}{3000}$ or $\frac{3200}{4800}$.

To show the need for using a common unit of measure in forming a ratio, the teacher can give the children a problem of comparing 4 feet with 3 yards. There is a temptation to write $\frac{4}{3}$, which is greater than 1, but surely 4 feet is less than 3 yards, as a diagram such as that shown indicates. If both measures are expressed in feet (3 yards is 9 feet), the ratio becomes $\frac{4}{9}$, which is correct. Of course, we could change 4 feet to $1\frac{1}{3}$ yards. Then the ratio is

$$\frac{1\frac{1}{3}}{3} \quad \text{or} \quad \frac{4}{3} \div 3 = \frac{4}{9},$$

which is the same as comparing the number of feet.

Two new properties of ratio emerge from this example. The first—and it is easy to establish—is that the ratio of the two like magnitudes remains the same even though a new unit is chosen to measure both magnitudes. The second is that there can be a ratio of two fractions, and the simple fractional form is found by dividing the fractions. Children measure a piece of paper and find that it is $8\frac{1}{2}$ by $11\frac{1}{4}$ inches. Then the ratio of the width to the length is

$$\frac{8\frac{1}{2}}{11\frac{1}{4}} = \frac{\frac{17}{2}}{\frac{45}{4}} = \frac{17}{2} \times \frac{4}{45} = \frac{34}{45}.$$

Then a large cardboard which had the same width-to-length ratio, if it were 34 inches wide, would be 45 inches long. Children can review computation with fractions by verifying that

$$\tfrac{34}{45} \text{ of } 11\tfrac{1}{4} \text{ is } 8\tfrac{1}{2} \qquad \text{and} \qquad \tfrac{45}{34} \text{ of } 8\tfrac{1}{2} \text{ is } 11\tfrac{1}{4}.$$

Many other examples of this type should be given to the pupils, involving problems in which they must change one unit to the other to obtain the ratio in common-fraction form. Examples are: 5 sec:3 min; 1 in. on a map:4000 ft on earth; $7\frac{1}{2}$ oz: $2\frac{1}{2}$ lb.

After children have had experience expressing ratios in common-fraction form and using these ratios, they should learn how to express a given ratio either exactly or approximately in decimal-fraction form. At first a few of the simpler ratios should be expressed decimally. For example, 1:2 or $\frac{1}{2}$ is also written 0.5; $\frac{3}{4}$ is written 0.75; and so on. However, the ratio $\frac{1}{3}$ can be expressed only approximately, but to any precision desired, in decimal form.

We cannot say

$$\tfrac{1}{3} = 0.3 \quad \text{or} \quad \tfrac{1}{3} = 0.33.$$

That would be a false statement, because $\tfrac{1}{3}$ is greater than 0.3 or 0.33. For this purpose we introduce a new symbol

$\approx$', read "is approximately equal to"

and write

$$\tfrac{1}{3} \approx 0.3 \quad \text{or} \quad \tfrac{1}{3} \approx 0.33 \quad \text{or} \quad \tfrac{1}{3} \approx 0.333,$$

and so forth. These are true statements.

Thus, in the foregoing problem, the ratio of the width to the length, when changed to decimal form, becomes approximately 0.7555 and we write $\tfrac{34}{45} \approx 0.76$, or more precisely, $\tfrac{34}{45} \approx 0.756$. Pupils should become accustomed to reading a decimal fraction as a ratio in tenths, hundredths, or thousandths, etc., for two reasons. First, this notation will serve as readiness activity for the study of percent; and second, most mathematical tables of ratios, such as those for the trigonometric ratios, always present these in decimal notation to a given degree of precision.

```
        0.755
   45)34.000
      31 500
       2 500
       2 250
         250
         225
          25
```

The ultimate objective is for children to conceive of a ratio as an operator, a multiplier which, when we use it to multiply the measure used as a base, yields the measure which was compared to the base. This thinking can be symbolized by the implication

$$\frac{\text{measure of } A}{\text{measure of } B} = r(\text{atio}) \iff m(A) = r \cdot m(B).$$

In this way, the ratio becomes a single mathematical entity, a fraction, that relates two like magnitudes.

12-2 RATE

Some textbooks do not distinguish a comparison by division of like and unlike magnitudes. Thus a comparison of distance with time, for example 184 miles to 4 hours, written as

$$\tfrac{184}{4} \text{ miles per hour,}$$

is also called a ratio. In this book, we prefer to call this a *rate*. In particular, the fraction shown is a rate of speed. The fraction can be simplified to $\frac{46}{1}$ miles per hour, which is the same rate as $\frac{184}{4}$ miles per hour. Although it is not commonly used, we could also compare the time to the distance and write

$$\frac{4}{184} \text{ hours per mile,} \qquad \text{or } \frac{1}{46} \text{ hour per mile.}$$

Children should take similar examples and tell their meaning, for example "2 oranges for 15 cents" is a rate of "$\frac{2}{15}$ orange per cent" or a rate of "$\frac{15}{2}$ cents per orange."

Rates and ratios behave as if they were the same in some situations, but in others they behave quite differently. A study of a ratio expressed by using different units of measure and of a rate expressed by using different units of measure will show the difference.

a) A ratio is independent of the unit used to measure both magnitudes. Thus a ratio of $\frac{2}{3}$ in which the unit is a foot remains $\frac{2}{3}$ if we convert the measurements to yards, inches, or miles. So the ratio is a number, and the unit used in the measure need not be mentioned.

b) A rate, as a fraction, depends on the units of measure. Thus a rate of $\frac{8}{3}$ miles per hour becomes $\frac{704}{3}$ feet per minute, because 8 miles is 8 × 5280 feet, 3 hours is 3 × 60 minutes, and

$$\frac{8 \times 5280}{3 \times 60} = \frac{704}{3}.$$

Surely $\frac{8}{3} \neq \frac{704}{3}$. Thus rates will behave like ratios only if they are expressed in the same unit of rate.

Once children understand this distinction, they can use rates for comparison in the same way they use ratios. It is necessary to remember only that when we use rates, we always keep the same unit of rate when we compare several different situations. Suppose we give children two ratios of measures of length: 2 feet is to 3 feet and 12 feet is to 17 feet. We then ask which is the greater, and what does it mean to say that one ratio is greater than another? The understanding of problems of this type, including both rates and ratios, will lead to the study of proportion. In the present problem, the pupils will probably resort to fractions and say that the ratio of 12 feet to 17 feet is the greater because

$$\frac{12}{17} > \frac{2}{3}.$$

It means that, for *any* base, $\frac{12}{17}$ is more than $\frac{2}{3}$. Similarly, a rate of 3 for 5 cents is less than 20 for 25 cents because

$$\tfrac{3}{5} < \tfrac{20}{25}.$$

This means that a rate of 3 for 5 cents gives fewer items for a given amount of money than a rate of 20 for 25 cents. Children should also express this as a rate of so many cents for so many items, obtaining

$$\tfrac{5}{3} > \tfrac{25}{20}.$$

This means that a rate of $\frac{5}{3}$ requires more money for a given amount of oranges than a rate of $\frac{25}{20}$. It should be stressed that children must practice with rates, expressing them in the two ways shown, until they understand what a rate really expresses.

12-3 PROPORTION AND PROPORTIONAL RELATION

The principal use of ratio is found in a proportional relation, which involves an equivalence class of ratios. The ratios

$$\left\{\frac{2}{3},\ \frac{4}{6},\ \frac{6}{9},\ \frac{8}{12},\ \ldots,\ \frac{2n}{3n},\ \ldots\right\}$$

are in the same class because any one ratio is equal to any other in the class. The ratios in this class, however, may arise when we compare different magnitudes.

To introduce this concept to children, we can begin with a situation such as the following: John spent 90 cents for 6 bars of candy, which he cut up into 18 servings. Bill spent $1.20 for 8 bars of the same candy, which he cut up into 24 servings. How do the amounts of money spent, the bars bought, and the servings compare? Children write the ratios:

$$\tfrac{90}{120}, \qquad \tfrac{6}{8}, \qquad \tfrac{18}{24},$$

and by various means find that the three ratios are equal. The children may be asked to find other ratios equal to these, including the simplest ratio equal to these ratios. We then say that the ratio of costs, the ratio of the number of bars, the ratio of the number of servings, and any other ratios equal to these are in the same proportional relation. We also say that a statement that any two ratios are equal is called a *proportion*. Thus to say

$$\tfrac{90}{120} = \tfrac{18}{24}$$

is to say that the ratio of the expenditures is proportional to the ratio of the number of servings. This is merely saying that if money is assigned in a certain ratio, and if the number of servings is in the same ratio, then the costs are proportional to the number of servings.

A similar statement can be made about rates, using the same rate unit. If one store sells 2 apples for 16 cents and another store sells 5 apples for 40 cents, what about the costs? First we can compare the ratio of the number of apples to the ratio of the prices paid. The ratio for the apples is $\tfrac{2}{5}$, for the prices is $\tfrac{16}{40}$, and these ratios are equal. But the first rate is $\tfrac{2}{16}$ apple per cent and the second rate is $\tfrac{5}{40}$ apple per cent, and these rates are equal. We can thus say that the ratio of the apples and the costs are in the same proportional relation, which is

$$\left\{\frac{2}{5}, \frac{4}{10}, \frac{6}{15}, \frac{8}{20}, \ldots, \frac{16}{40}, \ldots\right\}.$$

The rates are also in a proportional relation, but one that is different from that of the ratios; it is

$$\left\{\frac{1}{8}, \frac{2}{16}, \frac{3}{24}, \frac{4}{32}, \frac{5}{40}, \ldots\right\}.$$

After several examples of this type, the teacher should call attention to the distinction among ratio, proportion, and proportional relation. A ratio expresses a comparative relationship; it is obtained by dividing one of an ordered pair of numbers by the other, and is expressed by a fraction such as $\tfrac{2}{3}$ or $2:3$, or generally

$$\frac{a}{b} \qquad \text{(a ratio or a rate)}.$$

A proportion is a true statement that two ratios are equal, $\tfrac{2}{3} = \tfrac{8}{12}$, or generally

$$\frac{a}{b} = \frac{c}{d} \qquad \text{(a proportion)}.$$

A proportional relation is a collection of equal ratios, $\frac{2}{3} = \frac{4}{6} = \frac{6}{9} = \ldots$, or generally

$$\left\{ \frac{a}{b}, \frac{2a}{2b}, \frac{3a}{3b}, \ldots, \frac{na}{nb}, \ldots \right\} \qquad \text{(a proportional relation).}$$

Although in ratios the numerators and denominators may themselves be fractions, these ratios may be transformed into equivalent fractions of the form a/b. Later in their mathematical study, children will be introduced to other numbers called *irrational numbers*, but the same principles will hold. Thus the ratio of a circumference of a circle to its diameter is an irrational number π, the value of which is approximately 3.14159.

Proportions are used mainly to find one of the missing terms in one of the ratios. For example, we may know a ratio $\frac{2}{3}$ and another one equal to it with the second term missing, for example $\frac{10}{?}$. One way to teach this is to refer pupils to the principle of transforming fractions. Then there is no new mathematical language or process needed. If $\frac{2}{3} = \frac{10}{\square}$, surely the numeral to put in the box is a numeral for 3×5; the choice is usually 15. This is determined by comparing the numerators. Similarly, if $\frac{\square}{5} = \frac{12}{8}$, the child is asked, "By what must 8 be multiplied to yield 5?" Answer: $\frac{5}{8}$. Then he multiplies 12 by $\frac{5}{8}$ to obtain $7\frac{1}{2}$. So,

$$\frac{7\frac{1}{2}}{5} = \frac{12}{8} \qquad \text{or} \qquad 7\frac{1}{2} \text{ is to 5 as 12 is to 8.}$$

However, some books prefer to find a rule for equal ratios (or fractions) and give names to the terms in a proportion according to the order in which they occur. Thus, if we write

$$\frac{7\frac{1}{2}}{5} = \frac{12}{8},$$

$7\frac{1}{2}$ and 8 are called *extreme terms* or *extremes*, and 5 and 12 are called *mean terms*, or *means*. However, if we write

$$\frac{12}{8} = \frac{7\frac{1}{2}}{5},$$

the means and extremes are interchanged: 12 and 5 are extremes, 8 and $7\frac{1}{2}$ are means. The use of these words comes from reading the proportion in the form:

$7\frac{1}{2}$ is to 5 as 12 is to 8.

A consideration of a number of these ratios always reveals the same result, as follows:

The product of the extreme terms equals the product of the mean terms.

We can prove this by changing the fractions so that they have a common denominator which is the product of the two denominators in the proportion. This is a good place to introduce letter symbols which can be replaced by any numerals, except that '0' may not occur in a denominator. The proof should be discovered from a number of special cases and then be generalized:

$$\left.\begin{array}{c} \dfrac{2}{3} = \dfrac{8}{12} \\[2mm] \Downarrow \\[2mm] \dfrac{2 \times 12}{3 \times 12} = \dfrac{8 \times 3}{12 \times 3} \\[2mm] \Downarrow \\[2mm] 2 \times 12 = 8 \times 3 \end{array}\right\} \quad \text{and} \quad \left.\begin{array}{c} \dfrac{5}{16} = \dfrac{15}{48} \\[2mm] \Downarrow \\[2mm] \dfrac{5 \times 48}{16 \times 48} = \dfrac{15 \times 16}{48 \times 16} \\[2mm] \Downarrow \\[2mm] 5 \times 48 = 15 \times 16 \end{array}\right\} \quad \text{imply} \quad \left\{\begin{array}{c} \dfrac{a}{b} = \dfrac{c}{d} \\[2mm] \Downarrow \\[2mm] \dfrac{a \times d}{b \times d} = \dfrac{c \times b}{d \times b} \\[2mm] \Downarrow \\[2mm] a \times d = c \times b \end{array}\right.$$

Pupils who use this principle to find a missing term should always, when they write the proportion, use a letter symbol, such as x, n, r, etc., for the missing numeral. Purely arithmetic problems can be given, as well as practical problems. For example, pupils should be asked to find the missing term in the proportion

$$\frac{75}{25} = \frac{n}{4}.$$

Using the above principle, they write $75 \times 4 = n \times 25$. They then divide by 25, and

$$n = \frac{75 \times 4}{25} \quad \text{or} \quad 12.$$

In this problem, it is simpler to use this method than to change a fraction to an equivalent fraction, since 25 is not an exact whole-number multiple of 4. Pupils should practice working examples which have missing terms at any position in the proportion:

$$\frac{n}{4} = \frac{15}{12} \; ; \qquad \frac{4}{n} = \frac{12}{15} \; ; \qquad \frac{4}{12} = \frac{n}{15} \; ; \qquad \frac{12}{4} = \frac{15}{n} \; ,$$

and eventually all these problems should appear exactly the same.

Many Similar Figures

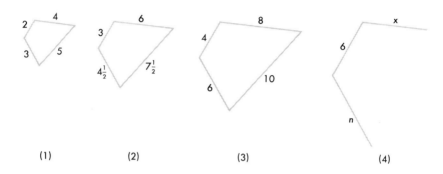

(1)   (2)   (3)   (4)

The study thus far can be nicely illustrated and unified for pupils by considering a set of similar polygons: triangles, quadrilaterals, or pentagons. Thus, in the diagram, a good study is to proceed as follows.

a) Select a ratio of two sides in one figure; for example, $\frac{2}{3}$.

b) Find the ratio of corresponding sides of other figures:

$$\frac{3}{4\frac{1}{2}} \; ; \qquad \frac{4}{6} \; ; \qquad \frac{6}{n} \; .$$

c) State the proportional ratio of

$$\left\{ \frac{2}{3} , \; \frac{3}{4\frac{1}{2}} , \; \frac{4}{6} , \; \frac{6}{n} , \; \ldots \right\} .$$

d) Write a proportion useful for finding n.

What conclusion can you draw regarding the ratio of two sides and the ratios of the corresponding sides on any other similar figure?

Any Two Similar Figures

a) Select a ratio of two corresponding sides: for example, $\frac{3}{4}$ [Figs. (1) and (3)].

b) Find the ratios for the other corresponding sides: $\frac{3}{6}$, $\frac{5}{10}$, $\frac{4}{8}$.

c) State the proportional relation of $\{\frac{1}{2}, \frac{2}{4}, \frac{3}{6}, \frac{4}{8}, \frac{5}{10}, \ldots\}$.

d) Pair Figs. (2) and (4) and write a proportion to solve for x.

The study of proportion can be greatly extended, but in the elementary school it can be limited to the treatment given above. That is, all children should learn the following ideas:

1. A ratio or a rate can be represented by a fraction.

2. A ratio is an operator which, when used to multiply a denominator of another ratio, yields the numerator of a ratio equivalent to the given ratio.

3. If two or more ratios (or rates) are equal, they are in proportional relation.

4. The true statement that two ratios (or rates) are equal is called a *proportion*.

Children should learn how to apply these ideas to social, business, and scientific affairs within their realm of understanding. Examples of such uses are numerous and can be found in the home, in the newspaper, in the science class, and in textbooks intended for use in Grades 6, 7, and 8. Much of the material in seventh- and eighth-grade textbooks can and should be introduced in the sixth-grade study of ratio and proportion.

12–4 PERCENT

Percent is a special ratio idea that is used by businessmen, scientists, engineers, and all knowledgeable citizens in making comparisons of like magnitudes. This idea used to be, and in some books still is, expressed as two words: "per cent." This comes from the original Latin *per centum* ("by the hundred"). People given any ratio (for example, $\frac{6}{47}$) would ask themselves: 6 for 47 is about how many (or how much) for 100? They felt that if all ratios could be changed to hundredths, they would have a better comparison because they could readily compare numerators. Such a system is, of course, quite common in today's school grading system. Very few teachers mark a paper "6 correct out of 11" or $\frac{6}{11}$. Instead they change $\frac{6}{11}$ to the nearest hundredth, $0.545 \approx 0.55$, and give the grade 55, which means that for the paper being graded, the work is of the grade 55 correct out of 100.

The fact that people made comparison "by the hundred" is merely due to the type of comparisons that they needed. To compare "by the ten" was too small a number of items for most comparisons, and "by the thousand" was beyond most thinking. So goods were sold "by the hundredweight" or a hundred pounds; money was borrowed in hundreds of dollars and thinking was geared to "that would be so many out of one hundred." This is still a good way to make comparisons, since it transforms all denominators into the number 100. However, for computational purposes and for solving problems it is more convenient to think of percents as single numbers as hundredths.

Our goals in teaching percent will be:

1. To develop the concept of percent as one-hundredth.
2. To develop the way to use percent as a ratio for comparative purposes.
3. To develop the use of percent in computations involving the fraction-as-an-operator idea.
4. To adapt the mathematical idea to the everyday language of *base*, *percentage*, and *rate* in solving banking, business, and social problems.

The first goal is to have the pupils always associate percent with the fraction one-hundredth, written either in the form '0.01' or '$\frac{1}{100}$'.

To do this, let us take a square region which is cross-sectioned into 100 congruent square regions. We shall speak of the square as having an area of 1; that is, it is 1 square unit. Then each of the small square subregions represents $\frac{1}{100}$ of the square, and as such is one percent of 1, or $\frac{1}{100}$ of 1, or 0.01.

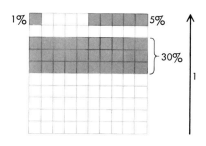

Having stressed the hundredth idea, the teacher may introduce the new symbol for percent, '%'. It should be stressed that '%' is another way of writing '$\frac{1}{100}$'. As such, it can be looked on as a numeral, another name for $\frac{1}{100}$, or 0.01. Having given this meaning, the teacher may ask the pupils to tell the meaning, give other numerals, and illustrate on the square the areas represented by the following percents:

$$5\% \quad (5\% = 5 \times \tfrac{1}{100} = \tfrac{5}{100} = 0.05 = \tfrac{1}{20}),$$
$$30\% \quad (30\% = 30 \times \tfrac{1}{100} = \tfrac{30}{100} = 0.30 = \tfrac{3}{10}),$$
$$64\% \quad (64\% = 64 \times \tfrac{1}{100} = \tfrac{64}{100} = 0.64 = \tfrac{16}{25}),$$
$$100\% \quad (100\% = 100 \times \tfrac{1}{100} = \tfrac{100}{100} = 1.00 = \tfrac{1}{1}).$$

The last line is especially important, since 100% is to be associated with 1, a unit. The expression 100% is sometimes associated with the words 'all' or 'whole'. The latter word is acceptable, since a whole of a given magnitude may be used as a unit. The word 'all', however, is misleading, since it implies that there can be no percent greater than 100. This, of course, is false, for if one thing (the square, for example) is 100%, then two squares would be 200% or 2, and 500% would be $500 \times \tfrac{1}{100}$ or 5 wholes.

Children must thoroughly comprehend the use of 100% as one of a certain quantity. If, in a class, 80% of the students (or of the class) is present, then pupils know that 20% of the class is absent. But the 1, or 100%, refers to the class or the number of pupils in the class. If there are 30 pupils in the class, 100% of the pupils is 30; the whole class is 100%. It is 1 class of 30 pupils. Then 50% of the class is $\tfrac{50}{100}$ (or $\tfrac{1}{2}$) of 30 pupils, or 15 pupils. This can be illustrated by diagrams in which the class is separated into subsets, and the number of pupils in each subset is represented as a fractional part of the whole class in which the fraction is given, or converted to hundredths. Thus 18 pupils is $\tfrac{18}{30}$ or $\tfrac{3}{5}$ or $\tfrac{60}{100}$ or 60% of the class.

This activity leads to a study of representation of ratios by means of decimal fractions or percents. Since the pupils have already learned decimal equivalents for common fractions, this work is merely a new view of the use of fractions. If the ratio of two numbers is 3:8 or $\frac{3}{8}$, it can be expressed as 0.375 (found by division). In turn, this is

$$\frac{375}{1000} \quad \text{or} \quad \frac{37.5}{100} \quad \text{or} \quad 37.5\%.$$

Thus the ratio $\frac{3}{8}$ is also the ratio 37.5:100 or 37.5%. An interpretation of this is: if 3 problems are correct out of 8 problems that were attempted, the ratio of correct to attempted problems is $\frac{3}{8}$. That is, $\frac{3}{8}$ of the attempted problems are correct. This is also 37.5% of the attempted problems, because $37.5\% = \frac{3}{8}$. This means that at the same rate a pupil would get $37\frac{1}{2}$ problems correct out of 100 attempts. By the study of many similar examples, pupils learn how to express any ratio (fraction) as a percent, either exactly or approximately. This is the first goal of the study. Probably the most reliable way to ensure that pupils will reach this goal is to encourage profuse use of graph paper on which a 10×10 square represents 1 unit, that is, 100%.

In this work pupils should gradually learn to think of one number, the percent, as relating two like magnitudes that are compared by division. If we refer to these magnitudes as the percentage and the base, the pattern is

$$\frac{\text{percentage}}{\text{base}} = \text{percent (or the number of hundredths)}.$$

The pupils now recall from the previous study of division that if

$$\frac{a}{b} = c, \quad \text{then} \quad a = c \times b.$$

Applying this to the fundamental pattern, they discover that

$$\frac{\text{percentage}}{\text{base}} = \text{percent} \quad \text{implies that} \quad \text{percentage} = \text{percent} \times \text{base}.$$

Sometimes the percent is also called a *rate*, or a *rate percent*. It is a rate in the sense of so many on a basis of 100, and pupils may refer to a *rate* as a ratio expressed in terms of hundredths as a particular use of the word in percent problems.

Care must be taken to distinguish the words *percentage* and *percent*, if the first of these is used at all. For example, in a spelling test of 50 words, 30 are correct. Then the percentage is 30 (a number of words), the base is 50 (a number of words), but the ratio or percent correct is $\frac{30}{50}$ or 60%. This is not a number of words. Thus 60% × 50 = 30 is equivalent to saying $\frac{30}{50}$ = 60%. It is this relation of the nature of percent to both division and multiplication that gives a unified concept of the topic and enables children to solve problems. Children must learn to select the *base* (equivalent to 1 or 100%) or the measure to which we compare the measures of other magnitudes. Then they select the measure being compared, which may be called the percentage. The quotient expressed in *hundredths* is the percent (or number of hundredths) the percentage is of the base. Literally hundreds of problems should be given to pupils in which they select these three elements and tell which two are given and how the third is found.

The first two situations expressed above—finding the percent or finding the percentage—usually cause little trouble in learning because each idea is an inverse of the other. The most difficult problem has traditionally been to find the base when the percent and percentage are given. There are several ways to approach this problem, and any or all of them can be taught, since the study of each procedure gives more insight into the nature and use of percent.

a) We can return to the basic division-multiplication relation which the child has learned and review the fact that

$$a \times b = c \quad \text{implies that} \quad a = c \div b \quad \text{or} \quad b = c \div a.$$

As a particular case, the pupils know that

$$0.45 \times 200 = 90$$

implies that

$$200 = 90 \div 0.45 \quad \text{or} \quad 0.45 = 90 \div 200.$$

When we compare this with the pattern for percent, it follows that percent × base = percentage implies that base = percentage ÷ percent. Hence, if we know a percentage and percent, we can obtain the base by division. Suppose that 30% of a number is 27; then by the pattern $(0.30 \times N = 27)$ we know that the base is $27 \div 0.30 = 90$. This can be checked by reversing the operation, $0.30 \times 90 = 27$.

Some teachers assert that if, as soon as children learn multiplication facts as such (expressions of the general form $a \times b = c$, $a \neq 0$, $b \neq 0$), they learn that given *any two* of the occurrences of the numbers they can find the third one, and if the children practice finding the missing number in such number sentences as they progress from working with only whole numbers through working with the various fraction notations, then working with percents becomes merely a matter of thoroughly understanding the concept implicit in the word *percent*. Hundreds of different vocabularies can be imposed on the mathematical model $a \times b = c$ (see Chapter 14), and the vocabulary associated with the concept of percent furnishes a huge class of applications of this model.

Since this method stresses the mathematical model of a percent-percentage-base situation, for further study it is preferable to any special methods, such as those that follow.

b) We can use the unitary method. The teacher should discuss this method in a simpler form before applying it to percents. The method depends on first finding a unit fractional part of a number and then the number itself. The class is presented with the problem of finding a number, given that $\frac{2}{3}$ of it is 50. The teacher can give a clue to the solution by asking how they can find $\frac{1}{3}$ of a number if they know $\frac{2}{3}$ of it. Of course, since $\frac{1}{3}$ is $\frac{1}{2}$ of $\frac{2}{3}$, then $\frac{1}{3}$ of the number will be $\frac{1}{2}$ of $\frac{2}{3}$ of the number. Thus $\frac{1}{3}$ of the number is $\frac{1}{2}$ of 50, or 25. Then, if $\frac{1}{3}$ of a number is 25, $\frac{3}{3}$ is 3×25 or 75. In essence this is using the principle of ratio and proportion without the formality of expressing the ratios and proportions involved.

In teaching this procedure, the teacher who wants to avoid just teaching a method should direct the pupils' attention to the algorism so that they can discover a pattern. Thus if $\frac{2}{3}$ of a number is known, we divide by 2, then multiply the result by 3. But this double process is exactly that obtained by operating with the fraction $\frac{3}{2}$. Hence we have actually multiplied by the reciprocal of $\frac{2}{3}$ to obtain the number. Similarly, if we are given $\frac{3}{7}$ of a number, to find the number we divide by 3 and multiply the result by 7, or we multiply the part by $\frac{7}{3}$. Children gradually generalize this situation to the point at which they omit the unitary process of finding $\frac{1}{7}$ and then multiplying by 7; instead they immediately multiply by the reciprocal of $\frac{3}{7}$. This can ultimately be put into a formula:

$$\text{If } \frac{a}{b} \text{ of } N = P, \qquad \text{then} \qquad N = \frac{b}{a} \times P.$$

This generalization is important. For example:

$$\text{If } \tfrac{3}{8} \text{ of } N \text{ is } 63, \qquad \text{then} \qquad N \text{ is } \tfrac{8}{3} \times 63 \text{ or } 168.$$

Since a percent is a ratio, then we can apply the same rule to a problem in which we know a stated percent of a number (or in which we know a percent and percentage), and we want to find the number or base. Suppose that 46% of a number is 138. We divide by 46 to obtain 1% of the number and multiply this result by 100. Thus

$$0.46 \times N = 138 \qquad \text{implies that} \qquad N \text{ is } \tfrac{138}{46} \times 100.$$

But this is merely saying that $\dfrac{138}{0.46}$ yields N, and the general rule emerges:

$$\text{Base} = \text{percentage} \div \text{percent.}$$

c) Some authors prefer to treat the whole subject by means of proportion. Children have already learned how to find a missing term in a stated proportion. They also have learned that

$$\frac{\text{percentage}}{\text{base}} = \frac{\text{number of percent}}{100}.$$

Given that 46% of a number (base) is 138, they merely want

$$\frac{138}{N} = \frac{46}{100} \qquad \text{and} \qquad N = \frac{100 \times 138}{46},$$

by the rule of proportion. Of course, one can use this process if the percentage or the percent is the value to be found.

12–5 APPLICATIONS AND LANGUAGE

One difficulty pupils encounter in the solving of problems involving percent is the language that is used in the world at large.
Whatever the language, in a given situation pupils must learn how
to select those elements which we have referred to as 'percentage',
'base', and 'percent'. The use of percent is found daily in newspapers (especially in sports and financial sections), in magazines,
in stories, in banks, in school savings and school statistics. Teachers
should collect a scrapbook of these applications in which there are
all the types of thinking that involve the percent concept. Such a
collection will convince any teacher or pupil of the need for every
member of society to know thoroughly the interpretation of percent.

Among other things, pupils should learn to recognize incorrect
uses of percent, and later in life to recognize misleading ones.
Thus if someone says that prices have risen 100%, this means that
they are doubled. However, suppose that prices are said to fall
100%. We understand that this would mean that prices were
zero, and no one would believe such a thing about prices of goods
in general. Also percent as a rate frequently refers only to percent
during a stated period of time, but the time period is not always
explicitly stated. Thus a 5% increase in a population of 1,000,000
means an increase of 50,000, but this may be a large or a small
increase depending on whether the 5% refers to a one-year or to a
ten-year period. Bank interest rates are given in percents, and the
period implied is usually a year. Thus "$4\frac{1}{2}$% interest, compounded
quarterly" does *not* mean that at each quarter-year the interest
granted is $4\frac{1}{2}$% of the principal. The fact is, it is only $\frac{1}{4}$ of this
amount of interest, or it is $1\frac{1}{8}$% of the principal which is paid
quarterly. The correct statement is "$4\frac{1}{2}$% interest *per year*, compounded quarterly." All these implied ideas must be examined
and clarified when we are solving problems in percent.

As an example of identifying the terms in a problem, consider
the problem of a bank book showing a balance of $168 to which
interest is added at the rate of $4\frac{1}{2}$% compounded quarterly. What
interest will be added? Here the balance (or principal) $168 must
be associated with the 'base' (or the basis on which the comparison
is made). The interest rate is $\frac{1}{4}$ of 0.045 or 0.01125 and is associated
with 1.125% or $1\frac{1}{8}$ percent. Then 0.01125 × 168 or $1.89 is the
interest which is associated with 'percentage'.

As a second example consider the problem: If the school population increases from 356 to 417, what is the percent of increase? Here pupils who do not think through the problem are likely to write the ratio $\frac{346}{417}$ which of course does not answer the question asked by the problem. An *increase* always raises the question "increase over what amount?" So pupils must determine that the 'base' of the problem is 346, and that the increase is $417 - 346$ or 71. Hence the percent of increase is the hundredth that is nearest to $\frac{71}{346}$, or approximately 21% (more precisely, 20.5%).

This latter problem can be illustrated geometrically with a graph (see Chapter 13) as shown. In this manner children can learn to comprehend the nature and use of percents greater than 100%.

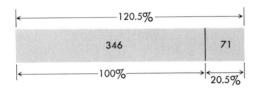

They should learn to think of 200% as a ratio of $\frac{2}{1}$, where 1 represents the base of the comparison. They should frequently compare 2% with 200% by considering any base and showing the percentage in each case.

A percent of increase means something in addition to the amount (or base) used as 100%, as the pupils may see in the above diagram. When the language *percent of decrease* is introduced, children should be asked to explain what this means (a) by telling what the base is that represents 100%, and (b) by drawing a diagram. Suppose that 417 was the school population last year, and this year it is 361.

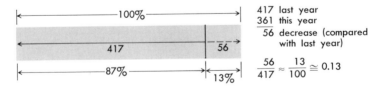

417 last year
361 this year
  56 decrease (compared
       with last year)

$$\frac{56}{417} \approx \frac{13}{100} \cong 0.13$$

Only after they have correctly interpreted the problem should pupils proceed to computing the percent of decrease.

For the more able pupils, the teacher can present the relation of a percent of a first quantity compared with a second quantity to the percent of a second quantity compared with the first. In every case pupils will note that the ratios of the quantities are reciprocal fractions and hence their product is 1. Thus if a ratio of $\frac{a}{b}$ is 80% or $\frac{80}{100}$, then the ratio of $\frac{b}{a}$ is $\frac{100}{80}$ or 125%. Thus 80% $\times$ 125% = 1. They note that these ratios do not *differ* from 1 by the same number of percent. Thus if one man makes $80 a week while another makes $100 a week, the difference of their salaries is $20. The ratio of the smaller to the larger is 80% but the ratio of the larger to the smaller is 125%. This ability to distinguish between comparing the smaller with the larger of two numbers, and the reverse, is essential if the pupil is to have a genuine understanding of the use of percent.

The pupil must learn the distinction between 2% and 2, 3% and 3, and the like, by changing these to ratios and working problems with them. He must learn to make a similar distinction between the number $\frac{1}{2}$ and the number $\frac{1}{2}$%. Thus $\frac{1}{2}$ is a ratio of 1:2 and as a percent this is $\frac{50}{100}$, or 50%. At the same time $\frac{1}{2}$% is $\frac{1}{2}$ of $\frac{1}{100}$, or $\frac{1}{200}$, and this is not the ratio $\frac{1}{2}$. By geometric illustration we note that if a small region represents 1%, then $\frac{1}{2}$% is represented by $\frac{1}{2}$ of this region, while $\frac{1}{2}$ is represented by 50 of these square regions.

Thus $\frac{1}{2}$ of a quantity or number is 100 times as much as $\frac{1}{2}$% of the same quantity or number. Finally, pupils compare $\frac{1}{2}$%, 50%, 200% by changing them to the form $\frac{1}{200}$, $\frac{1}{2}$, 2; and $\frac{1}{5}$%, 20%, 500% by changing them to the form $\frac{1}{500}$, $\frac{1}{5}$, 5, in order to recognize the distinction between *a number of something* and *a percent of something*.

Another difficulty in the use of percents or hundredths lies in the use of a number other than a whole number of percent. It is easy to comprehend 0, 1, 2, . . . , 99, 100 percent, or 0.00, 0.01, . . . , 0.99, 1.00. Thus if a ratio can be represented exactly as a decimal in hundredths between 0 and 1, the problem is relatively simple. A ratio of two numbers in which the denominator of its simplest form contains prime factors other than 2 or 5 cannot be represented by any finite decimal fraction. Thus it cannot be represented in whole numbers of hundredths. What should we teach in these cases?

Children have already learned that $\frac{1}{3}$, when changed to decimal notation, becomes a repeating decimal $0.333\dot{3}$, where the dot over the 3 indicates that the expanded decimal will continue this way. To the nearest hundredth, this value is 0.33 and we can write:

$$\frac{1}{3} \approx 0.33 \quad \text{or} \quad \frac{33}{100} \quad \text{or} \quad 33\%.$$

We cannot write $\frac{1}{3} = 33\%$, for this is false. If we desire to have greater precision, then we must learn how to express this. When we use $\frac{1}{3} \approx 0.333$ and change it to common form $\frac{333}{1000}$, we are not expressing the approximation in hundredths. To express this fraction in hundredths, we may divide numerator and denominator by 10 to obtain

$$\frac{33.3}{100} \quad \text{or} \quad 33.3\%.$$

Similarly, a more precise representation is 33.33%. However, in popular usage $\frac{1}{3}$ is usually represented exactly as $33\frac{1}{3}\%$. Children should be asked to explain how this number is obtained. Different suggestions may be given, for example: (a) Multiply numerator and denominator by 100 and then divide each by 3:

$$\frac{1}{3} = \frac{100}{300} = \frac{33\frac{1}{3}}{100}.$$

b) Multiply numerator and denominator by $33\frac{1}{3}$:

$$\frac{1}{3} \times \frac{33\frac{1}{3}}{33\frac{1}{3}} = \frac{33\frac{1}{3}}{100}.$$

$$\begin{array}{r} 0.33\frac{1}{3} \\ 3\overline{)1.00} \\ \underline{90} \\ 10 \\ \underline{9} \\ 1 \\ 1 \\ \underline{} \\ 0 \end{array}$$

c) Divide 3 into 1 and express the answer exactly as a number of hundredths, as shown in the margin at left.

In all these cases, the pupil must recognize that the $\frac{1}{3}$ appearing in the percent is really $\frac{1}{3}$ of 1% and that is why we say "thirty-three and one-third percent."

Now we can express a non-hundredth decimal ratio (or fraction) either approximately in decimal notation or exactly in whole-number and proper-fraction form. Children learn that

$$\tfrac{3}{8} \approx 37\% \quad \text{or} \quad \tfrac{3}{8} = 37.5\% = 37\tfrac{1}{2}\%,$$
$$\tfrac{2}{7} \approx 29\% \quad \text{or} \quad \tfrac{2}{7} = 28\tfrac{4}{7}\% \quad \text{or} \quad \tfrac{2}{7} \approx 28.6\%.$$

The distinction between the use of $\approx$ and $=$ is important and must be constantly brought to the pupils' attention:

$$\tfrac{2}{3} = 66\tfrac{2}{3}\% \quad \text{but} \quad \tfrac{2}{3} \approx 67\% \quad \text{or} \quad \tfrac{2}{3} \approx 66.7\%.$$

In grading papers, 9 correct responses out of 13 attempts is represented by

$$\tfrac{9}{13} \approx 69\% \quad \text{or} \quad \tfrac{9}{13} = 69\tfrac{3}{13}\%.$$

In all cases the fractional part, whether expressed in common form as in $67\tfrac{1}{2}\%$ or in decimal form as in 67.5%, represents less than $\tfrac{1}{100}$ or less than 1% of the base under consideration. The teacher must illustrate the double use of decimal representation for percent and for parts of one percent by a number of examples before most children comprehend the difference.

Thus 33.33% really means 33% plus $\tfrac{33}{100}$ of 1%. This can be shown by writing

$$33.33\% = \frac{33}{100} + \frac{.33}{100} = \frac{33}{100} + \left(\frac{33}{100} \times \frac{1}{100}\right) = \frac{33}{100} + \frac{33}{10,000},$$

and the second addend is very small compared with the first. It certainly is not 33%; it is 33 ten-thousandths. Similarly,

$$66.7\% \quad \text{means} \quad 66\% \text{ plus } \tfrac{7}{10} \text{ of } 1\% \ (\tfrac{7}{1000}).$$

Another way to develop the idea of percents less than 1% (or 0.01) is to count by tenths of one percent. Thus

(a) $0.001, 0.002, \ldots, 0.009$

are all less than 0.01, so they are less than 1%. Hence we can write

(b) $0.1\%, 0.2\%, 0.3\%, \ldots, 0.9\%$

instead of thousandths. This can be referred to baseball statistics, which are frequently (and imprecisely) called 'percents' or 'percentages', but are usually written as thousandths. Thus, as a percent, a statistic written in the form 0.568 is really 56.8%. Practice can be given in transforming percents into thousandths and thousandths into percents, accompanied by a discussion of why it is necessary to use percents less than 1% in practical situations.

12–6 GRADE PLACEMENT IN TEACHING RATIO, PROPORTION, AND PERCENT

In the first half of this century, the only one of these topics taught before the seventh grade was that of ratio. Today all these topics are at least introduced in Grades 5 and 6, and their study is continued in the seventh and eighth grades.

At a very early age, children make comparisons of collections of objects and of amounts of materials. By age 7 or 8, they are able to know which is more than, less than, or the same when they are comparing two groups of objects or amounts of material, regardless of the arrangement or shape of the objects or material concerned. They then begin to state comparisons in terms of numbers. In Grades 2 and 3, there should be in every program comparisons which involve relating the differences of two measured quantities. At the same time, children can be taught to compare sets of objects by describing a situation in terms of the two numbers; for example, "He has 3 to my 4." This is merely a readiness activity for the subsequent teaching of ratio. At this time no attempt should be made to make a fraction (a ratio) of the two numbers. Comparison by subtraction (finding the difference) and by stating the relative measures of quantities or lengths should continue throughout Grade 4.

In Grade 5, as soon as multiplication of fractions has been taught, the meaning of ratio should be introduced. The rewriting of '3 is to 5' in the form '3:5' and then '$\frac{3}{5}$' should occur very rapidly. After the pupils have learned ratio as a comparison, it should be introduced as an operator or multiplier and the inverse relation should be used:

$$\frac{m(A)}{m(B)} = \frac{a}{b} \Leftrightarrow m(A) = \frac{a}{b} m(B).$$

In Grade 6, the idea of ratio should be extended to include the concept of percent as a ratio with base 100. The use of percent as a ratio and the terms *base*, *percentage*, and *rate* should be introduced. The use of percent and ratio should be extended to a proportional relation. Proportion and its use should be taught by means of ratios and percents:

$$\frac{a}{b} = \frac{c}{d} \Leftrightarrow ad = bc.$$

The nature of a rate or a percent as a unique concept with which we do our thinking and reasoning is as important as the computational skill involved.

For bright and highly interested students, the teacher may introduce the use of percents greater than 100% and less than 1%, and should apply these to comparisons involving increases and decreases. The extension of properties of proportions, and the use of ratio and proportions in geometry and in practical problems, may be deferred to junior high school study.

12-7 THE FORM $A \times B = C$

In the entire study of ratio and percent, there should be a genuine attempt to stress the form

$$A \times B = C \Leftrightarrow A = C \div B \Leftrightarrow B = C \div A, \qquad A, B \neq 0.$$

Thus when a product of two numbers, neither one zero, is involved in any problem, either of the factors is a divisor of the product; that is, in a given problem, when there are two factors and a product, provided that we know any two of the numbers, we can always find the third.

1. *A ratio is the quotient of two given numbers.* This signifies that

$$\frac{a}{b} = r \Leftrightarrow a = r \times b,$$

and we are back to the form $C = A \times B$. Then the solution of any percent problem is immediately referred back to a product and its two inverses.

2. *A percent is a ratio expressed in hundredths.* This signifies that

$$\frac{a}{b} = \frac{c}{100} \Leftrightarrow a = \frac{c}{100} \times b.$$

If we think of $\frac{c}{100}$ in decimal notation, we are back to the form $C = A \times B$.

3. *A proportion is a statement that two ratios are equal.* This signifies that

$$\frac{a}{b} = \frac{c}{d} \Leftrightarrow a = \left(\frac{c}{d}\right) \times b \Leftrightarrow c = \left(\frac{a}{b}\right) \times d.$$

If we think of $\left(\frac{c}{d}\right)$ and $\left(\frac{a}{b}\right)$ as fractions, we are back to the form $C = A \times B$.

4. *Comparison of two magnitudes by division of their measures* signifies that

$$\frac{m(a)}{m(b)} = \text{a number} \Leftrightarrow m(a) = (\text{a number}) \times m(b),$$

and all the work of this chapter culminates in the form

$$C = A \times B.$$

EXERCISES

1. Make a list of 15 everday events which involve ratios. In each case give a problem involving the use of the ratio. All the problems should be suitable for use in the sixth grade.

2. Ratios are sometimes referred to as proportional relations. Show how one can use the equality of fractions to teach the proportional relation of ratios.

3. Distinguish between a ratio and a rate as used in this chapter. Explain the statement that a ratio is a pure number. In the sense that we use *rate* in everyday life, why would rate be considered not so much a measure as a measurement?

4. Distinguish between a *proportional relation* and a *proportion*. Give two illustrations of proportion, one involving ratios, the other rates. Cite an instance in which you would be concerned with a proportional relation and another in which you would be concerned mainly with proportion.

5. Show how ratio, percent, and proportion are closely related, and how meanings and operational procedures for them are found in meanings and operations with fractions.

6. Discuss several ways of introducing the meaning of percent. Criticize the statement, "Convert 0.04 to percent." Defend and explain the statement, "Convert 0.418 to percent."

7. Define the symbols '$=$' and '$\approx$' as used in this textbook. Ascribe a meaning to (a) $\frac{3}{8} \approx 37\%$; (b) $\frac{3}{16} = 18.75\%$; (c) $\frac{2}{3} \approx 66.7\%$. Explain how you would teach children the proper use of these two symbols.

8. The meaning that *percent* can have if interpreted as *per centum* or *by the hundred* has value in enhancing the concept. Explain what you believe to be the advantages of the use of *per centum* and explain how you would teach it.

9. Explain the advantages and disadvantages of teaching percent (a) as having three cases, (b) as a relation of two numbers or like measures in hundredths, (c) as an idea represented by the equation $P = R \times B$.

10. Explain both the unitary and the inverse methods of teaching how to find the base in a proportion or a percent. Give advantages and disadvantages of each method.

11. Make a list of applications of *percent* in business, in banking, in foods and drugs, in science, and in sports, which you may use in teaching the subject. Some books refer to this topic as *percentage*. Tell which of these two words most accurately describes the subject and why.

12. Design a wall chart which has a title something like "The Meaning of *Percent*."

13. Suppose that children were preparing a bulletin-board display or a notebook to illustrate the meaning and use of percents. Where would you suggest that they look and what might you suggest that they look for?

REFERENCES

HAUCK, E., "Concrete Materials for Teaching Percentage," *The Arithmetic Teacher* **1,** 1, December 1954, pages 9–12

KENNEY, R. A., and J. D. STOCKTON, "An Experimental Study in Teaching Percentage," *The Arithmetic Teacher* **5,** December 1958, pages 294–303

Teaching ratio, proportion, and percent

RAPPAPORT, D., "Percentage—Noun or Adjective?" *The Arithmetic Teacher* **8,** 1, January 1961, pages 25–26

TREADWAY, D. C., and G. E. HOLLISTER, "An Experimental Study of Two Approaches to Teaching Percentage," *The Arithmetic Teacher* **10,** December 1963, pages 491–495

VAN ENGEN, H., "Rate Pairs, Fractions, and Rational Numbers," *The Arithmetic Teacher* **7,** December 1960, pages 389–399

WENDTH, A., "Percent Without Cases," *The Arithmetic Teacher* **6,** October 1953, pages 209–214

measures extended;
coordinates; graphs

After children have become acquainted with concepts and techniques of measurement, and have learned that angles with the same degree measure are congruent angles and that segments with the same length are congruent segments (and conversely), they can extend their understanding of classification of and relations among geometric figures. They should learn how triangles are classified according to the relative lengths of their sides or the relative sizes of their angles, they should learn a mathematical definition of similarity, and they should develop experimentally some of the theorems having to do with bisectors, medians, and altitudes of a triangle. Also the teacher can introduce the number π (pi) and show the children how they can use this number to find lengths, surfaces, and volumes of circular objects. Further, they can use their concepts and skills in measurement to construct many kinds of charts and graphs.

13–1 CLASSIFICATION OF TRIANGLES

The set of triangles contains a large number of subsets, of which some overlap and some do not. By the time children leave sixth grade, they should get a correct mental picture from phrases such as *obtuse triangle, isosceles right triangle*, and the like. The least desirable route to this goal is the memorization of definitions. A much better approach is through activities devised to give the children experience in working with characteristics specified in one definition or description and to discover elaborations and implications.

For example, the teacher may pass out three different worksheets, each with a drawing on it labeled (correctly) *scalene triangle*, and ask the children to use rulers, compasses, and protractors to find out whatever they can about these triangles. Aside from insisting that they keep a record of any measurements they make, the teacher should let the children tackle this problem their way. The class should discuss what they have found out, and eventually they may be asked what characteristics they think all scalene triangles have in common. They should say, "No two sides are congruent" or "No two angles are congruent." If they do not say either one, the teacher should define a scalene triangle in one of those ways. Then the children should insist that when one of those conditions exists, the other does also.

The teacher should exploit whatever other properties the children mention. Did someone notice that, in all these cases, the longest side was opposite the largest angle? This should cause everyone to check whether the shortest side is opposite the smallest angle. If the teacher is lucky, someone will wonder whether a triangle with two sides the same length has two congruent angles. How can they test this? They need a way of making an accurate drawing of an isosceles triangle. There are many ways to do this. How could you start with a circle and draw a triangle with exactly two congruent sides and with its vertices on the circle? How could you use folded paper? This is a good time to introduce straightedge and compass constructions.

Such constructions are of value not only because children would cheerfully spend months at a time doing straightedge and compass constructions, but also because these constructions can contribute to intuitive feelings about what constitutes a proof. Aside from these considerations, an adequate reason for teaching these constructions is that they are so handy and so dependable when you want an accurate picture of certain figures. The construction of a triangle with sides congruent to three given segments is a simple matter. The children should have a commonsense understanding of why the construction works. In the first few examples, start with three segments no one of which is longer than the other two combined. Now speculate: How shall we go about this?

We have to start somewhere. We know how to copy a segment, using a compass. Let's just draw a segment longer than any of those given and copy one of the segments on it. Does it matter which one? Let's choose one, and use that this time. We'll try another choice later. (Be sure to do this with both other choices, and find out that all triangles constructed with sides congruent to three given segments are congruent.) Now we know the location of two vertices of the triangle.

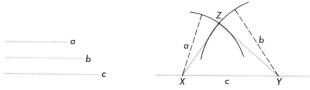

How can we locate the third vertex? What do we know about it? The other two segments meet there. Oh, we can put one end of the segment congruent to a at an end of c. The other end has to be a specified distance from that point. Where are all the points at a specified distance from a given point? On a circle with the given point as center and the specified distance as radius. Then we need a part of another circle with its center at the other end of c and a radius the same length as b. Where is our third vertex? It has to be a place where these circles intersect. Why? Letter the vertices, say X, Y, and Z. The segment $\overline{XY}$ is congruent to c; we drew it that way. All the points at a distance a from X are on the circle we started with X as center. All the points at a distance b from Y are on the other circle we started. A point which is *both* a distance a from X and a distance b from Y has to be on the intersection of those circles. The point Z is a point like that. In this case, common sense is formality.

Now the children should practice constructing triangles with given lengths as sides. The teacher may give measurements in inches or centimeters, choosing these so that some result in scalene triangles, some in isosceles triangles, some in right triangles, and some in no triangles (impossible). The children should try to find a way of predicting, just from the measurements, what kind of triangle will appear. They should test their conjectures. No one should have to be told how many measurements he would need, or how to do the construction, to construct an equilateral triangle in this way (there are other ways).

The children should compare angle measures and side measures of a variety of triangles. The teacher may ask whether it is possible for a triangle to have exactly two 60° angles, 45° angles, 90° angles, 30° angles, 72° angles, 105° angles, and so on. Children need their protractors for making drawings to explore this. There is no end to what one simple construction, unhampered by restrictions against the use of other tools, may produce in the way of highly motivated and mathematically fruitful learning.

Copying an angle using a protractor is a useful skill. Copying an angle using compass and straightedge is easy once everyone realizes that it amounts to copying a triangle whose sides are furnished by what you do to the angle you are copying. Drawing, or constructing, a line through a given point parallel to a given line is a matter of copying an angle. This last construction will be merely operating in reverse from discovery exercises in which the children start with two parallel lines (they can trace two lines about three inches apart on lined paper), draw any line which intersects both of these, and measure all the angles. Make this "any line" oblique to the others at first; eventually make it perpendicular to them.

Sometimes we want a quick way of drawing a line perpendicular to another line. We can do this with a ruler. The scale marks on a ruler are perpendicular to the edge. Suppose that we want a line (or segment) perpendicular to line ℓ at point P in the drawing. Line up the ruler so that one of the longer scale marks looks like a part of ℓ. Position the ruler so that, allowing for the width of the lead in the pencil, a line drawn along its edge passes through P.

Paper-folding is another exceptionally productive vehicle for discovery of geometric relations. When paper is folded once, then folded again so that the first fold falls along itself, four right angles appear when the paper is unfolded. If the paper remains folded, there is one right angle. Knowing this, middle graders should be able to take any irregularly torn piece of newspaper and fold a rectangle or a right triangle. They can fold an isosceles triangle— right, acute, or obtuse—if they first fold the vertex angle, then pinch the spot on one of the folds to indicate the length of one leg, match this distance on the other fold and pinch the appropriate

350

spot there, and fold again through the pinch marks. The reader is urged to experiment with paper-folding. Waxed paper is excellent for this purpose because it makes sharp folds and because it is transparent. An elementary school pupil can learn a large part of all the geometry he needs to know by means of paper-folding.

The preceding paragraphs in this section have assumed that the reader knows the applicable subject matter and have described techniques to use for making adequate models for discovering properties of triangles and other geometric figures. Definitions are not, as such, subject to discovery, but activities which lead to understandings which make a definition meaningful are surely both desirable and proper. Furthermore, these activities lead to other understandings fundamental to a functional knowledge of geometry.

By the end of sixth grade, the children should be able to make a chart for the classification of triangles, headed somewhat like this:

Name of triangle	Sides	Angles	Typical picture

At this time, also, if they have had the kind of experiences suggested here, they will know a great deal more about these triangles than is apparent from a look at the charts.

13-2 SIMILAR POLYGONS

Two polygons are similar if and only if their corresponding angles are congruent and their corresponding sides are proportional. After children have had an informal introduction to the notion of similarity (see Chapter 7) and after they have assimilated the requisite concepts of congruence of angles and of ratio and proportion, they are ready to learn this precise definition and to work with it.

The part of the definition that deals with angles is easy for them to contend with. They know several ways to test angles for congruence, and sometimes congruence of angles is implicit in the distinguishing characteristics of the figures they are working with, as is the case for rectangles, for example. The part of the definition which deals with proportionality of sides is harder for children to understand. The teacher must help them with this. The stretcher-shrinker idea usually contributes positively toward this end.

Consider two rectangles which are to be tested for similarity. The corresponding angles are congruent because all right angles are congruent. Suppose we measure the sides and find that, in terms of some unit, the first is 5 by 2 and the second is 10 by 4. Are the corresponding sides proportional? How is 5 related to 10? Is 2 related to 4 in the same way? If we could run the first rectangle through a stretcher which would double each segment and leave the angles unchanged, would the output be congruent to the second rectangle? If so, the rectangles are similar. They are. The *ratio of similitude* is $1:2$ or $\frac{1}{2}$.

Consider two more rectangles. A pupil measures the sides. He tries the inch scale on his ruler and finds that the measures are "funny fractions." He tries the centimeter scale and finds that the measures of one rectangle are 10 by 15 and the measures of the other rectangle are 11.25 by 7.5. These numbers seem more friendly, but where does he go from here? First he must pick out corresponding sides. What does that mean? For rectangles, the question is easy to answer: long sides with long sides and short sides with short sides. Now he records the measures he obtained for his second rectangle as 7.5 by 11.25. The 10-cm sides of the first rectangle correspond to the 7.5-cm sides of the second rectangle. What is a simpler expression for the ratio $10:7.5$?

$$\frac{10}{7.5} = \frac{100}{75} = \frac{4}{3}.$$

Is a simpler expression for $15:11.25$ also $4:3$? One way to test this is to run an 11.25-cm segment through a hookup of a $\overline{3}$-shrinker and a 4-stretcher and see whether the output is a 15-cm segment. What happens to an 11.25-cm segment in a $\overline{3}$-shrinker? It shrinks to 3.75 cm. What happens when this output goes through a 4-stretcher? It stretches to 15 cm. The longer sides of the two rectangles have the ratio $4:3$. The shorter sides also have the ratio $4:3$. If we picked an appropriate pair of vertices and "marched around the rectangles," we would get the following result.

15 cm   11.25 cm

(1)   10 cm   (2)   7.5 cm $\dfrac{15}{11.25} = \dfrac{10}{7.5} = \dfrac{4}{3}$

This is what we mean when we say that corresponding sides are proportional. Since the corresponding angles are congruent, these two rectangles are similar. The ratio of similitude is $4:3$, or $\frac{4}{3}$. If we had considered the rectangles in the opposite order, the ratio of similitude would have been reported as $3:4$, or $\frac{3}{4}$.

It is interesting to lay out a supply of drawing and measuring materials—rulers, protractors, compasses, graph paper, lattice paper, lined paper, unlined paper—and pose a problem to the children and see what they do with it. For instance, they may be told that their problem is to draw two similar irregular pentagons. Each should do this in his own way, and then the variety of solutions should be discussed. Each child should test his solution for congruence of corresponding angles and proportionality of corresponding sides. Methods of testing should also be compared.

A quick, mathematically impeccable way to determine whether corresponding sides are proportional employs the principle

$$\frac{a}{b} = \frac{c}{d} \Leftrightarrow a \times d = b \times c.$$

For most classes, however, the writers do not recommend the use of this principle in work with similar polygons because: (1) Some pupils will use the principle in places where it does not apply. For example, they may say that

$$\tfrac{2}{3} = \tfrac{5}{9} + 3 \text{ because } 2 \times 9 = 3 \times 5 + 3.$$

(2) Some pupils understand where it applies, but do not see how to use it with more than two fractions (see the example below). (3) Even the pupils who use it effectively in this context do not, from it alone, get an "in-the-bones" feeling for proportionality. However, when a course of study includes it, the teacher must make sure that his pupils understand that they use this principle with two fractions (or ratios) at a time and that showing three or more fractions to be equivalent also involves the transitivity of equality. Consider two triangles with sides measuring 3 in., 4 in., 7 in., and $4\frac{1}{2}$ in., 6 in., and $10\frac{1}{2}$ in. Are corresponding sides proportional?

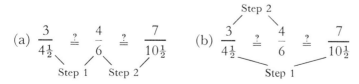

We test two fractions at a time. Does it matter whether we use scheme (a) or scheme (b)? Why not? Are there other schemes, not shown? In each of these schemes, there is a comparison of one pair of fractions that we have ignored. Is this an oversight? What would we find out if we did test them? Some pupils are confused when, using scheme (a) they find that

$$\text{(Step 1)} \quad \frac{3}{4\frac{1}{2}} = \frac{4}{6} \qquad \text{because} \qquad 3 \times 6 = 4\frac{1}{2} \times 4 = 18$$

and

$$\text{(Step 2)} \quad \frac{4}{6} = \frac{7}{10\frac{1}{2}} \qquad \text{because} \qquad 4 \times 10\frac{1}{2} = 6 \times 7 = 42,$$

but $18 \neq 42$. Then the teacher must call attention to what this test shows. It shows that the first fraction is equivalent to the second fraction, since the appropriate products are equal. The *size* of these products has nothing to do with the matter. The test also shows that the second fraction is equivalent to the third fraction. Again the size of the products is immaterial. Now with any three numbers, if $A = B$ and $B = C$, is $A = C$? Are all three numbers equal? Then the corresponding sides of these triangles are proportional. If their corresponding angles are congruent, the triangles are similar.

Sixth-graders should be given activities which lead to the discovery that, for triangles, congruence of corresponding angles guarantees proportionality of corresponding sides, and conversely. Such activities are not hard to devise, and their description is left as an exercise for the reader.

13-3 PAPER-FOLDING CONSTRUCTIONS

The teacher who experiments himself to see what he can do with paper-folding will have a gold mine of ideas to use with his class. He should try using pages torn out of discarded magazines, the different kinds of paper supplied by his school, waxed paper, and even old newspapers.

The discussion here will be restricted to descriptions of some activities with waxed paper. Because small pieces of waxed paper are awkward to handle (it is thin), and because waxed paper is transparent, we usually do not suggest that the figures we are working with be cut out. With other kinds of paper, it is often wise to have the figures cut out.

With waxed paper, it is a very simple matter for anyone who knows the meaning of bisection to fold the bisector of an angle. This same person can fold the perpendicular bisector of a segment by folding the paper so that the ends of the segment coincide. He can find the midpoint of a segment by proceeding as if he were going to fold the perpendicular bisector, and just pinching the place on the segment without folding the rest of the line. He can fold a perpendicular from a point to a line by folding the line on itself in such a way that the fold goes through the point. He should practice these four things until he has a reasonable skill. Then he is ready to make some interesting discoveries.

He can find out that, at least for all the triangles he tests, the angle bisectors are concurrent. This is a good theorem to start with because it always turns out well for a child who has no more than two thumbs. The child should test a great variety of shapes of triangles. The teacher may, for enrichment, suggest that he measure the shortest distance from the point where the bisectors meet to each side of the triangle. The child will find out that, for each triangle, these three distances are the same. Now the teacher may ask what would happen if a circle were drawn, using the point at which the bisectors meet as center and this "shortest distance" for the given triangle as radius. The circle "just fits" inside the triangle. We call this the *inscribed circle*.

In analogous fashion, the child can discover that the perpendicular bisectors of the sides of a triangle are concurrent in a point which is the center of the circumscribed circle.

By first locating the midpoint of each side as described above, the child can fold the medians of a triangle, note that they are concurrent, and find the ratio in which this point of concurrency divides each median. He can even do this last by folding. The point of concurrency of the medians is the center of gravity of the triangle, and a cardboard model of a triangle will balance on the point of a thumbtack if the triangle is set very carefully on the tack (the tack being point up) at its center of gravity.

The altitudes of a triangle can be folded and found to be concurrent also. Acute triangles should be used at first in this activity, so that the point of concurrence will be inside the triangle. With a right triangle, the altitudes meet in the vertex of the right angle, since two of the sides are altitudes. With an obtuse triangle, the altitudes meet at a point outside the triangle, so the teacher should direct the original placement of the triangle on the paper so that the orthocenter will be on the paper.

13-4 STRAIGHTEDGE AND COMPASS CONSTRUCTIONS

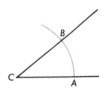

It has been suggested previously that the straightedge and compass construction for copying an angle amounts to constructing a triangle, given three sides. Thus, to copy $\angle C$ by the standard construction, we locate points A and B by drawing an arc with a compass (see margin), and then construct a triangle with sides congruent to $\overline{CA}$, $\overline{CB}$, and $\overline{AB}$. Only convenience dictates that we make $\overline{CB} \cong \overline{CA}$. We could just as well have used different lengths, but that would have been a little more trouble.

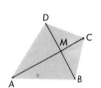

The other simple standard constructions—bisectors of angles and segments, perpendiculars to a given line—can all be tied together by relating the mechanics of these constructions to the framework of an ordinary kite. Study the figure in the margin. Which angles are bisected? Which segments are perpendicular? Is there a segment which is the perpendicular bisector of another segment? Do you see that constructing bisectors and perpendiculars can become a matter of building missing parts of a kite?

Define a kite as any quadrilateral which has two pairs of congruent adjacent sides, with or without crossbars. By this definition, all the figures below are kites.

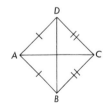
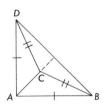
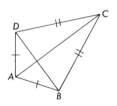

Do you want to bisect the angle shown below? Label it A and build a kite.

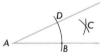

Locate points B and D by using any convenient radius with your

compass, the same radius for each point, of course. Now you must
locate point C. What do you know about it? It is the same distance
from B as from D. What distance? It doesn't matter, except that
this distance has to be at least half the distance from B to D.
Locate point C and draw a crossbar AC. $\overleftrightarrow{AC}$ is the bisector of $\angle A$.

The commonsense explanation of why this works might go
somewhat as follows: A bisector goes through the middle of the
angle. A bisector is a line. If you know two points of a line you
can locate the line. The vertex of an angle is on its bisector, so you
already have one point. You located point C by going the same
distance from A to B and D, and the same distance from B and D
to C.

If you postulate the congruence theorems, you can prove this
construction easily. In the completed construction, consider
triangles ABC and ADC, shown in the margin. You constructed
$\overline{AB} \cong \overline{AD}$ and $\overline{DC} \cong \overline{BC}$. $\overline{AC}$ is the third side of both triangles (it
is a wise procedure to draw a separate picture to show this) and
$\overline{AC} \cong \overline{AC}$. Therefore

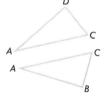

$$\triangle ABC \cong \triangle ADC$$

by the side-side-side congruence theorem. Since corresponding
parts of congruent figures are congruent, $\angle CAB \cong \angle CAD$, so
$\overrightarrow{AC}$ bisects $\angle A$ by the definition of an angle bisector.

Now suppose that you have a segment and you wish to construct its perpendicular bisector. Which part of a kite is the perpendicular bisector of which other part? Draw the segment, label
it DB, and build the rest of the kite (see the illustration in the
margin).

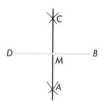

The commonsense justification for this also involves the
"down-the-middle" idea: same distance from each end.

The proof is a bit more difficult because the triangles you wish
to prove congruent ($\triangle DCM$ and $\triangle BCM$) do not show themselves
congruent as an immediate consequence of the construction. First
you must prove that $\triangle ABC \cong \triangle ADC$, either by the side-side-side
theorem or by having accepted it as a theorem already proved for
kites. That gives you $\angle DCA \cong \angle BCA$. Then you have
$\triangle DCM \cong \triangle BCM$ by the side-angle-side congruence theorem,
$\angle DMC \cong \angle BMC$ by corresponding parts, $\overline{DM} \cong \overline{MB}$ by
corresponding parts, and the angles at M right angles because

they are congruent and supplementary. No sixth-grader should be required to learn a proof like this. But all sixth-graders who have had several years' experience with physical, active geometry can follow the argument; even those who have no patience with proofs of something they already believe can get an informal acquaintance with formality. The teacher should make it clear that his purpose in introducing this sort of proof is not to convince anyone of the "truth" of something, but rather to provide initial acquaintance with this type of argument.

The construction of perpendiculars to a line at a point on a line and from a point not on the line fit into the kite pattern. If the point is on the line, label it M and build the rest of the kite, as shown on the left below.

If the point is not on the line, label it A or C and build the rest of the kite, as shown on the right above.

Work with these constructions should not be considered complete until the children are aware of the uniqueness of bisectors of angles, perpendicular bisectors of segments, and perpendiculars to a given line through a given point. The teacher should ask questions such as "How many bisectors does an angle have? Now that you have finished the construction of the bisector of this angle, repeat your work on the same drawing, using different settings for your compass. What do you notice about the new points you are locating? (They are all on the same line, *the* bisector.)"

13–5 CIRCULAR OBJECTS AND THE NUMBER π

It took the best minds of the human race many centuries to figure out exactly how the length (perimeter, *circumference*) of a circle is related to the diameter of the circle, so no one should expect this relation to be intuitively obvious to young children. It is possible to do some work in finding lengths and areas of circles before the

children have the requisite proficiency with fractions and decimals
to enable them to compute with rational approximations to the
number π, and some of this work is a necessary prerequisite to the
introduction of π.

Beginning in fourth grade, the teacher may ask children how
they might find the distance around some circular object. There
are two particularly productive suggestions: (1) Use a tape measure; or equivalently, use some heavy cord pulled taut (but not
stretched) around the object, and measure the cord. (2) Roll the
object on a flat surface and measure the distance it travels in one
complete turn.

Now what might we mean when we say "the distance across a
circle?" There are many different distances across a circle. If we
are going to speak of *the* distance, we had better decide which one.
The easiest distance to identify is the longest distance, and we soon
find out that the segment of which this distance is the length
contains the center of the circle.

After the children know how to measure the distance around a
circle and the distance across a circle, they can measure several
circular objects (preferably quite large objects for which they can
round the measures to the nearest whole inch without having a
large relative error) and compare the distance around each circle
with the distance across each circle. They soon find out that, for
each circle, the distance around is a little more than 3 times the
distance across. Now is the time to introduce the words *circumference*, *diameter*, and *radius*, if the children do not already know
them. The word *pi* and the corresponding symbol need not be
introduced at this time. Knowing that the circumference of any
circle is just a little more than 3 times its diameter, the children
can find approximate answers to questions involving situations in
which the diameter is known. (For example: A circular race track
has a diameter of 1 mile. About how long is the track?) They
can also answer questions about objects whose circumference is
easy to measure but whose diameter is not. (For example, what is
the diameter of the trunk of a growing tree whose circumference
is 6 feet?) The children cannot help knowing that the results they
get by using 3 as the relation (ratio) of the length of a circle to its
diameter are not exact. However, this realization may help them a
couple of years later to understand the approximate nature of the
results they get when they use any rational approximation to π.

To find areas of circles, the children may draw circles on graph paper and count the little square units of area inside each circle, taking a unit square on the graph paper as a unit of area. The children must devise ways of counting the parts of squares which always appear around the boundary. This may be enough to expect them to do with areas of circles in fourth grade. The next step requires the teacher to take care that the center of each circle be placed at the point where two grid lines cross so that diameters and radii in terms of linear units on the graph paper may easily be found. Now the children can see that the area of any circle (meaning, of course, the area of the plane region bounded by the circle) is less than the area of a square one side of which is the same length as a diameter of that circle: $A_\odot < d^2$ (left-hand illustration). This implies that $A_\odot < 4r^2$ (middle illustration). By counting the units of area inside the circle, using applicable shortcuts, and doing some simple arithmetic, the children may discover that the area of the circle is just a little bit more than $3r^2$. When they are asked, later, to believe that the area of a circle is very close to $3.14r^2$, they are likely to think that this is reasonable.

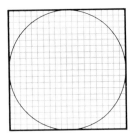 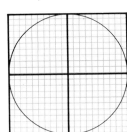 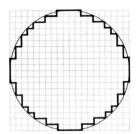

When the children are able to compute well with fractions, in common or decimal form, the number π (pi) may be introduced. The teacher must understand, and be able to convey to the children, that π is an exact number. It has a place on the number line just as definite as the points for 1 or $\sqrt{2}$. Like $\sqrt{2}$, π is irrational, so that no fraction or rational number is a value for π. A numeral to a million decimal places would never be a means for defining π. So if we use rational numbers as an approximation to π, our computation is also approximate. The area of a circle whose radius is exactly 10 units is exactly 100π square units; it is also approximately 314.159 square units. Note that 'π' is a numeral for an irrational number.

One of the major thrills in store for the student of higher mathematics comes when he discovers that the number π appears in a miraculous assortment of mathematical situations, some of them having nothing whatever to do with circles. Historically, π evolved as the ratio of the circumference of a circle to its diameter, and it is in this context that we introduce the number to children. An effective way to do this will now be described.

Ask each child, preferably as a homework assignment, to find three circular objects—the largest such objects he can locate, in order to minimize relative error—and measure their circumference and diameter as carefully and precisely as possible. Have him record his results in a table constructed somewhat as follows.

Object	Circumference	Diameter	Circumference ÷ diameter
Bicycle wheel	87.9 in.	28.0 in.	
Table			
Drum			
		Average of quotients	

When he has found these measures, he should decide whether it would be better for him to report the fractions in common or decimal form, and then do the required division. If he is using decimal notation for the fractions, he should carry out the results to thousandths. He should notice that the results in his last column are suspiciously alike. Then he should find the average of these three results. In the next mathematics class, the children pool their results. In order to keep the computation manageable, it is a good plan for the children in each row (or some other grouping) to find the average of the averages found by everyone in the row. Read the individual averages aloud so that everyone may be impressed by the fact that these results are nearly the same. Also, the children usually suggest that the class throw out results which are obvious mistakes. (If they do not, the teacher should!) Then the average of these second averages is found. In a class of thirty careful workers, this final average seldom differs from 3.14 by more than 0.01. Now is the time to tell the class about the number π, pronounced like 'pie', but spelled without the 'e' (π is a letter of the Greek alphabet). Bring in something about the history of this number, if possible. Perhaps some of the children would like to make a report on it.

Knowing where they got the number π leads the children immediately to the formula $C = \pi d$. Going back to their old friend, the mathematical model

$$a \times b = c \Leftrightarrow b = \frac{c}{a}$$

produces the formula $d = C/\pi$. From this point on their major difficulty is likely to be in remembering that π is the ratio of the circumference of a circle to its *diameter*, and for problems in which the radius is involved specifically, they must double or halve a number somewhere, as the context of the problem may indicate. There is no need even to mention the formula $C = 2\pi r$. If the pupils know the formula (and they really do not have to know it as a formula, but just as an expression of a relation they are familiar with) $C = \pi d$, and the fact that the diameter of any circle is twice its radius, they can find the circumference when the radius is given. Also they are less likely to confuse the formulas for circumference and area if they always associate diameter with circumference and radius with area.

When the time comes to teach the children how to find areas of circles, assuming that they have done the preliminary work of counting unit squares inside a circle drawn on graph paper, the teacher will find that one heuristic development of the formula which usually is convincing is the following.

Cut a circular disk out of heavy paper and cut it up into 8 congruent sectors, as in the left-hand illustration. Put these wedges together as shown on the right. Ask the children what the resulting figure looks like to them. Ask what it would look like if there were 16 pieces instead of 8. Suppose there were 32, 64, 128? Everyone agrees that, as the number of pieces increases, the figure looks more and more like a parallelogram. Now you have to ask the children to believe that if there were more such pieces than anyone could possibly count, the figure would be almost a parallelogram; indeed, it would be almost a rectangle. The base of this parallelogram would be half the length (or circumference) of the circle; the height of this parallelogram would be the radius of the circle. The length of a circle is πd, so half the length would be πr. Since the area of a parallelogram is found by multiplying measures of its base and height, and the area of this parallelogram must be the same as the area of the circle we started with, the area of the circle must be $\pi \times r \times r$, or πr^2.

Now the children are ready to work all sorts of problems in which circumferences and areas of circles must be computed. One class of applications of these ideas has to do with finding surfaces and volumes of cylinders and volumes of cones. In elementary school, we focus our attention on right circular cylinders and cones because these are the kinds which most often are found in everyday situations.

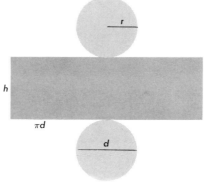

Consider the ordinary tin can. It is a right circular cylinder. It has a radius r, a diameter d, and a height h. Think about what the parts that were used to make it must have looked like before they were put together. If you are not sure, get a can opener and cut a can apart. Actually, you can tell what the curved (lateral) surface would look like flattened out by carefully removing the label. The total surface of a right circular cylinder is a rectangle and two congruent circles. Once we have found this out, it is an easy matter to find the area of this surface. The radius of each of the circles is the radius of the cylinder, so their combined area is $2\pi r^2$. The height of the rectangle is the height of the cylinder. What is its base?

Its base is the circumference of one of the circles, πd. The lateral area of the cylinder, then, is πdh. The total area is $\pi dh + 2\pi r^2$. A formula need not be memorized.

A good first way to develop the volume of a cylinder is to use the principle of conservation of material, no matter in what shape it may be. If we have a square-inch region, no matter what shape, the amount of surface (the measure of region) is 1.

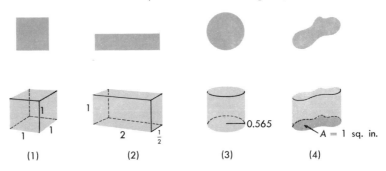

(1)   (2)   (3)   (4)

Suppose that we build a solid on each of these shapes by piling the like shapes one on top of the other until the solid is 1 inch high. Then each of these solids occupies the same space region, that is, they are each 1 cubic inch. If these solids are made out of putty, each of (2), (3), and (4) can be remolded to be congruent to (1). Thus for each square inch of surface built up into a solid 1 inch high, we have 1 cubic inch of volume.

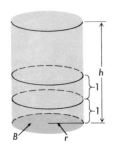

Then, in a manner similar to that used for a rectangular solid in Chapter 8, we can find the volume of a circular cylinder (see illustration in margin). We know how to find the area of the circular base: it is πr^2 square units. For each unit of height in this area there will be πr^2 cubic units. Then in any number h units of height there will be a volume of $\pi r^2 \times h$, or simply $\pi r^2 h$ cubic units. So we find the measure of the base and multiply this number by the altitude. If we want to use a formula, we can write

$$V = \pi r^2 h \quad \text{or} \quad V = Bh, \quad \text{where } B = \pi r^2.$$

The volume of a cone is $\frac{1}{3}$ that of a cylinder having the same base and altitude as the cone. The volume of a pyramid is $\frac{1}{3}$ that of a prism having the same base and altitude as the pyramid. $V = \frac{1}{3}Bh$ is the applicable formula in both cases. For a circular cone, the formula may be written $V = \frac{1}{3}\pi r^2 h$, of course. It is not intuitively obvious that $\frac{1}{3}$ is the factor which applies in these cases. The teacher may make a hollow cone which "just fits" inside a cylindrical can and have the children fill the cone with sand or water and pour it into the cylinder. It takes 3 conesful to make 1 cylinderful. Similarly, models for a pyramid which "just fits" inside a prism will have the same 1:3 volume ratio. Commercially made models are available for this purpose.

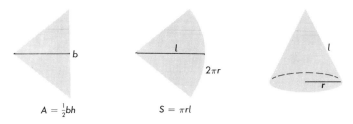

$$A = \tfrac{1}{2}bh \qquad\qquad S = \pi r l$$

For enrichment, some children may wish to learn about surface areas of pyramids, cones, and spheres, and about the volume of a sphere. Since the faces of a pyramid are triangles and the base is a polygon, areas of pyramids may be found by making the appropriate measurements, finding the area of each face, and adding. The teacher should just give the formula for the lateral area of a cone without much explanation. Then he can show that this formula has something in common with the formula for the area of a triangle, as illustrated here.

The surface of a sphere has the area of four great circles, $S = 4\pi r^2$. There is no way to demonstrate this which is both simple and convincing. One teacher had reasonable success by measuring the diameter of a volleyball using three rulers arranged as in the illustration in the margin, and having the children cut out paper disks with the same diameter. Then the children were told to fit the disks like blankets on the ball, using a jigsaw-puzzle approach where necessary, until the surface of the ball was covered. They found that they needed four of these disks, and even though the experiment was not very neat, they were ready to believe $4\pi r^2$. The formula for the volume of a sphere is $V = \frac{4}{3}\pi r^3$, and since π is not much greater than 3, $V \approx 4r^3$. The teacher who wishes to demonstrate this latter relation by way of demonstrating the reasonableness of the exact formula may make two hollow cubical boxes, one having the diameter of a given available model of a sphere for its inside dimensions and one having the radius of the

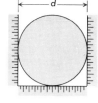

sphere for its inside dimensions. The children can find the capacity of those boxes: respectively, d^3, which equals $8r^3$, and r^3. The sphere is now placed inside the box it "just fits," and the smaller box is used as a cup for filling the empty space around the sphere with sand. It takes just about 4 of those little boxfuls of sand $(4r^3)$ to fill up this space, so the sphere must occupy the remaining $8r^3 - 4r^3$ $(4r^3)$. Almost everyone is astonished to find that a sphere has just about half the volume of a cube whose sides have the same length as the diameter of the sphere. Having found this out, they are ready to believe that the exact factor is $\frac{\pi}{6}$, and that the formula for the volume of a sphere is $V = \frac{4}{3}\pi r^3$.

13–6 100% GRAPHS

Everyone is familiar with "pie charts," circle graphs which show 100% of something (one unit) partitioned to show relative sizes of its parts. As soon as children are able to work with written symbols for fractions, they can learn to read charts like the one shown below.

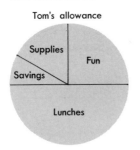

Tom's allowance

Even without reference to fractions, the children can discuss the relative sizes of the parts: Tom spends as much of his allowance for lunches as for anything else. He spends more on fun than on supplies. He saves just a little bit. When fractions are readily understood, the children can use numbers (actually relations) like $\frac{1}{2}, \frac{1}{4}, \frac{3}{8}$, and make absolute comparisons

As soon as children know how to use protractors, or make straightedge and compass constructions for drawing angles of specified sizes, they can construct circle graphs. The items for the graph have to be given as fractions of some whole (unit). If the items provide data such as those given in the example below, fractional parts must be found and reported in one of the fraction forms: common fractions, decimals, or percents. Then these fractions must be used to find the number of degrees in central angles of a circle. When these angles are drawn, each with its vertex at the center of the circle, the graph is complete, except for the labeling. Here is an example.

Joan's doll collection		Fraction	Degrees
American	10	$\frac{10}{24} = \frac{5}{12}$	$\frac{5}{12} \times 360 = 150$
French	6	$\frac{6}{24} = \frac{1}{4}$	$\frac{1}{4} \times 360 = 90$
German	4	$\frac{4}{24} = \frac{1}{6}$	$\frac{1}{6} \times 360 = 60$
Japanese	2	$\frac{2}{24} = \frac{1}{12}$	$\frac{1}{12} \times 360 = 30$
Mexican	2	$\frac{2}{24} = \frac{1}{12}$	$\frac{1}{12} \times 360 = 30$
Total	24	Total 1	Total 360

The fractions should always add to 1 (or 100%) and the degrees should always add to 360. This furnishes a check on computation. Once the children know the degree measures, they have only to draw the requisite angles, label the sections, and put in the title (and any other desirable information, such as "total, 24 dolls").

The teacher should realize, and the children should sense, that even though this is an area graph, the important features of it could just as well have been shown as a graph on a line, on which the circumference of the circle was taken as a unit and fractional parts of that unit were marked and labeled.

The 100% bar graph is made in this way. The lengths (or heights, if the bar is vertical) of the sections marked on the bar are the only relevant feature. The width of the bar has nothing to do with the interpretation of the graph; it is usually determined by how much space is needed for labeling. Here is a 100% bar graph of Joan's doll collection. The specific data for this graph were obtained by altering the title for the third column in the example from *degrees* to *percent* and doing the requisite computation.

Joan's doll collection

The length of the bar is the unit, 100%. The bar is divided, vertically in this case, just as points on a number line would be located if the left-hand corner of the graph were labeled 0, the right-hand corner of the graph were labeled 1, and the other points of division had as coordinates $\frac{5}{12}$, $\frac{5}{12} + \frac{1}{4}$, $\frac{5}{12} + \frac{1}{4} + \frac{1}{6}$, and $\frac{5}{12} + \frac{1}{4} + \frac{1}{6} + \frac{1}{12}$ (see top of next page).

One important use for 100% bar graphs, or equivalently, graphs on a unit segment, is showing pictorial solutions to problems involving percents of increase or decrease. The greatest trouble children have with problems of these kinds is to determine the number to which other numbers in the problem are related: the base, the number taken as 100%, the unit. Suppose that a problem states that last year there were 690 pupils enrolled in Fox school and this year there are 897, and asks for the percent of increase. Increase over what? What number do we start from? The number for last year's enrollment; thus 690 will be associated with 100%, or 1 unit. The number 897, then, will be associated with some percent greater than 100. We have to build the picture out beyond the 100% mark, as here.

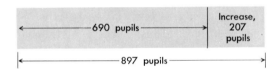

Now what we have to find amounts to finding the coordinate of a point on a number line set up as follows.

What numeral should replace the question mark? Well, 897 ÷ 690 = 1.3, and 1.3 = 130%. Then 130% of 690 must be 897. (Check this.) We were to find the percent of increase. That means the percent in excess of 100%. The percent of increase is 30%. Would we get the same answer if we divided 207 by 690? We should. Test it and see.

Problems asking for percents of decrease are handled in the same way, except that the amount of decrease is included in the unit (it is less than 100% of the unit, and is a part of the unit), so the base is the largest number used in the graph.

13–7 COORDINATES

In the preceding section, it was suggested that graphs in *one dimension* are marks on a line and that, once a unit is chosen, just *one coordinate* will locate a point. If children are in a line, and someone asks, "Where is Charles?" the answer, "Charles is third in line" locates him exactly.

Suppose we move to two dimensions. A good model for the background needed for two-dimensional graphing is the seating chart for a standard classroom. Now if someone asks, "Where is Charles?" the answer, "In the third row" does not locate him exactly. We still need to know which seat in that row Charles is occupying. We need more than one number, specifically two numbers, to locate a seat exactly. Each point of a graph in *two dimensions* has *two coordinates*. (How many coordinates would you expect a point of a graph in three dimensions to have?)

Even if a teacher has no plans to work with graphs for several weeks after school starts, he can introduce (or practice) the concept of an ordered pair of numbers associated with a point in a plane and get acquainted with the children on the first day of school, provided his classroom can be arranged so that the seats are in columns from front to back and rows from left to right, as shown.

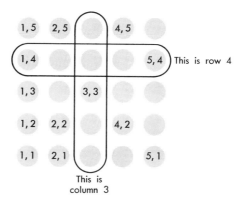

The teacher and the children agree that in a given pair of numbers, the first number will tell which column and the second number will tell which seat in the column or the row. They decide how to number the columns and rows. If it is not extraordinarily awkward, the teacher should try to influence the decision so that a seating chart made during the activity would look like a standard graph on the number plane. Now the teacher calls on children by name, one at a time, and asks each child to give the ordered pair of numbers (column, row) which locates his seat. After it is apparent that everyone understands this, the teacher may say (if the children know one another), "Paul Tundo, where is Andrew Sheldon's seat?" or "Alberta, who is sitting in seat (5, 2)?" Then he may ask, "Where is seat (5, 1)? Where is seat (1, 5)? Where is a seat for which both numbers in the pair are the same? How many such seats are there? If we list the ordered pairs of numbers for seats in the first column (front to back, by our agreement) and reverse the order of the numbers in each pair, which seats would these new pairs locate? Does everyone know the *coordinates* for his seat? Each of you reverse the order of the coordinates for your seat and move to the seat that goes with the new coordinates. Who has to move the farthest? Is there anyone who does not move at all? . . ."

The word *graph* means *picture*. Children from first grade up make pictorial representations of quantitative relations in science classes and in social studies classes. Each such picture is some kind of graph. It is possible to make graphs that actually are graphs in the number plane long before the children have any facility with numbers. For example, in a science class, first-grade children may plant corn seeds on five or six successive Mondays and watch the seeds germinate and grow. If the plants are set on a table placed near the chalkboard, lined up from youngest to oldest, marks may be made on the chalkboard to indicate the height of each plant. Then, if the table is removed, the marks may be connected by a smooth curve which is a graph of the growth of the corn. With just this much of a picture, the children may discuss certain general implications of the graph: Corn grows faster at some stages than at others; it takes it a while to get started, etc.

In a third-grade class, coordinate axes may be introduced in a graph like this, the horizontal axis labeled to show time in weeks and the vertical axis labeled to show height in inches. The teacher must take care that this height is established so that everyone knows "height above what?" Usually, it will be height above the level of the top of the soil in the pot. Children in the middle grades can learn to make tables which are records of the results of experiments and then graph the data from these tables. Once they know how to associate ordered pairs of numbers with a point in a plane (and they learn this easily), their principal difficulty lies in choosing appropriate scales for the coordinate axes. The teacher should help them with this, discussing how to decide, and leaving the impression that there is more than one workable choice; the final choice is usually determined by convenience.

In certain types of graphs, negative numbers appear as a matter of course. For instance, when children keep a record of temperature on successive days in winter, they may record below-zero temperatures. They have seen the minus sign used to report below-zero temperatures on weather maps and they may use the minus sign in their own records with no particular thought about it. If the children are puzzled about how to record temperatures (or anything else) when the magnitudes alone are not adequate, the class should discuss the necessity for having some sort of symbolism which will report both magnitude and direction. Then they should agree on some scheme—using arrows with numerals, circling the numerals for "in-the-hole" numbers, using positive and negative signs, or whatever else they may suggest—so that each child can communicate with his classmates.

The teacher must know that coordinate axes do not have to be perpendicular; it is frequently just more convenient to have them that way.

The children should learn the use of coordinates in locating places on a map—a street map of their city, a map they make themselves of their neighborhood, a road map—and when they know about longitude and latitude, they should learn to locate places on a globe. They should realize that a given ordered pair of numbers is associated with exactly one point in a plane or on a globe, once the axes are established (you have to have a place to start, and directions to go from there).

An interesting activity for sixth-graders which not only contributes to their understanding of graphs and coordinates, but also strengthens their knowledge of ratio is the following: The teacher has each pupil set up a pair of axes on graph paper and then gives three ordered pairs of numbers to be graphed. (These ordered pairs are chosen judiciously, in the first few examples, so that computation will be easy.) The children are told to draw a triangle having these three points as vertices. Then they are to locate the midpoint of each side by some reliable method and find the coordinates of each of these midpoints. Then they should compare the coordinates of the midpoint of each segment with the coordinates of the endpoints of the segment. "It turns out to be the average!"

They should wonder about the coordinates of points which divide the segments into thirds or fourths. They should make predictions and test them.

For enrichment, sixth-graders may do some work with graphs of linear functions, usually with equations of the form $y = ax + b$. They should note what happens to the graph when the value for a is held constant and the value for b changes, and vice versa. They should find out for themselves that the graph of each such equation is a straight line. They should determine coordinates for points on the line not listed in their tables and should note that the coordinates of all such points could be listed, if a person had several years to spend on one graph. With exceptional classes, graphic solutions for two equations in two variables may be found. This should not be done by rote. There is no better way to illustrate the intersection of two sets than by a cognitive approach to the solution of simultaneous equations.

Children can learn to read graphs before they can learn to make them, and at all stages, they should have an opportunity to develop an appreciation of the great convenience of a graphic presentation. This appreciation is reinforced in a situation which comes out of their daily experiences. For example, suppose that they are doing an experiment for a science lesson in which they need centigrade temperatures, and they have only a Fahrenheit thermometer. If there is available a graph of the formula $F = \frac{9}{5}C + 32$ or the formula $C = \frac{5}{9}(F - 32)$, they can read directly off the graph the centigrade temperatures for any Fahrenheit temperatures they use, without having to compute them. If there is no such graph available, and they know how to make one, doing so would be well worth the time it takes if they have more than three or four temperature readings to convert.

The alert teacher will seize every opportunity to relate whatever mathematics he is teaching to the daily lives of his pupils.

EXERCISES

1. Make a chart showing how triangles are classified according to relations among their sides and among their angles.
2. Give a commonsense explanation of why the standard compass-and-straightedge construction for copying an angle works. Which of the

congruence theorems would be needed if a formal proof of this construction were to be given?

3. Describe a sequence of activities by which sixth-graders should discover the simple theorems for similarity of triangles, given the general definition of similar polygons.

4. Would you advocate teaching the simple compass and straightedge constructions in elementary school? Give reasons for your answer.

5. A pair of coordinate axes in a plane is sometimes referred to as a pair of number lines. This is unfortunate, since they are graphs of sets of points in a plane, and each point in a plane is associated with a pair of numbers. Which coordinate is usually omitted in labeling an axis of abscissas? Why is it omitted? Which coordinate is usually omitted in labeling an axis of ordinates? Why? How much point should you make of matters like this in a fourth-grade class? In a sixth-grade class? Give reasons for your answer.

6. Children are given coordinate paper and asked to select axes and the unit (the same) on both axes. Some children use a quarter-inch, others a half-inch, and others an inch as a unit. They are asked to locate the points $(0, 0)$, $(5, 0)$, and $(2, 4)$ and connect them by segments. For the various graphs:

   a) What is the ratio relation between the measures of corresponding segments?

   b) The measurement in inches of the corresponding segments?

   c) The measure of the angles of the triangles?

   d) The measurement of the areas of the triangles in square inches? Explain why the measures are the same, and why the measurements have the ratios they do have.

7. Outline what appears to you to be a reasonable study of graphical representation for Grade 5.

8. A pupil made a sign like the one shown in the margin. How would you use this sign to discuss the selection of axes and the unit on each axis to use in constructing a graph? (This is an introduction to flowcharting.)

PLAN AHEA

9. All figures which have four sides and two opposite pairs of sides parallel are called parallelograms. Parallelograms with right angles are rectangles; without right angles they are rhomboids; rectangles with all sides equal are squares; rhomboids with all sides congruent are rhombuses. Make a diagram to illustrate this classification. Compare this classification with that illustrated by Venn diagrams on page 170 and tell why it differs.

Measures extended; coordinates; graphs

REFERENCES

GOLD, S., "Graphing Linear Equations—A Discovery Lesson," *The Arithmetic Teacher* **13,** 5, May 1966, pages 406–407

PHILLIPS, J. M., "Bisecting Angles and Segments," filmstrip H in *Seeing the Use of Numbers, Set VII*, Eye Gate Productions, Jamaica, N.Y.

problem-solving

It has been said that the overall objective of all education is to develop the ability to solve problems. Here *problems* refers to problems of all kinds, quantitative and otherwise. In this context, a problem is defined as a situation for which no ready-made procedure toward a solution is available to the person facing such a situation. It follows that a situation which is a problem for one person may be an exercise for another and a frustration for a third, depending on the experience, knowledge, skill, and attitude brought to the situation.

Much has been written on strategies for problem-solving. Step 1 in all such strategies refers to identifying the problem. Most certainly, no one can solve a problem if he does not know what the problem is. The principal difficulty some children have in solving "story problems" in mathematics textbooks lies in the inability of these children to understand what the problem is. Most of the problematic situations people experience in their personal lives could be solved readily if the people were able to identify these problems properly.

An admittedly oversimplified strategy for problem-solving asserts that the solutions of problems of all kinds—getting a date for the prom, passing a mathematics test, landing on the moon—depend on finding appropriate answers to three questions, not necessarily in the order given:

1. What do I have?
2. What do I want?
3. How can I use what I have to get what I want?

Most of the content of this book deals with helping children solve problems involving quantitative or spatial relations. In this sense all learning is conceived of as being achieved by means of problem-solving. How to tell "how many" is a problem which may be solved by counting. Then children are faced with the problem, "How do you count?" Similarly all algorisms for finding the results of the fundamental operations are posed first as problems, as "How can we find the answer?" Thus to learn how to find the product of 65 × 287 is as much a problem as to find the answer to a word problem.

The reader who thinks back over the developments of topics discussed in the chapters preceding this one will be able to see that the three questions mentioned above were answered in some appropriate way in each case. However, when teachers speak of problem-solving, they usually refer to story problems (verbal problems, worded problems). This chapter will present a number of strategies for solving the problem of helping children learn to solve story problems. It is not suggested that these strategies be used in the order given, except that the first-mentioned obviously has to come first. Indeed, several of them should be used at almost the same time, and repeatedly.

14–1 BEGIN WITH BEGINNERS

The problem-solving program should start before the children are able to read and before they know how to write any number facts. Little stories about numbers of things should be given orally by the teacher and should be made up, and given orally, by the children. As soon as the children know how to count—i.e., to find the cardinal number of a set—they can act out number stories in some way. Sometimes the children themselves pretend to be whatever objects are mentioned in the story. Sometimes they use toys or counters to represent the objects. Children can play. "Play that you are a pony" or "Play that your counters are ponies" make perfectly good sense to them. Somewhat later, they may make tally marks as a streamlined procedure for keeping a record of the events in a story, adding more marks or crossing some out as the story may indicate.

Suppose that a class of beginners has mastered counting through 6. The teacher may suggest that the class play some number stories, and proceed somewhat as follows: "*Three children are playing in the sandbox.* Who wants to be one of those children? David, Marie, come to the sandbox. Do we have three children there now? How many more do we need? All right, Albert, you come to the sandbox. Do we have three children there now? *Three children are playing in the sandbox. Two more children come to join them.* Clara, would you like to choose two more children to join the three at the sandbox? *How many children in all are playing in the sandbox?* How do we find out? (Sometimes we can tell just by looking; sometimes we count to find out.) We had three children at first, two more came, and now we have five. *Three children and two children are five children.* I'll make up one more story and then I'll ask you for one."

Obviously, the stories do not have to be about children. A child may say, "See this part of the floor right here? Well, that's a pond, and I'm a duck, and I'm swimming in the pond." His story can go on from there.

It is desirable, at first, that each child have a supply of toys, or paper or flannel cutouts, to use in dramatizing stories in which the child plays the role of director rather than actor; but if such supplies are not available, any kind of counters will do. The teacher may say, "As I tell you this story about ponies, show the ponies with your counters (cutouts, toys). *Five ponies are eating grass.* Show just the ponies. (Check to see that each child has exactly five counters together at a designated spot on his desk.) *Three of the ponies go away. How many ponies are there now?* Louis, can you tell us the whole story?" Louis should say something like, "There were five ponies at first. Three of them went away. There are two ponies still there." The teacher should not put words in Louis' mouth, but should prompt him, if necessary.

When children are learning to recognize number symbols, the teacher may write number facts on the chalkboard (casually and, at first, just for the children to see) as a shorthand way of keeping a record of the story. When the time comes for the children to read an expression like '2 + 3 = 5', they should read it as 'two plus three is five'. They should read '5 − 3 = 2' as 'five minus three is two'.

All through kindergarten and in the early part of the first grade, children should dramatize number stories. In this way, they become acquainted with addition and subtraction facts, and acquire the necessary beginnings of readiness for multiplication and division, before they even try to write one of these facts. The child confronted with the physical task of recording a number fact can do this much more easily if he is already familiar with the content he is recording.

14-2 GIVE CONSCIOUS ATTENTION TO TEACHING READING

A child who cannot read a story problem and know what the story tells and what it asks cannot possibly solve the problem. Even children who are good readers of the kinds of stories which appear in their reading books need instruction and practice in reading content material of the kind found in mathematics textbooks.

The teacher of children just learning to read may record on the chalkboard a simplified version of number stories made up by the children. Suppose that a child says, "I went to visit my grandfather and he asked me if I had any money and I said, 'Yes, I do. I have three pennies. They are in this box right here. Do you want to see them?'" The teacher should write:

I had 3 pennies.

He should point out to the children exactly what he has written. The teacher should realize that, in deciding what to write in a case like this, he is using a skill which the children have to acquire eventually, that of picking out those items in a story which are pertinent to the problem.

Now suppose that the child continues, "My grandfather fished around in his pocket and got out his change and gave me all the pennies he had. After he gave me all his pennies, I counted mine and I found out I had seven pennies then. Now here is my puzzle: How many pennies did my grandfather give me?" The record of the whole story might be:

I had 3 pennies.

My grandfather gave me more pennies.

Then I had 7 pennies.

How many pennies did my grandfather give me?

The children may solve the problem using real money, or play money, or counters, or some kind of tally marks, or number facts $(3 + ? = 7)$, depending on the level at which they can operate comfortably at the time.

Obviously the reading in a story like this is much more difficult than that found in the story problems first encountered in the primary-level mathematics texts, but in this case, the children heard the story before the written version was made. Furthermore, they are usually highly motivated to read their own stories, especially if the teacher plans a display of one story for each child in the class, possibly illustrated in each case by the child who made up the story.

When the children are able to read most of the words in the story problems in their texts, the teacher should help them develop the skills necessary for comprehending the ideas conveyed. One reading of a problem is seldom enough. A good problem-solver usually reads a problem through quickly, just to get the gist of it. Then he goes back and reads it again slowly and carefully, several times, if necessary, until *he can restate it in his own words*. He has to do this, in effect, for every problem he solves. The teacher should help every child to learn to do this. A problem may be read aloud by one child with the other children following the text, or silently by everyone. Then the teacher should ask the class to think how to restate the problem in their own words and call on several children to do this. The teacher should not insist that this restatement be elegant, or even grammatically correct. The purpose at hand is to be sure that each child understands correctly, on his own terms, what the problem says.

Problems in which the solver has to pick out the information relevant to the question he wants to answer, or to use some information which he probably knows but which is not given in the problem, or to search for more information of a certain kind, come closer to real-life problems than anything else in a classroom. Problems children make up themselves, especially if they are not required to write them, are often embellished with details not necessary for finding the answer to the question the problem asks. This is fine. The child who makes up the problem, as well as the rest of the class, should pick out the data needed for solving the problem. They will probably decide that the extra details make the story more interesting. Incomplete stories are also interesting. A child who is able to say, "There's something more I need here," or "I don't have to use this," is well on his way to becoming a good problem-solver. The teacher should provide experiences such that the children can discuss and solve problems with too much, or too little, data.

Once a child is able to *read* a problem—to know what it *tells* and what it *asks*—he has part of the answer to the question, "What do I have?" The rest of the answer to "What do I have?" is the knowledge and skills he has at his command. He has all the answer to the question, "What do I want?" In order to decide "How can I use what I have to get what I want?" he must be able to see the relations among the numbers (or geometric entities) in the problem. This is the hardest thing for the teacher to help him with. If the teacher tells the child what to do, it is the teacher who has solved the major part of the problem. The teacher must develop the ability to ask the kind of questions that will lead the child to see the appropriate relations for himself. Certain techniques for developing the child's ability to see "How can I use what I have to get what I want?" will now be described.

14–3 TEACH THE WHEN, AS WELL AS THE HOW AND THE WHY

There is no doubt that children should know both the *how* and the *why* of the mathematics they learn, but for problem-solving, there is something just as important as either of these: the *when*. If a child does not know *when* to add, it is little use (except for tests in computation) to him to know how to add and why he adds that way.

When children are learning the meaning of a mathematical operation and are learning to write some of the number facts, they learn to associate certain actions—maneuvers with counters or motions along a number line—with a specific operation. When they put two or more bunches of counters (or other objects) together, this suggests the union of sets, and the analogous operation on numbers is addition. Combining forward motions along a number line should also make the children think of addition. When they act out a problem story—by dramatizing it themselves, by using counters, by using number lines, or by drawing some sort of picture or diagram—the teacher may ask, "What did we do with

these things?　What does that tell us to do with the numbers?''
When the day comes that the teacher no longer needs to ask questions like these, the children can see for themselves *when* to add (subtract, multiply, divide).　When the sets being joined, or the forward moves along the number line, are all the same size, multiplication is a more efficient way to find a total than addition, if the children know the requisite multiplication facts and skills.

Removing a part of a group of things, or moving backward from a given point along a number line, should be associated in the children's minds with subtraction.　So also, somewhat later, should situations in which they have to decide how many more of something they need, or how much farther they have to jump, to arrive at a certain number.　When a set is partitioned into two or more subsets, all the same size, or when two or more backward moves along a number line are all the same size (length, distance), division is a more efficient way to find the answers than iterated subtractions, if the child knows the requisite division facts and skills.

When a story can be illustrated by counters lined up in rows with the same number of counters in each row, multiplication or division is suggested, depending on which parts of the story are told in the problem.　If, in effect, the number of rows and the number of counters in each row are given and the question involves finding the total, this is a typical multiplication situation.　If the total and one of the two factors is given and the question involves finding the other factor, this is a typical division situation.　Only when we are interpreting the answer does the matter of which factor (the number of rows or the number in each row) is given require pointed attention.

The technique of dramatizing or diagramming a problem is far from childish.　It is used by good problem-solvers of all ages and at all levels of mathematical sophistication.　Before anyone can solve a problem, he has to visualize the problem situation in some way.　Some children are good at constructing, in their minds, make-believe cartoons in which a problem story is acted out.　Others get better results by going through certain motions themselves, with other children, with counters, with cutouts manipulated on the flannel board or on their desks or on an overhead projector, or with drawings and diagrams.　The teacher should encourage each child to use his own best way to "see" a problem, to visualize the action, and to interpret all this in terms of operations on numbers.

14-4 AT ALL LEVELS, USE PUPIL-MADE PROBLEMS

One of the very best ways to help a child learn to solve problems is to have him make up problems for himself, and his classmates, to solve. This procedure has all sorts of perquisites: it helps the child to read, it helps to correlate mathematics with other subjects, it helps a child to verbalize his thoughts clearly, it helps him to analyze quantitative situations. The instructions may be to make up a problem which can be solved by division, or to make up a problem to go with a particular number fact, or to make up a problem about some specific story line or using some given data, etc., or to make up just any problem. The one thing common to most such assignments is that the child should be able to solve the problem he makes up himself.

The teacher may also ask the children to produce a problem to represent a given kind of expression. For example, "Make up a problem to illustrate $a + (b + c)$." A reply is "Billy has 5 articles, Sam has 3 of them. I have 6. If I add the number of their articles to the number of mine, how many shall I have altogether?" By posing $(a + b) + c$ as another example, children can learn the associativity of both the union of sets and the addition of numbers. In similar fashion, children learn that $a + (b - c)$ and $(a + b) - c$ give the same result, but $a - (b + c)$ and $(a - b) + c$ do not. In this way problem-solving of word situations can help to establish the fundamental principles of commutativity, associativity, and distributivity.

The results of such assignments are normally a revelation. They furnish an excellent, and easy, way to provide for individual differences. Some children will make up, and solve, problems much more difficult than any which have yet been covered in class. Others are apparently comfortable only with problems less difficult than those the class is working on at the time. This helps the teacher in diagnosing the progress of each child, and to provide assistance, encouragement, or challenge as circumstances may dictate.

Some experienced teachers have formed the habit of reading the daily newspaper with a pair of scissors at hand for clipping out items which give data for problems which are timely and which may be interesting to the children. The teacher should not assume, however, that a problem an adult regards as realistic and interesting will impress a child in the same way. Pupil-made problems dispel that myth. One sixth-grader who had seen some data in which distances were given in kilometers made up a problem which asked for the volume of a rectangular solid whose dimensions were 5 kilometers, 3 kilometers, and 6 kilometers. Realistic? To that child, and to the rest of the class, yes.

Sometimes some of the data, or the results, in pupil-made problems involve numbers the children have not yet learned to compute with, such as fractions or negative numbers. The teacher should seize the opportunity to develop concepts associated with such numbers, with little attention to formality, at times like these.

Most children are highly motivated to solve a problem made up by one of their classmates.

14–5 USE PROBLEMS WITHOUT NUMBERS

Problems without numbers are valuable in that they focus attention on the process which might be used to solve the problem if the numbers were given. A teacher cannot ask a child, in these words, "What is the essence of an addition situation?" He can, however, ask him to react to this: "John had several toy airplanes. He got some more for his birthday. How many airplanes did John have then?" If the child says, "If I knew how many he had at first and how many he got for his birthday, I could tell you how many he had then," the teacher should ask him how he would tell. Usually, his answer will show that he knows *when* to add, at least part of the time, and also it will help other children who need reinforcement of their concept of addition.

If a child cannot see that this is an addition situation, even though no numbers are given, and the problem as stated cannot be solved, have him work with heaps of counters (no counting) or with number lines without numerals (from here to here, this much more) until he sees what he might do if the numbers were supplied.

Then different pupils should supply different pairs of numbers so that the problem can be solved. The teacher may write the problem on the chalkboard, leaving a blank space where 'several' and 'some' appear, and ask children, one at a time, to suggest ways to fill in the blanks. They should find the answer in each case and should note how they found it. They should see that this problem is an addition problem regardless of the numbers used.

Similar problems may be given for the other operations. Two categories of questions can be answered by division, and the teacher must give pointed attention to each category.

This activity can be capped by making universal generalizations. The child learns that if the objects of two disjoint sets are joined into one set, the pattern for finding the sum is

$$\square + \triangle = \pentagon .$$

He also learns that if a number of sets, all with the same number of elements, are joined into one set, the pattern for finding the number of the joined set is

$$\square \times \triangle = \pentagon .$$

In each case, if one of two given numbers appears on the right-hand side of the equality, he knows that an inverse operation is required to find the number to use for the empty frame.

All children must learn eventually that it is not the numbers nor the specifics of the story line, but the relations among the numbers, which determine the process (or processes) to use in solving problems.

14-6 USE PROBLEMS WITHOUT LABELS

The things a problem talks about, except for subjects like gravity or certain geometric entities which have numerical implications, have little to do with determining the method used for its solution. One way to develop this understanding is to give a problem like the one following, with instructions to fill in the blanks so that the problem makes sense.

> I have 11 _____ in my desk drawer.
> I have 7 more _____ in my closet.
> How many _____ do I have in all?

The child who says, "It doesn't really matter what I write in those blanks so long as I write the same word in each one. I could just make up a word. Whatever it is, there are 18 in all," has the requisite concept. This is an addition problem regardless of how the blanks are filled in.

A bonus attached to this sort of insight is the fact that the problem-solver does not always have to know what something is before he can solve a problem which mentions it. If he can see the relations among the numbers in a problem, he can solve the problem and guarantee his answer. Try this:

> One zyxure may be exchanged for 3 badefs. How many badefs could you get for 5 zyxures?

What's a zyxure? What's a badef? Does it matter?

14–7 USE PROBLEMS WITHOUT QUESTIONS

Pupils who make arbitrary or irrelevant decisions about what to do with the numbers in a problem can be helped to think more clearly if they are given a problem situation without the question, or statement, which tells what is to be found. The accompanying instructions require the pupils to ask separate questions leading to solutions by at least two, and preferably three, of the four operations. (It is difficult to find a social situation, except those dealing with geometric shapes, where four suitable questions, one for each operation, make sense. You come out with square eggs, or some such thing.) Here is an example:

> In the Easter-egg hunt, Sally found 12 eggs and Ruth found 4 eggs.

Ask a question to make this an addition problem; ask another question to make it a subtraction problem; and another question to make it a division problem.

The pupils see that they cannot tell what to do with the 12 and the 4 until they know what it is they have to find.

At a higher grade level, if the 12 and the 4 are given as measures in the same unit of the sides of a rectangle, a question which asks for the perimeter will produce an addition problem, a question which asks for the difference of the dimensions will produce a subtraction problem, a question which asks for the ratio of the dimensions will produce a division problem, and a question which asks for the area will produce a multiplication problem.

14-8 ESTIMATE EACH ANSWER

The habit of estimating answers should begin in first grade, at the latest. Even with very simple problems, a child may be asked, "Should the answer be more than 5? How can you tell?" As the level of maturity rises, the children should be encouraged to make judgments such as: It has to be at least 50. It can't possibly be as much as 100. It should be between 1000 and 2000. It ought to be about 30. When children have learned to round numbers—and this can be done informally until about fifth grade—they can use rounded numbers in making estimates: "These baseball caps cost 97¢ apiece. That's almost a dollar. Three of them should cost just about $3." "We went 287 miles yesterday. Call that 300. We went 408 miles today. Call that 400. We went about 700 miles in two days."

There are some children who appear to hit a mental block whenever they are faced with a problem in which the numbers are large whole numbers or fractional numbers of any size. Sometimes these children are helped to get over this hurdle if they are taught to replace, temporarily, these "troublesome" numbers by small whole numbers. This technique is especially fruitful if the small whole numbers appear in some form of rough approximation to the exact numbers. For instance, 2,000,000 is a rough approximation to 1,687,942 and the children can write this as '2 million' and ignore the 'million' while they are figuring out the process to use in solving the problem. Fractional numbers greater than 1 can always be rounded to a convenient whole number. Fractional numbers less than 1 can be rounded to 0 or 1, depending on whether they are less than $\frac{1}{2}$ or not less than $\frac{1}{2}$, but sometimes this rounding introduces so large a relative error in the estimate as to make it useless. In these latter instances, it is better to replace the fraction symbols in the statement of the problem by expressions like '1 eighth' and '7 tenths'. Again, the children can ignore the word in these expressions temporarily and think in terms of the small whole numbers (in this instance, 1 and 7) while they are figuring out the method they should use to solve the problem.

The child who habitually asks himself "*About how much* should this answer be?" will avoid mistakes which would make his answers ridiculous. In real-life problems, estimating the answer is often the only way to check the solution of a problem before it is actually tried out. Checking the computation is only one part of checking a solution. The important part of the check is testing whether the solution makes sense (checks out) in the problem situation.

The teacher who wishes to develop in his pupils the habit of estimating answers is ill advised if he requires the estimating process to be so structured, or so laborious, that it is more trouble for the pupils than finding the exact answer. The teacher should encourage each pupil to develop a way of estimating which is both reliable and easy, and to acquire progressively more mature judgment about how close an estimate is adequate for a given purpose.

14–9 ENCOURAGE A VARIETY OF SOLUTIONS

Only in the case of a counting problem in which there is not more than one object to count is there only one correct way to solve a problem. Sometimes one of the several correct ways is shorter, faster, or more adroit than the rest, but even when this is the case, this "neat" solution is of no use to the child who would never think of it.

A problem-solver needs some sort of plan for each of his solutions, but his teacher (or his boss) is unwise if he insists that these plans follow a prescribed form. Conceptually,

$$\begin{array}{r} 231 \\ -76 \\ \hline \end{array}$$

is just as much an open sentence as

$$231 - 76 = n \qquad \text{or} \qquad 76 + \square = 231.$$

In the vertical form, the bar under the '76' takes the place of the '=' in the horizontal form. There is substantial evidence that requiring children to follow certain "steps" in solving problems leads to poorer overall performance than helping them acquire the requisite general concepts and skills and then letting each child use these concepts and skills in his own best way.

There is also substantial evidence that children gain more problem-solving skill by solving the same problem in several ways than by solving several similar problems in the same way. Furthermore, if a child solves the same problem by two or more methods and gets the same answer each time, he can be reasonably confident that his answer is correct.

Contrary to what one might suppose, this multiple approach to problem-solving does not confuse the slow learner. Instead he avoids the frustration which is inevitably his lot when he does not understand what someone has decreed (mistakenly) to be *the* correct method. Of several methods, all of which lead to a correct solution, he may choose the one which makes sense to *him*. He learns to have confidence in his own way of thinking.

Of course, his teacher will help him to develop the most efficient methods of which he is capable.

14–10 HAVE EACH ANSWER GIVEN IN AN ENGLISH SENTENCE

There are some students, even in college classes, who can get the correct numerical answer to a problem and then have no idea how this number fits the problem situation. Surely interpreting the answer is just as important as getting the answer, and should receive commensurate emphasis. If a child says, "The answer is $4\frac{1}{2}$," he should be asked, "What about this $4\frac{1}{2}$?" "The shorter side of this rectangle is $4\frac{1}{2}$ feet long," might be his reply.

What does the answer tell you?

Sometimes the result of a correct computation for an acceptable method of solving a problem is not a sensible answer to the question the problem asks. Consider the problem: How many buses with 29 seats each should we hire to transport our Field Day teams, 138 people in all, to the stadium? This is clearly a problem which can be solved by division. (How else? There are at least two more processes which could be used.) Suppose that our plan for solving the problem is recorded as

$$138 \div 29 = \square.$$

We divide 138 by 29 and we get $4\frac{22}{29}$. The problem asked how many buses. We can't hire a fraction of a bus. Shall we ignore the fraction? If it is permissible to have standees, we might be able to get the job done with 4 buses. Suppose that it is not permissible to have standees. Then the answer to the problem is "We should hire 5 buses." Standees or no standees, the answer to the computation ($4\frac{22}{29}$, or alternatively, 4 remainder 22) is not the answer to the problem.

What does the problem require? What is your answer? Whatever it is, say it in an English sentence.

14–11 CHECK EACH SOLUTION IN THE PROBLEM SITUATION

It has been suggested previously that checking the computation is only a part of checking the answer to a problem. Some people are very good at getting the right answer to the wrong question. After the computation has been checked and the answer to the problem has been stated in an English sentence and this latter statement has been compared to an estimate of what a sensible answer should be, there is one further check to be made. The answer should be inserted at appropriate places in a restatement of the problem to see whether it "fits."

Consider this problem: Last year Stow School had 1024 pupils. This year it has 1156 pupils. To the nearest tenth, what is the percent of increase in enrollment? Suppose that two pupils each estimate the answer to be about 10%. Both know that an increase is added to the smaller number. One divides 1024 by 1156, gets 88.6%, subtracts this from 100% and states as his answer, "The percent of increase in enrollment is 11.4." His answer is close to his estimate. His computation is correct. Is his answer correct? To be sure that it is, he should check to see that 11.4% of 1024, added to 1024, yields 1156, or a number very close to 1156. (Why not exactly, in this case? Between what limits must his results lie?) The other pupil divides 1156 by 1024, gets 112.9%, subtracts 100% from this, and states as his answer, "The percent of increase in enrollment is 12.9." His answer is close to his estimate. His computation is correct. Is his answer correct? If it is, 12.9% of 1024, added to 1024, should yield 1156, or a number appropriately close to 1156. Which of these pupils has the correct answer? If the pupil whose answer is incorrect does not check his answer in the problem situation, will he suspect that his answer is less than perfect?

14–12 DEVELOP AN AWARENESS OF BASIC MATHEMATICAL MODELS

Mathematics has been described as the art of killing many birds with one stone. This description refers to the remarkable range of applicability of the basic mathematical models. Most of the numerical problems in elementary school mathematics fit one of the following two models:

$$a + b = c, \qquad a \times b = c.$$

Shortly after a child makes his first formal acquaintance with addition or multiplication facts, as such, he should be encouraged to see that, given any two of the occurrences of number in these operations, he can find the third. One way to help him see this is to ask each child in the class to make up a problem to go with a specific number fact, not necessarily one of the basic facts, depending on the grade level. Have each child state his problem. It will be most unusual if all the problems together do not contain examples of all three possible "missing numbers."

A person who would like a picturesque way to go insane could spend the rest of his sane years imposing different vocabularies on just one of these basic models. Consider the model $a \times b = c$. Any problem involving the cost of several articles each at the same price; any problem involving the area of a rectangle; any problem involving a percent of a number; any problem involving time, uniform rate, and distance; any problem involving amperes, volts, and ohms; and an endless number of other large categories of problems fit this model. Think what problem-solving power, coupled with appreciation of mathematics, a child who comprehends this must have. He can distill the essence of the problems he faces. He knows that, with this model, sometimes he multiplies to find the missing number and sometimes he divides to find it. Furthermore, the child knows when to multiply and when to divide.

It is not unrealistic to expect all average sixth-graders to appreciate, and to use effectively, the basic mathematical models, provided these children have been properly guided in their mathematical instruction.

14–13 SUMMARY

Helping the children learn to solve story problems is a problem for all elementary teachers. What do these teachers have? They have some knowledge of mathematics, psychology, and pedagogy, and a profound interest in children together with a roomful of children they wish to help. What do they want? They want to help these children learn to solve problems. How can they use what they have to get what they want? They can use the strategies in the following list, augmented by any others they can devise.

1. Begin with beginners.
2. Give conscious attention to teaching reading of mathematical content.
3. Teach the *when*, as well as the *how* and the *why*.
4. At all levels, use pupil-made problems.
5. Use problems without numbers.
6. Use problems without labels.
7. Use problems without questions.
8. Estimate each answer.
9. Encourage a variety of solutions.
10. Have each answer interpreted and checked in the situation the problem describes.
11. Develop an awareness of basic mathematical models.

The teacher who really believes that everyone can think, but not everyone can think in the same way, and who has genuine respect for all productive thought processes, including those far different from his own, is usually successful in solving the problem of teaching problem-solving.

EXERCISES

1. Why should an elementary mathematics program include verbal problems?

2. Predict the education outcomes of an instructional program which develops mathematical concepts and skills and gives no external applications versus an instructional program which stresses applications as well as concepts and skills.

3. Criticize the following step procedure for problem-solving.
   a) Read the problem.
   b) Tell what is given.
   c) Tell what you wish to find.
   d) Find the answer.
   e) Check the answer.

4. Make up a problem which can be solved by division. List at least three acceptable plans for its solution, not all of which need necessarily involve division.

Problem-solving

5. Describe a problem situation which lends itself to a variety of questions. List at least three questions. Give two acceptable methods for finding the answer to each question.

6. The following algebraic expressions indicate problematic situations. Construct a problem for each of them.

   a) $a - b$ b) $a + b$ c) $a \times b$ d) $a \div b$ e) $a - (b + c)$

   f) $\dfrac{a - b}{c}$ but not $\dfrac{a}{c} - \dfrac{b}{c}$ g) $\dfrac{a}{b} \cdot c$ h) $a \cdot (b + c)$ i) $a \cdot (b - c)$

7. How is a desirable problem-solving attitude developed?

8. How is the maturity of an individual related to his ability to solve problems?

9. Describe the role of everyday environmental experience (speaking vocabulary, reading vocabulary, actions, observations) in the development of problem-solving ability.

10. There is an analogy between maneuvers with physical objects and certain arithmetical and geometrical relations. Discuss the "transfer of training" from one to the other.

REFERENCES

GROSSNICKLE, F. E., "Verbal Problem Solving," *The Arithmetic Teacher*, **11**, 1, January 1964, pages 12–17

HANNON, H., "Problem Solving—Programming and Processing," *The Arithmetic Teacher* **9**, 1, January 1962, pages 17–18

NATIONAL COUNCIL OF TEACHERS OF MATHEMATICS, *Learning Mathematics: Its Theory and Practice.* Twenty-First Yearbook, 1953, Chapters 1 and 8

PHILLIPS, J. M., "Solving Problems," filmstrip H in *Seeing the Use of Numbers, Set IV;* "Many Birds with One Stone," filmstrip J, *Set VI;* "Using What You Know," filmstrip J, *Set VII;* Eye Gate Productions, Jamaica, N.Y.

enrichment topics
in elementary school
mathematics

It is well known that bright children can master the general curriculum in mathematics in less time than that allowed for teaching the subject. There are also less-than-talented children who are interested and motivated to learn mathematics. For both these groups, especially in the intermediate grades, it is of real educational value to offer a challenge through enrichment of the subject. *Enrichment* means giving children material that will prepare them for later study and that will give them a deeper insight into the content of the regular program of study. It is not an accelerated program.

There are many topics that can be used for this purpose, more topics than can be taught. The teacher should select those topics in which he also has a real interest and in which he can guide the children's study. In every case the teacher should have in mind a definite objective or goal to be attained by the pupils engaged in enrichment study. In this chapter this type of study is illustrated with a number of topics from the so-called "modern mathematics."

15-1 VENN DIAGRAMS

In ordinary addition we are concerned with the problem of finding the number of elements in the join (union) of two nonoverlapping (disjoint) collections. To prevent children from thinking that the sum of the numbers of two sets will *always* give the number in the union of these two sets we resort to diagrams, consisting of rectangular and circular regions.

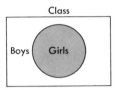

Class

A given region is used to represent or to contain the elements of a well-defined set. Thus the circular region (on the left) is thought of as containing the elements (as points) of all members in one set. This set could be a subset of another set. In this case, the rectangular region (on the right) can be thought of as containing all the children in the class, and the circular region as being a subset of the class, the set of all girls in the class. Then the region of the rectangle not in the circular region represents the set of boys in the class. (The teacher is not considered a member of the class.) The pupils should be encouraged to make many representations of this type, as the initial work in this study. Numbers may be assigned to each set and subset.

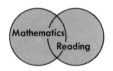

Next consider two overlapping sets, for example, the set of honor pupils in mathematics and the set of honor pupils in reading. Here there are some pupils that belong to both sets and the Venn diagram would appear as shown here. This example, or a similar one, permits the study of the *union* and *intersection* of two sets.

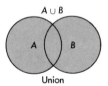

$A \cup B$

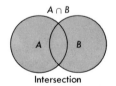

$A \cap B$

Union
All members belonging to one set *or* the other (i.e. either set)

Intersection
All members belonging to one set *and* the other (i.e. both sets)

Again the pupils should collect and illustrate many examples of the union and intersection of two sets. They should also give the number of elements in each set, in the union, and in the intersection. The teacher may introduce the symbols '∪' for union and '∩' for intersection. The pupils should learn to stress the logical words *or* (in the inclusive sense) and *and* (in the sense of *both A and B*).

From a study of the numbers of the sets, pupils will discover the following facts:

a) If sets do not overlap, then

$$n(A \cup B) = n(A) + n(B).$$

b) If sets overlap, then

$$n(A \cup B) = n(A) + n(B) - n(A \cap B),$$

since the intersection has been counted twice in counting A and B separately. Now the teacher may give several problems in finding numbers of sets, subsets, and the union and intersection of two sets. For example, if

$$A = \{2, 3, 5, 7\} \quad \text{and} \quad B = \{1, 3, 5, 7, 9\},$$

then

$$n(A) = 4, \; n(B) = 5, \; n(A \cup B) = n(\{1, 2, 3, 5, 7, 9\}) = 6,$$
$$n(A \cap B) = 3,$$

and it is easy to verify that $n(A \cup B) = 4 + 5 - 3 = 6$.

As a final part of this study, pupils can be asked to find a missing number for one of the parts of a Venn diagram. Consider a party at which there are 29 children. Seventeen children have cake, 22 have ice cream, and 15 children have both cake and ice cream. How many took no refreshments?

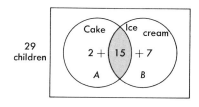

$A \cap B = 15$	Both refreshments
$A = 17 = 15 + 2$	(cake)
$B = 22 = 15 + 7$	(ice cream)
$A \cup B = 2 + 15 + 7 = 24$	(refreshments)
$\therefore 29 - 24 = 5$	(no refreshments)

A '5' should be written in the part of the rectangular region outside the circular regions. Again many examples of this type can be collected, illustrated, and solved by the children. No attempt to put the problems in equation form is necessary unless this technique has been previously taught. Many examples can be found in current junior high school textbooks and in the references at the end of the chapter. The study of sets and set operations by using Venn diagrams may be taught in Grades 4, 5, and 6.

15-2 CLOCK OR DIAL ARITHMETIC

One of the aims of extended mathematical study is to enlarge a number system so that subtraction and exact division become operations. That is, no matter what ordered pair of numbers is given, one can find the difference, or, except for the divisor zero, the quotient. To give bright children an idea of a finite number system in which all four operations exist, the teacher can resort to the use of a dial or clock with a single hand.

Begin with the little hand of the clock on the wall (ignore the large hand) or a dial, as shown here. This dial of 5 spaces is easier for a start. Tell the pupils that *all the new arithmetic will be done on this dial.* How many numbers are there? Only five; our number system has only the elements 0, 1, 2, 3, 4. This is all the dial counts, for after 4 it reverts to 0.

b

a	+	0	1	2	3	4
	0	0	1	2	3	4
	1	1	2	3	4	0
	2	2	3	4	0	1
	3	3	4	0	1	2
	4	4	0	1	2	3

Now define addition in terms of spaces covered by the dial. When the dial returns to 0 the counting must start all over. Thus the addition table shown above can be constructed. This table can be verified by turning the dial a spaces, followed by b spaces, and the result entered in the proper cell. A study of the table shows that addition is commutative and associative. The number 0 is the identity element of addition. But now, while we are using this dial, subtraction is always possible.

To show this, define a subtraction as an inverse of an addition:

$3 - 2 = \square \Rightarrow 3 = \square + 2,$ | $2 - 3 = \triangle \Rightarrow 2 = \triangle + 3.$

In the table for the column headed 2 we go down to the sum 3 (in row 2) and opposite it at the left is the difference, 1: | In the table for the column headed 3 we go down to the sum 2 (in the last row) and opposite it to the left is the difference, 4:

$3 - 2 = 1$ because $1 + 2 = 3.$ | $2 - 3 = 4$ because $4 + 3 = 2.$

The children can verify this subtraction by first turning the dial the spaces designated by the minuend, and then reversing the dial the number of spaces designated by the subtrahend. The endpoint is the difference. This last activity leads to a very interesting fact. Every row has a 0, and only one 0. Hence for any number, there is one and only one other number such that the sum is 0. For example, $1 + 4 = 0, 2 + 3 = 0, 3 + 2 = 0,$ $4 + 1 = 0, 0 + 0 = 0.$ We say that a number which, when added to another number, yields the sum 0 is an *additive inverse* of that number. Thus 1 is the additive inverse of 4 and vice versa, 2 of 3 and vice versa, and 0 of itself.

b

$\times$	0	1	2	3	4
0	0	0	0	0	0
1	0	1	2	3	4
2	0	2	4	1	3
3	0	3	1	4	2
4	0	4	3	2	1

a

The pupils can now build a multiplication table in the following manner. We have a panel board with a hookup to the dial, as shown at right. If button '0' is pressed, nothing happens on the dial. Press it 1, 2, 3, or 4 times and nothing happens. Thus $0 \times N = 0$. Again, if the 1, 2, 3, or 4 button is not pressed, we interpret this as $N \times 0 = 0$. If button '1' is pressed, the dial turns 1 space. For each successive pressing the dial moves an additional space; hence $1 \times 1 = 1$, $1 \times 2 = 2$, etc. Similarly, if button '2' is pressed, the dial moves 2 spaces. If this button is pressed 3 times, the dial spins around to 2, to 4, to 1, so that $2 \times 3 = 1$. In this way the entire multiplication table is filled in, as shown on the previous page.

It is easy to verify that the operation is commutative and associative, that 1 is the identity multiplier, that is, $1 \times n = n \times 1 = n$. It is also easy to show that every number except zero has a multiplicative inverse, since each row has one and only one '1' occurring in it. Thus $1 \times 1 = 1$, $2 \times 3 = 1$, $3 \times 2 = 1$, and $4 \times 4 = 1$. Because of this, division, except by zero, is always possible. We define

$$a \div b = c \Rightarrow a = c \times b, \qquad b \neq 0.$$

So if $4 \div 3 = \square$ means $4 = \square \times 3$, from the multiplication table in the column headed '3' we find the product '4' opposite '3' (at the left of this row). Hence $4 \div 3 = 3$ because $3 \times 3 = 4$. Now the pupils should solve all possible division problems, $1 \div 3 = 2$, $3 \div 1 = 3$, etc.

Finally it is easy to verify that multiplication is distributive over addition because

$$4(3 + 2) = 4 \times 3 + 4 \times 2,$$
$$4 \times 0 = 2 + 3,$$
$$0 = 0.$$

This whole clock (or dial) number system should be presented with stress on the properties of the operation. It should be compared with the whole-number system and the rational-number system. As an end product, the pupils should construct their own clock system with 3 numbers, then 7 numbers, and, as a method of comparison, with 6 and 8 numbers. The difference in properties which results when we use a prime number of elements on a dial and a non-prime number of elements on a dial is of real significance. Finite-dial arithmetic is a new number system; if the number of basic elements in it is a prime number, the system behaves beautifully.

Clock arithmetic may be introduced in either Grades 4, 5, or 6, at the time the teacher reviews the properties of a number system.

15–3 MODULAR ARITHMETIC

When we present this topic there are three important objectives that we can attain if we direct our teaching toward these goals. First, children can learn the idea of periodic phenomena. That is, as one progresses from 0 through the ordered set of whole numbers, there is a relation (same remainder as) which places the numbers in distinct classes. Second, children become acquainted with a way of separating numbers into disjoint classes, a way other than that of classifying them as odd-even or prime-composite. This method is one in which the difference between any two numbers in any one of the classes is a multiple of the modulus. Third, and most important if considered in relation to rational numbers, children learn that all the members of a whole class or set of numbers can be regarded as equivalent. Hence we can add and multiply classes of numbers by selecting elements in the classes, and no matter which elements we select in the classes, the result is always in one particular class. Therefore clock arithmetic is an instance of modular arithmetic.

When we begin the work, we should ask the children to start with the set of whole numbers, and divide each of them in turn by a selected number. At first let this selected number be prime, for example, 3, 5, 7, or 11. Then we should ask them to collect these numbers into separate sets according to the rule: "gives the same remainder as." They discover two important facts:

1. There are as many classes as the number which was used as a divisor.

2. If in any class the numbers are ordered, they form an arithmetic progression. That is, in any class, successive numbers differ by the divisor.

3. Another way of stating (2) is: In any class, the difference of any two numbers is a multiple of the divisor.

Then the divisor should be called a *modulus*. Since in any class, any two numbers behave the same way with regard to division by the modulus, or to the difference being a multiple of the modulus, we say that in any class any two of the numbers are *congruent* (i.e., they behave the same way) *modulo d*, the divisor. For example, 7 is congruent to 12, modulo 5. The pupils should write the *remainder* or residue (what is left over or remains) in brace notation and on a series of concentric circles, as shown here.

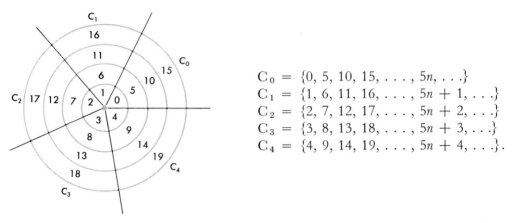

$$C_0 = \{0, 5, 10, 15, \ldots, 5n, \ldots\}$$
$$C_1 = \{1, 6, 11, 16, \ldots, 5n + 1, \ldots\}$$
$$C_2 = \{2, 7, 12, 17, \ldots, 5n + 2, \ldots\}$$
$$C_3 = \{3, 8, 13, 18, \ldots, 5n + 3, \ldots\}$$
$$C_4 = \{4, 9, 14, 19, \ldots, 5n + 4, \ldots\}.$$

If the pupils are apt, the teacher may wish to introduce modular notation:

$a \equiv b \pmod 5$ means that $a - b$ is a multiple of 5,

$a \equiv b \pmod 5$ means that a and b give the same remainder on division by 5,

$a \equiv b \pmod 5$ means that if $a = q \cdot 5 + r$, and if $b = q' \cdot 5 + r'$, then $r' = r$.

After they have studied one modulus, for example, 5, as above, the children should repeat the same study for other moduli by themselves. As a final aspect of this study in the elementary school, the teacher should discuss addition of classes. First we ask the children to select any element of class C_i, for example C_1. Then we ask them to select an element of another class, for example C_3. Add them. In what class is the sum? Answer: C_4. Now repeat this several times until the children generalize:

Any number in class C_1 added to any number in class C_3 gives a sum in class C_4. We write this in the form

$$C_1 \oplus C_3 = C_4,$$

where the $\oplus$ has a very special meaning. It means: whatever C_1 represents, and whatever C_3 represents, the result $C_1 \oplus C_3$ represents C_4. This is a binary operation (internal law of composition) which the children can verify. Then we ask the children to complete the "class addition" table and verify that compared with ordinary arithmetic this addition has $C_0 \to 0$, $C_1 \to 1$, and that it is associative and commutative.

$\oplus$	C_0	C_1	C_2	C_3	C_4
C_0					
C_1			C_3		
C_2		C_3			
C_3					
C_4					

They can solve sentences such as

$$C_3 \oplus \boxed{x} = C_4, \qquad \boxed{x} = C_1,$$

and find that there is always a solution. This means that subtraction is always possible. They can solve

$$C_i \oplus x = C_0, \qquad i = 1, 2, 3, 4,$$

and find that every class has an "opposite class." This can be called the *additive inverse class*. Thus this class arithmetic is superior to the ordinary arithmetic of whole numbers, where $4 + \square = 2$ has no solution.

Similarly, if time allows, the same discussion should be carried over to class multiplication designated by $\otimes$. Here the teacher must be careful to use a prime number as a modulus in all the introductory examples. As a final exercise, the pupils can construct a $\otimes$ table for modulo 4, or 6, or 8, or 9. They will discover that irregularities occur. For example, in modulo 6,

$$C_2 \otimes C_4 = C_2 \qquad \text{and} \qquad C_2 \otimes C_1 = C_2$$

and $C_2 \otimes \square = C_2$ has two solutions. Again this system does not behave like the whole-number system. The teacher should ask the pupils to explain why prime-number moduli behave well and nonprime moduli do not. The answer lies in the factorization of a prime number as compared with the factorization of a composite number.

It must be stressed that, although we do have a lot of fun doing this modular arithmetic of classes, its primary object is to build a frame of reference which will serve the children well when they study rational numbers. Although it is beyond the ability of most children to comprehend the structure of a modular system, they can associate what is taught with a system of numeration, and thus use it to develop rules for divisibility of a number expressed in decimal (or any other) notation.

15-4 DENSITY OF THE RATIONALS

One concept to be developed in mathematical study is that of the real number line; it is a concept that will eventually prove essential. It is fairly easy to show how to attach (or map) whole numbers or particular rational numbers to points on a line, once a '0' and '1' point have been selected. However, the fact that there is an infinity of points on any segment, no matter how small, of this number line is a fairly abstract idea. That there is a number to be assigned to any point on the line is even more abstruse. One way to prepare the way for this concept, and to lead to the eventual study of irrational real numbers, is to study the density of rational number points on any small part of the number line.

In this study we introduce the first intuitive idea of a least upper bound of a sequence of numbers. The primary ideas here are decimal fractions, repeating decimal fractions, approximation sequence, and least upper bound. This study may be introduced after the children have learned the operations with rational numbers both in common-fraction notation and in decimal notation, perhaps in the second half of the sixth school year.

As a first enterprise, the children use the symbol $<$ to show that for any two fractions, no matter how close in value, there are other fractions with values between those two. For example, they know that $\frac{1}{2} < \frac{2}{3}$. Ask the pupils to find another number between these two numbers, and prove their answer.

This study with a number of similar special cases should lead to the three generalizations:

1. If $\frac{a}{b} < \frac{c}{d}$ then $ad < bc$; $\frac{1}{2} < \frac{2}{3}$ because $1 \times 3 < 2 \times 2$.

2. If $\dfrac{a}{b} < \dfrac{c}{d}$ then $\dfrac{a}{b} < \dfrac{a+c}{b+d} < \dfrac{c}{d}$;

$$\frac{1}{2} < \frac{1+2}{2+3} < \frac{2}{3} , \text{ that is, } \tfrac{1}{2} < \tfrac{3}{5} < \tfrac{2}{3}.$$

3. If $\dfrac{a}{b} < \dfrac{c}{d}$ then $\dfrac{a}{b} < \dfrac{\frac{a}{b} + \frac{c}{d}}{2} < \dfrac{c}{a}$;

$$\frac{1}{2} < \frac{\frac{1}{2} + \frac{2}{3}}{2} < \frac{2}{3} , \text{ that is, } \tfrac{1}{2} < \tfrac{7}{12} < \tfrac{2}{3}.$$

In the special example shown, children can then find another number between $\tfrac{1}{2}$ and $\tfrac{3}{5}$, for example, $\tfrac{4}{7}$; then another between $\tfrac{1}{2}$ and $\tfrac{4}{7}$, for example, $\tfrac{5}{9}$, and so on, forever. Thus there are an infinite number of numbers between $\tfrac{1}{2}$ and $\tfrac{2}{3}$. Using other fractions, and the same procedure, and attaching each newly found "between number" to a point on the line, children begin to get a feeling for the density of numbers between two given numbers.

A second activity consists in learning the nature of decimal fractions, that is, those fractions which can be represented exactly by a finite decimal notation. It is easy to show that any finite decimal notation can be changed to common-fractional form. Thus

$$23 \text{ is } \tfrac{23}{1}, \qquad 2.31 \text{ is } \tfrac{231}{100}, \qquad 6.4 \text{ is } \tfrac{64}{10} \text{ or } \tfrac{32}{5},$$

and so forth. The decimal is written with a whole-number numerator and the proper power of ten in the denominator, and if necessary transformed to its simplest form. It is a bit more complicated to establish the reverse of this process; that is, when can a common-form fraction be changed into a finite decimal?

First the children study the prime factors of powers of ten:

$$10 = 2 \times 5, \qquad 10^2 = 2^2 \times 5^2, \qquad 10^3 = 2^3 \cdot 5^3,$$

and so on. In this way they discover that the only prime factors in the denominator of a decimal fraction are 2 and 5. Any other prime factors cannot be changed, by multiplication by a whole number, to a power of ten. Thus 3 can never be multiplied by any whole number to give a power of 10. Neither can 7, 11, and so on. How about 4, 6, 8, or 9? Well, since $4 = 2^2$ we can multiply it by 5^2 to obtain $2^2 \times 5^2$ or 100. Since 6 is 2×3, we cannot change it to a power of 10 by multiplying it by a whole number. But since $8 = 2^3$, we can change it to a power of 10 (1000). Since $9 = 3 \times 3$ we cannot; and so on.

Thus children discover that any fraction whose denominator has only the prime factors 2 or 5, or both, can be changed to a finite decimal representation; all others cannot. We say that all the other fractions represent nondecimal rational numbers. Thus they know that $\frac{1}{3}$ is a nondecimal rational number. Practice must be given in determining which common fractions can be transformed and what the transformed decimal notation is.

Now pupils can make a study of the approximation to nondecimal rational numbers by using decimal representation to as many decimal places as desired. They do this by using the usual division process. For example, consider $\frac{17}{7}$. By dividing 7 into $\frac{170}{10}$ or 17.0, they find that

$$\frac{24}{10} < \frac{17}{7} < \frac{25}{10}, \qquad 2.4 < \frac{17}{7} < 2.5.$$

By extending the division process, they find that

$$2.42 < \frac{17}{7} < 2.43 \text{ (between 2 successive hundredths)}$$
$$2.428 < \frac{17}{7} < 2.429 \text{ (successive thousandths)}$$
$$2.4285 < \frac{17}{7} < 2.4286 \text{ (successive ten-thousandths), etc.}$$

In this manner, the children derive a sequence (ordered set of numbers) 2, 2.4, 2.42, 2.428, 2.4285, 2.42857, 2.428571, $\cdots$, in which each successive number is greater than the one before it and yet all these numbers are less than $\frac{17}{7}$. By extending the sequence, we can get decimal rationals as close to $\frac{17}{7}$ as we desire, yet we never reach $\frac{17}{7}$. We call $\frac{17}{7}$ the *least upper bound* of the sequence. Why? Because if we select any rational number less than $\frac{17}{7}$, there will be a number in the above sequence greater than the number we select. Children should practice this procedure with many rationals, for example, $\frac{5}{3}, \frac{3}{14}, \frac{4}{9}, \frac{120}{11}$, etc. Then we ask them to do it for $\frac{5}{16}$, and they find that the process terminates. This can lead to a new way of representing such a number as an upper bound of an infinite sequence.

Consider $\frac{1}{2}$, which can be written 0.5. Surely $0.49 < 0.5$. Then $0.499 < 0.5$ but $0.49 < 0.499$. Hence the sequence of numbers 0.4, 0.49, 0.499, 0.4999, $\cdots$, has a least upper bound which is 0.5. Similarly $\frac{5}{16} = 0.3125$, and thus 0.3124, 0.31249, 0.312499, $\cdots$ has $\frac{5}{16}$ as its least upper bound. (Here, if teachers

$$
\begin{array}{r}
2.428571 \\
7)\overline{17.000000} \\
14 \\
\hline
3\,0 \leftarrow \\
2\,8 \\
\hline
20 \\
14 \\
\hline
60 \\
56 \\
\hline
40 \\
35 \\
\hline
50 \\
49 \\
\hline
10 \\
7 \\
\hline
30 \leftarrow
\end{array}
$$

care to do so, they may introduce infinite repeating decimals, but this topic may well be left for later study.)

As a final part of this enrichment topic, children can be asked to do the reverse process, selecting a point at random on the number scale and approximating the number it represents by a decimal notation. For this purpose it is best to use a meter to represent the length of one unit. When they stop at a point along the edge, they know that the number of this point is such that

$$0 < n < 1.$$

When we look at the tenths scale we next find, for example, that

$$0.6 < n < 0.7.$$

Looking at the hundredths scale, we find that

$$0.64 < n < 0.65.$$

Looking at the thousandths scale, we find that

$$0.645 < n < 0.646.$$

Using a magnifying glass, we estimate that the point is

$$0.6452 < n < 0.6453,$$

and this is about as close as we can get.

If the point falls on a division mark, it is represented by a decimal rational. If it does not we can only estimate. Thus suppose we find that

$$0.3 < n < 0.4, \qquad 0.33 < n < 0.34, \qquad 0.333 < n < 0.334,$$

and the glass appears to show that $0.3333 < n < 0.3334$. We can surmise, but not be sure, that the point represents $\frac{1}{3}$. (Why can we not be sure? The next enlargement might show that $0.33335 < n < 0.33336$, and already 0.33335 is greater than $\frac{1}{3}$! Prove this.)

The above development could lead pupils to believe that every point on the line has a rational number assigned to it. They must not be led to this conclusion. We ask about numbers such as 0.12123123412345 ... and 0.10203040. ... Children will learn more about this in their subsequent study. Tell them that $\sqrt{2}$ is not rational, yet is assigned to a point on the number line. Remember that we cannot teach the whole theory of real numbers in the elementary school, not even to the brightest of pupils. Any treatment of rational approximation should be delayed until Grade 6.

15-5 PLACE SYSTEMS OF NOTATION

The purpose of teaching systems of notation to bases other than ten is *not* to develop computational skill. Rather it is to show that the nature and properties of whole numbers (and rational numbers) are not changed when we use a different method of naming the numbers. Thus zero always remains the identity element of addition, 1 is always the identity element of multiplication, 8 is always an even number, although '13$_{\text{five}}$', its representation in base 5, ends in an odd-number digit. An odd number or a prime number remains so, no matter what different numerals (in different bases) are used to name them. Children learn that in different bases numerals representing the same number are different, but the properties of the number remain the same. They also learn that rules of divisibility of numbers developed in a decimal system of notation do not necessarily hold if a different base is used.

The study of different bases can be used in two ways: one, as a readiness experience for learning to count in base ten, and two, as a method of giving children a deeper insight into a system of numeration after they have learned and used the base ten. The readiness activity may start as soon as children can count to five, six, or seven. For example, if children can count to three, they can count how many there are in a class. Suppose that we put a dot on the board for each pupil, like this:

Now we count off the dots in groups of three, putting a ring around each three until there are not enough remaining to make three. Thus there are groups of three (call them triads) and two left over. Now we count the triads by threes, putting a large circle around each three triads until there are fewer than three triads left.

Call one of the large circled sets a *triple triad*. There are two of the triple triads, one triad and two single dots. How many in all?

        2 triple triads,   1 triad,   and 2.

This same procedure can be carried out by having the pupils count off by threes, and recording the number by strokes. For each three strokes they erase and put a stroke in the triad column. They count as follows:

Triads	Ones

Now we do the same with the triads; that is, for each three triads we erase and place a stroke in the triple-triad column. Then we write the following:

Triple triad	Triad	Ones
2	1	2

We state the number of each kind of set and say that 2 1 2 means

        2 triple triads,   1 triad,   2 ones.

We can use the same procedure to count by fours, fives, or eights, inventing names for each new set in the columns to the left. For example, we can measure out water and counting by twos use the names from *right* to *left*,

gallon   flagon   quart   pint   cup   gill,

where any 2 of the one set makes 1 of the set next to the left. Thus 1011 means 1 quart, 1 cup, 1 gill (no pints). The use of the base two might well be deferred until other bases have been used. Then counting by tens leads to the decimal system of notation.

If children have learned the decimal system, then they should be ready to construct a system to the base five, seven, or eight. A good exercise is to use new words but to keep the symbols already learned. New symbols make the learning harder and are not necessarily conducive to learning the nature of place notation. If we use the base five, then we can give the names

zero	lā	lē	lō	lū	băh
$\{\ \}$	$\{a\}$	$\{a, b\}$	$\{a, b, c\}$	$\{a, b, c, d\}$	$\{a, b, c, d, e\}$
0	1	2	3	4	10_{five}

as the numbers of the corresponding sets shown, and write the symbols as shown. Of course the 10 is ten, but 10_{five} means one băh and zero lā. Then the counting and notation would go as follows:

0	zero	10_{five} lā-băh	20_{five} lē-băh	40_{five} lū-băh
1	lā	11_{five} lā-băh lā	21_{five} lē-băh lā	. . .
2	lē	12_{five} lā-băh lē	. . .	. . .
3	lō	13_{five} lā-băh lō	. . .	. . .
4	lū	14_{five} lā-băh-lū	24_{five} lē-băh lū	44_{five} lū-băh lū

and the next numeral is 100_{five} and is lā băh-băh, for which a new name can be created, just as "hundred" was created for ten-tens. The digits 0 to 4 are the same as in the base ten, but from then on each numeral has a subscript "five" to show that the numeral is in base five. Care must be taken to differentiate 234 and 234_{five}, because the first numeral is in base ten (since no subscript is shown) and the second is not.

Now that the children have learned how to write numerals to base five, they can by analogy learn to write them to any other base two to nine. Bases greater than ten demand new digits and can be left for later study. Although it is not necessary, some teachers may prefer to have pupils compute using a system of notation other than the decimal system. The purpose of this activity is to gain deeper understanding of the nature of an algorism, not to gain skill in computing in another base. In fact it is better not to use addition and multiplication tables in other bases, since this can cause the children confusion in remembering the fundamental facts of the base-ten system. The best procedure is to use the base-ten system and convert to the base under use.

Thus in the addition problem shown, the child should say $6 + 3 = 9$, $9 + 2 = 11$; this is 1 eight and 3, write '3' and carry '1'. $1 + 4 = 5$, $5 + 5 = 10$, $10 + 6 = 16$; this is 2 eights, write '0' and carry '2'; $2 + 3 = 5$, $5 + 1 = 6$, $6 + 7 = 13$; this is 1 eight and 5, write '15', answer 1503_eight.

$$
\begin{array}{r}
762_\text{eight} \\
153_\text{eight} \\
+ \quad 346_\text{eight} \\
\hline
1503_\text{eight}
\end{array}
$$

Similarly for the multiplication problem, the pupil says $6 \times 5 = 30$, this is 3 eights and 6; write '6', retain '3'. Then $6 \times 6 = 36$, $36 + 3 = 39$. This is 4 eights and 7. Write '7', retain '4'; and so on. In each case the pupil should explain how he is multiplying (or adding) the higher powers of the base.

$$
\begin{array}{r}
765_\text{eight} \\
\times \quad 46_\text{eight} \\
\hline
5676_\text{eight} \\
37240_\text{eight} \\
\hline
45136_\text{eight}
\end{array}
$$

As a final activity, perhaps in Grades 5 and 6, the pupil can convert a numeral in one base to one in another base to represent the same number. To do this, we must always use the decimal system for the necessary computations. For example,

$$643_\text{seven} = 6 \times 7^2 + 4 \times 7 + 3 = 294 + 28 + 3 = 325.$$

To change 325 to the system base seven, we use the counting procedure given at the start of this section. We divide 325 by 7. There are $46 \times 7 + 3$. Therefore 3 is the units digit. We then divide the 46 (7 sets) by 7. There are $6 \times 7 + 4$; hence 4 is the number of 7-sets. We divide 6 by 7, obtaining $0 \times 7 + 6$, and 6 is the number of seven-squared sets. Thus

		Rem.
7	325	
7	46	3
7	6	4
	0	6

$$325 = 643_\text{seven}.$$

The reader should now be able to teach the conversion of any base to any other base, by first transforming a given numeral into the base ten, and then converting the new numeral into the required base. For example:

$334_\text{five} = \boxed{}{}_\text{four}$ $334_\text{five} = 3 \times 25 + 3 \times 5 + 4 = 94$;

then, as shown at the right,

4	94	2
4	23	3
4	5	1
4	1	1
	0	

$$334_\text{five} = 94 = 1132_\text{four}$$

There are many other enrichment topics than can be developed. For example: transforming geometric figures by translating, reflecting, or rotating; topological puzzles; product sets and lattice points; elementary ideas of probability and statistics; proof and logic. These are described in the literature, and the teacher who cares to spend time on these topics can find an abundance of material. There is one topic that is more than enrichment, since it enters into everyday affairs and into the study of elementary science; teachers may wish to include it as a part of the instruction for all pupils. The topic is positive and negative numbers.

15–6 POSITIVE AND NEGATIVE NUMBERS AND ZERO

There are many mathematically correct methods of introducing positive and negative numbers, either just the integers or the rational numbers. However, at the elementary school level we are interested in the uses and meanings that these numbers may have, and so the presentation should be very informal and one for which immediate application can be made. A good readiness exercise is to discuss games in which points can be made and also lost, earning and spending money, going above and below sea level, gaining and losing weight, and so on. In all these cases there are quantities which may be considered as oppositely directed. To each one of them we can also associate a number of arithmetic—one that is not directed—for example, a number of points in a game, an amount of money (number of dollars), a distance from sea level, a weight, and so on. So children should first give examples of (1) quantities that are not directed and (2) quantities that are directed.

Then children can discover that to each quantity that is measured by an arithmetic number, there are two corresponding but oppositely directed quantities. The measure of these quantities we agree to represent by new numbers called *directed numbers*. Thus to a measure of weight 8 pounds, we have two new numbers: $+8$ meaning an increase or gain of 8 pounds and -8 meaning a decrease or loss of 8 pounds. These numbers should be read *positive* eight and *negative* eight; and not plus or minus, since the latter are operation terms. The symbols '$+$' and '$-$' may be written as pre-superscripts and not as operational signs. The first thing the pupils should learn is how to read and write these positive and negative numbers, and ascribe meaning to them in terms of measured quantities. Many illustrations can be found in first-course algebra textbooks.

Thus to each arithmetic number, except zero, children can now assign two new numbers which may be called directed numbers, rational numbers, or positive and negative numbers. Zero is neither positive nor negative, but it belongs to the set of rational numbers. For the purpose of talking about these numbers, if both numbers are positive, or both negative, we say that they are of *like sign;* otherwise they are of *opposite sign.*

Arithmetic	Directed
0	0
1	$+1, -1$
$2\frac{1}{2}$	$+2\frac{1}{2}, -2\frac{1}{2}$
$3\frac{3}{4}$	$+3\frac{3}{4}, -3\frac{3}{4}$
$\vdots$	$\vdots$

Since we have already studied the number line in detail, we may now use it (and extend it) as a new number line of directed numbers. Just as we scaled the line from 0 to the right, we now extend the scale from 0 to the left.

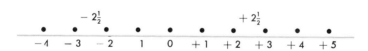

If we assign to the points on the right the positive numbers, corresponding to the arithmetic numbers, then, symmetric to 0, there is for each positive point another point to which we assign the oppositely directed (negative) number. In this way we build up a scale similar to the thermometer scale, and 0 becomes a number from which it is possible to make measurements in either direction.

Finally the pupils can learn how to combine two directed numbers by addition. For this purpose they may use the number line in the usual method presented in most algebra textbooks. Another interesting way is to give each pupil a number of small pieces of paper on which are written the numbers $+1$ and -1. Since '$+$' indicates a gain and '$-$' a loss, it is quickly apparent that if one '$+$' paper and one '$-$' paper are combined they neutralize each other and $+1 + -1 = 0$. Similarly, the 'n's in $+n + -n$, where 'n' is a numeral for any number of arithmetic, neutralize each other and $+n + -n = 0$.

Now children select several pieces of paper and two pupils combine their pieces to find the result. If three '$+$'s and five '$-$'s are combined, three '$+$'s neutralize three '$-$'s and the result is -2. We write this as

$$+3 \oplus -5 = -2,$$

where $\oplus$ indicates an addition different from ordinary arithmetic. After many such experiences, children develop their own rules for combining these numbers. Then more than two of these numbers can be combined by $\oplus$.

Any further development can be found in the books on algebra referred to previously. In a similar manner teachers can find ways of introducing variables, generalizations, and the solution of simple equations, but at all times this should be not merely interesting busy work, but it should have a genuine educational objective.

15–7 PROOF

In the last few years, the idea of *proof* or proving by logical reasoning has been suggested as a possible sixth-grade enrichment topic. Perhaps the easiest topic in which to introduce this enrichment is the proving of simple geometric relations and constructions by accepting the three congruence theorems and using the compass to construct equal radii. The teacher can find this material in current textbooks on plane geometry and extract it for use. He should take care, however, not to make these proofs too rigorous or give them in an axiomatic way. Such proofs are merely a way of getting children to see how to draw correct logical conclusions from the use of *modus ponens*. That is, from the acceptance of the two statements:

   a) If it is this, then a certain result follows,

   b) It is this,

we can logically conclude that

   c) A certain result follows.

As an example, from the two statements:

        a) If it is a Swiss watch, it is a good timepiece,

and

        b) It is a Swiss watch,

we conclude that

        c) It is a good timepiece.

15–8 SUMMARY

Many children can learn the entire regular course of study in elementary school mathematics in less time than that allotted in the program. These children can and should be challenged by enrichment work—that is, a study that gives an added and deeper insight—worked into the mathematics of the regular program. This material should not be the same as the more advanced study of later grades, since this may tend to disinterest bright children when they have to repeat it. The material can consist of topics not included in standard courses but sufficiently elementary to be learned by these students. It should not only challenge them to reason and to form new concepts so that they will develop a greater appreciation and understanding of mathematics, but it should provide them with the basic tools of logical reasoning.

Topics that meet these objectives are: (1) sets and Venn diagrams, (2) arithmetic that stresses the laws and nature of an operation, for example, clock and modular arithmetic, (3) decimal notation of rational numbers, leading to the density properties, (4) the number line, including its extension to represent all rational numbers, (5) systems of notation other than the decimal one, which will eventually tie in with number theory and make clear the distinction between number and numeral, (6) ideas about proof, so that, in learning mathematics, pupils may rely less and less on someone else's authority.

There are other topics that meet the same goals, and these each teacher must select according to his own tastes and knowledge. The essential matter to remember is that enrichment is secondary and it should not take time in the regular program until the required mathematics—that is, the regular course of study—has been studied and mastered.

EXERCISES

1. Describe what the terms *enrichment* and *acceleration* in mathematics study mean to you. Give arguments for and against each of these procedures and then state your position with regard to each procedure.

2. Enrichment has been advocated for the talented or able students. Argue as to the type of and reasons for enrichment for all students, not only the gifted.

3. A teacher wishes to introduce logic as an enrichment topic in Grades 5 or 6. Tell how you would go about creating a unit of four or five lessons on this topic at this level. Whenever you have an appropriate opportunity, teach this unit.

4. One of the most modern topics in mathematics is topology. Consult the references at the end of this chapter and outline a unit on topology that could be taught in Grades 4 or 5.

5. Probability is growing in importance in the study of modern science. Give reasons for introducing ideas about this topic in the elementary school and outline a unit of three lessons that could be taught in the intermediate grades.

6. The modular arithmetic in this chapter was limited to positive whole numbers and zero. It can be extended to include negative whole numbers, provided that the remainders are always positive. Thus $5 \equiv -1 \pmod 3$ because $5 \div 3$ has a *remainder of* 2 and also $-1 \div 3$ gives a quotient of -1 and a *remainder of* $+2$ (that is, $-1 = -1\,(+3) +2$. Now write the three residual classes modulus 3, including positive and negative whole numbers. How would you teach this to sixth-graders?

7. Explain how you would use enrichment as a means of conducting a mathematics club in a school. What pupils would you admit to the club and why?

8. Most elementary school teachers have not had an opportunity to hear of modern topics applicable to elementary school teaching. Explain methods that could be used to acquaint teachers with the mathematical background to teach these topics.

9. One movement in the reform of teaching elementary arithmetic has been the introduction of letters used as variables and the generalization of the laws of operation. Explain to what extent you would develop an introduction of algebra into the elementary school program.

10. Another form enrichment may take is applying mathematics to the teaching of science. Name six to ten topics in elementary school science where mathematics could be used to advantage, and tell how you would interweave the mathematics teaching into these science topics.

REFERENCES

D'AUGUSTINE, C. H., "Developing Generalizations with Topological Net Problems," *The Arithmetic Teacher* **12,** February 1965, pages 109–112

FEHR, H. F., and T. J. HILL, *Contemporary Mathematics for Elementary Teachers*, Boston: D. C. Heath, 1966

HILDEBRAND, F. H., "Experiment in Enrichment—Fourth Grade," *The Arithmetic Teacher* **10,** February 1963, pages 68–71

PEELER, H., "Enrichment Material for School Mathematics," *The Arithmetic Teacher* **9,** May 1962, pages 271–275

PHILLIPS, J. M., "Non-Decimal Numerals," filmstrip G from *Seeing the Use of Numbers, Set VII*, Eye Gate Productions, Jamaica, N.Y.

PHILLIPS, J. M., "The Real Numbers," filmstrip B from *Seeing the Use of Numbers, Set VIII*, Eye Gate Productions, Jamaica, N.Y.

SMITH, L. B., "Venn Diagrams Strengthen Children's Mathematical Understandings," *The Arithmetic Teacher* **13,** 2, February 1966, pages 92–99

SUPPES, P., "Mathematical Logic in the Schools," *The Arithmetic Teacher* **9,** November 1962, pages 396–399

a comprehensive view
of the elementary school
mathematics program

It is not sufficient for an elementary school teacher to know only a segment of the program for any subject, for example, only the material assigned to the particular grade he is working with. The teacher must reach a point in the mastery of the subject and its pedagogy which permits him to see the content and purpose of the entire school program from kindergarten through the first years of high school. This comprehensive view enables him to build each day's lesson toward future learnings, so that pupils have at all times an interrelated set of concepts and operational skills.

16–1 FUNDAMENTAL OBJECTIVES

The overall objective of elementary school mathematical education is to develop those concepts of number and of space, and the concomitant skills in using and applying these concepts, that are necessary to interpret and solve those quantitative and relational problems encountered by all individuals throughout their lives.

The diagram on the opposite page is presented to help the reader see the structure and relationship of the various subjects the child must learn. The reader should analyze it for sequence and for the scope of the fundamental mathematics to be learned. The well-informed reader may desire to construct other possible sequences. In any program, *the real numbers are central*.

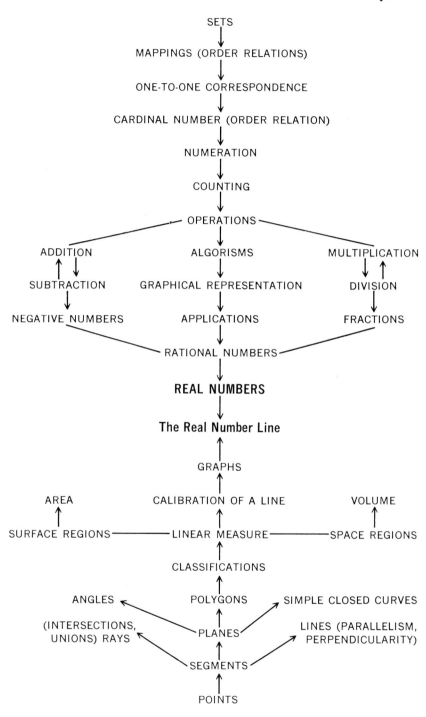

Of course, it is not possible for elementary school children to attain a comprehensive grasp of elementary mathematics as an interrelated discipline, as presented in the diagram, but they should acquire a basis so that subsequent study and use of mathematics deepens and enlarges their understandings of number and of space. The essential principle for a teacher to keep in mind is that, as children are introduced to new concepts, they should recall and use all previous learning. In fact the best way for a child to increase his efficiency is to use the material he has already learned to learn or solve a new situation. Furthermore, it is in this way that mathematics becomes a unified structure in the mind of the pupil. The child should learn the subject in such a manner that he will have a sound basis for extended study of mathematics in subsequent years of schooling. This demands skill in handling concepts and algorisms sufficient to enable the learner to work efficiently and with confidence in all the mathematics he does. The skills, concepts, symbolic processes, applications, and some methods for teaching them have been developed in the preceding chapters.

16–2 EVALUATION OF LEARNING

One of the major unsolved problems in education is the problem of evaluation. At the present time, we have only heuristic solutions. In the past, the major purpose of evaluation has been one of selection; that is, the teacher must select those pupils who have shown, by their record on a test, that they can do sufficiently well to pass on to higher study. Although this selective evaluation procedure is necessary for a limited number of persons—those entering universities for higher study or those entering a profession or career demanding the acquisition of high skills—it is not in accord with the general purpose of elementary school education. In elementary school, in which we recognize the wide divergence in inherited ability and environmental conditioning, evaluation makes it possible to help each child fit into a learning situation in which he can satisfactorily move ahead at a pace adapted to his past acquisitions and his overall ability.

A teacher who is to guide a class of individuals to possible maximum individual achievement must learn a great deal about each pupil. He can accomplish this only by using testing situations in which the purpose of the test has dictated its construction. In the past, for the most part, standard and teacher-made tests have sought to determine the pupil's speed and efficiency in computational processes, perhaps because it is easy to construct computational exercises ranging from the simple to the complex, and even easier to discover how far a given pupil can get in a given time, and with what percent of correct answers. Today, however, we stress the teaching of concepts and the understanding of them. But we find it difficult to know how to measure these two things, let alone how to create "discovery methods" which generate desired concepts in the minds of our pupils. If we itemize the purposes of testing, and the means of measuring progress toward what we aim at, we shall be in a better position to help our pupils learn.

One purpose of testing—never to be relinquished—is to establish standards of accomplishment, in skills, concepts, and applications, below which a pupil cannot be judged competent to perform his everyday duties as a citizen. A pupil who fails to meet these standards must be guided toward this goal even if this means he must continue the study of elementary school mathematics subsequently, when he enters secondary school. These standards must be set by the school, working with mathematically competent consultants. At present, the goals for achievement are usually stated in terms of standardized test scores, and the most reliable of these is the score for skill in computation. This book has given many suggestions for reasonable expectations as to understanding and problem-solving, as well as computational skill. The authors feel that, in general, time tests should be avoided and children should be encouraged to work in unhurried calm.

Tests designed to measure this achievement should be directed toward several outcomes:

1. To examine the pupil's inventory of acquired mathematical competence, that is, to find out what it is that each pupil already knows.

2. To discover what the pupils have mislearned or never learned of basic concepts and skills. It does a pupil no good to continue to practice erroneous ideas.

3. To make a prognosis for future mathematical study. Those pupils who can readily translate principles into algebraic formulas can be urged to begin the study of algebra in Grade 7 rather than deferring it to Grade 8 or 9.

4. To help the teacher improve his own teaching techniques. When most of the pupils in a class make the same error, it may be the mode of presentation that has led to misinterpretation. By modifying or changing a mode of presentation, a teacher may not only improve his teaching, but may also increase the amount of mathematics that the pupils can learn. The use of tests as an aid to self-improvement, by both teachers and pupils, yields the greatest return so far as the improvement of education is concerned. Tests should always be looked on as opportunities to discover what one knows, what one does not know, how the unknown may be learned, and how the erroneously learned may be corrected.

To test is not necessarily to evaluate. It is the purpose for which the test is used and the interpretation of the test results in the light of that purpose which constitute the evaluation. The same test may be used as a test for mastery, a test for diagnosis of pupils' difficulty, a test for diagnosis of the teacher's effectiveness, and a basis for predicting a pupil's success in future learning. A test is usually designed with one of these uses as its major purpose, and it may be expected to produce results which contribute more toward that purpose than another, but the alert teacher will find several uses for each test he gives. Usually a new test should be developed for each new attempt to evaluate. This does not preclude the use of past test items which a good teacher always keeps on file. A number of procedures will help the classroom teacher to develop such items.

1. Prepare a set of specific statements of desired outcomes. Always state these outcomes in terms of specific behaviors expected of the pupil. Instead of saying "an ability to multiply correctly," say "to be able to find the correct product of any two three-digit numbers" or "to solve a problem whose solution involves

$$\frac{a(b - c)}{d}$$

where $(b - c)$ must be found first."

2. After the specific goals have been stated, create test situations to meet them. These may consist of computational exercises, verbal problems, or exhibited material to which the pupil is asked to give a response. List possible responses that will be accepted as correct. Not all evaluation need be of the "paper-and-pencil" type.

3. Ask pupils to try to discover areas in which they lack knowledge as well as topics which they believe they know. Teachers can devise questions to help pupils see how correct they are in their own evaluation. On prepared charts children can keep a record of their growth in computational techniques, in concept interpretation, and in problem-solving ability. Samples of items measuring these aspects of mathematical growth may be found in the literature (see the references at the end of this chapter).

4. As we shall note later, the goals of educational achievement are set by the philosophy of school instruction to which any particular school subscribes. In any good situation this philosophy changes from time to time as new knowledge comes to light. Hence, from time to time, a teacher should reexamine the objectives in arithmetic and geometric study and adapt the teaching process to the achievement of the revised objectives. This will call for new test situations which the teacher may create for himself or which he may find in the newer publications on the teaching of mathematics in the elementary school.

When we count the number of items in a finite collection of distinct objects, we can be absolutely exact: e.g., there are 29 pupils in my class. The measure 29 is exact. However, as we saw in Chapter 8, when we attempt to find out how much there is of some continuous quantity, we can be only approximate in our answer. When it comes to the measure of intelligence, or the amount of mathematical knowledge, possessed by a child, we are in an even more nebulous situation; our approximation is one that must allow for great error. In the first place, we have to remember that there is no zero point on the scales we use for measuring mathematical knowledge or general intelligence, and that fact alone is sufficient guarantee that the measures we get are not absolute. No matter how objective we try to make our test items, we must realize that what the items really measure and how well they measure it (validity and reliability, respectively) are only matters of statistical interpretation.

However, measure we must, and helping pupils learn by a variety of test situations appears to be the best available procedure at present. Some situations are:

1. *Objective test.* A test item which has one (or at least a particular type of) response and is either correct or incorrect. Most standard test items are of this type.

2. *Practice test.* A series of exercises, usually timed, which reveal the degree of efficiency which a student has in certain types of mathematical thinking or computation.

3. *Problem situation.* Here a teacher expresses a problem in a genuine, or apparently genuine, situation and asks the pupil to discuss the procedure he would use to find a solution. By keeping a record of the pupil's responses, the teacher can tell whether or not the pupil makes the correct recall, penetrates to the key procedure, guesses or reasons, etc. This is subjective in part, but it tells the teacher much more than a list of responses to unrelated questions.

4. *Pupil self-evaluation.* This can be accomplished by giving outside-of-class assignment (homework assessments). Pupils should be asked to state their difficulties and to "talk out" unsolved problems.

5. *Questioning and interviewing.* A class period of questioning, not only concerning procedures and facts, but concerning concepts, understandings, and problem-solving or the same sort of questions, when used in interviews with individual pupils, may help to bring to light the pupils' strengths and weaknesses and to pinpoint the difficulties pupils may be encountering in learning. Although this method is time-consuming, it is perhaps the best method of evaluation if the teacher using it clearly sees the desired goals of his instruction.

It must always be borne in mind that all testing or evaluation in the teaching of elementary school mathematics is for the guidance of pupils and for the improvement of teaching procedures. A test should *never* be used as a disciplinary method, as a threat, or as a means of merely separating the good from the not-so-good mathematics pupil.

16–3 LEARNING MATERIALS; THE PUPIL'S TEXTBOOK

All learning of mathematics takes place in the mind of the pupil. It is the teacher's obligation to place before this mind the best possible material in the most strategic manner. Surely, if one of the ways learning takes place is by reading and reflecting, then the selection of textbooks and practice books is of crucial importance. The question most frequently asked by teachers is "How do I select a textbook for my class?" The teacher, or small committee of teachers and administrators, can measure possible textbooks against a number of criteria, and then select a most-likely suitable book.

1. The material in the book—its scope and sequence—should be compared with the established local school curriculum in elementary mathematics. The construction of a curriculum in mathematics is a very complex, professional task requiring the cooperative efforts of mathematicians, educators, and experienced teachers. This work is usually done by national, state, or large locality groups, and published as a guide. Then teachers from each local school district can study these guides, and in light of local conditions—type of pupils, teacher preparation, administration and school-board requirements and limitations—adopt a curriculum which in scope and sequence appears to be appropriate. Such study by all the teachers involved gives a fairly comprehensive overview of the development of the entire subject. Then the textbook that most clearly conforms to their curriculum guide can be considered as fulfilling one requirement for selection.

2. Every school should have a statement of the philosophy of instruction to which it adheres. This philosophy should state a position with regard to types of learning: rate, meaning, understanding, scientific inquiry, and the like. It should also indicate a balance among the time and stress to be given the various disciplines taught in the school program. The mathematics book which has a presentation most closely related to the school's philosophy of learning meets another criterion of acceptance.

3. Mathematics learning is sequential and each new year builds on the previous learning of the child. To this end a well-planned yearly sequence of textbooks lends itself better to a school program than separate books, each by different authors and selected for a special year of study. Hence, other things being equal, teachers should give weight to a unified series offering a complete program in elementary school mathematics.

4. The textbook is to be used daily by the child. He will carry it to and from his home, read it, turn pages, and sometimes treat the book roughly. Thus the format of the textbook is important. Does it have hard durable covers? Is it attractive in color and design? Is the print sufficiently large for easy reading? Is the paper durable? Are the pictures attractive and pertinent to the subject matter? These and other such questions should be asked concerning each textbook examined.

5. Elementary school teachers must instruct in many areas, and to learn all the pedagogical devices in each field is extremely difficult, especially when every discipline almost yearly reorganizes its scope and sequence, and in addition injects new material into its program. Every new series of textbooks should supply a teacher's manual which is specific in telling the teacher the aims of instruction, the materials other than the text that can be used as supplementary aids, how to use these aids, hints on presenting the material in the textbook, and sample tests to measure the results of the instruction. The manual should be written by the author(s) of the textbooks and thus should amplify the philosophy which the authors used as a basis for writing their arithmetic program. Textbook series without teacher's guides may easily be misinterpreted by the teacher.

6. The qualifications of the team of authors of a textbook series should be examined. A good series should be mathematically correct, educationally sound, and teachable. This calls for co-operative writing by mathematicians, mathematical educators, and classroom teachers (or persons with extensive experience in teaching mathematics to elementary school pupils). Does the authorship reflect all these facets? If not, the book may show a bias that may interfere with its best usage.

7. Consider the practice and problem-solving material. No skill, computational or logical (reasoning), can be learned without sufficient practice and periodic review for reinforcement of the learning. Some series of textbooks have special workbooks to accompany the textbook. This may be an added expense that could be avoided by properly providing the exercises in the textbook. Usually teachers have too much teaching to do to take time to create or reproduce mimeographed practice material, and so a textbook should be examined carefully to see that the children are not left wanting for practice material or problems to solve.

8. Among other criteria we mention readability. The vocabulary, the symbolic representation, the sentence structure, all should be

adapted to the level of reading ability the child has attained at the time he uses the book. If pupils cannot read the textbook with understanding, it serves no purpose other than offering a supply of exercises. Although the teacher may prefer to present a learning situation in a manner of his own, the book presentation should offer a complementary approach to the topic. Several views of a particular concept or algorism always give deeper insight into the mathematics than a single presentation. But the uppermost hope of all teaching is that the individual will continue to study through-out the rest of his life. To this end the ability to read and reflect must be developed, and only through readable textbooks can this goal be pushed forward.

16–4 LEARNING MATERIALS; SENSORY AIDS

Throughout this book we have stressed the use of sensory objects as a first means to approach concept formation. The arithmetic and geometry emerge or are abstracted from physical situations, through the use of scientific inquiry. The learning, however, does not stop here, but proceeds to application in new problem situa-tions. All educators recognize the value of the use of sensory materials in learning mathematics, but they also recognize that these materials are means to an end, never the end in themselves.

The variety and kinds of aid commercially available today are literally unlimited, but the teacher should carefully weigh their essential value for learning before purchasing them. For example, one type of commercial material may consist of rods of different colors keyed to different lengths. After children learn the number names in order by *rote*, the teacher assigns a number name to each color, or to each rod of that color. Then, by comparing the lengths of the rods through matching, children discover the addition facts. In all this teaching, color plays a dominant role, yet color has nothing whatsoever to do with cardinal numbers. The concept of *measure*, measuring lengths, is used to develop number relations, whereas in most developments of mathematics, number is used to develop the concept of measure. In this foregoing illustration learning by rote played a significant role, whereas the theory explained in this text outlaws pure rote learning, except for those few things—usually linguistic entities—which must be learned by imitation. This is merely an example to show that children may learn some things from the use of almost any materials and colors, but what they learn may be conceptually barren and useless in application. Before he uses any materials, the teacher should always think through the kind of concept that will be the outcome, and the probable use of the concept.

As stated in Chapter 1, the physical environment of the child is usually replete with materials for learning arithmetic and geometry. But after these environmental situations have been explored, it is well to replace them by representative materials such as counters, pegs, markers, clothespins. (These are useful for comparing sets of objects and for learning cardinal numbers, order relations, and fundamental operational facts.) The use of an abacus represents a further step toward abstraction. Here the position of a single counter replaces the collection of a set of ten counters; or, in the hundreds column, the same-sized counter represents ten sets of ten counters. Finally, numerical symbols replace all previous stages of abstraction, and a child has an accurate concept of a number such as 376 without any recourse to a physical representation. It is a mark of good teaching to recognize when a child is ready to go from physical collections to representations, and then to symbolic thinking, so that the child has a deep, broad, appropriate understanding of number.

In the same way, the use of physical objects, for which the child uses touch and sight, leads from an edge of a ruler or a cubical die to a line drawing, to a concept of a segment as a set of points in a given space. To jump too quickly from the physical object to a representation, or from a representation (drawing) to the formal concept and definition of a geometrical entity, may result in a child never learning what mathematics is, or how it can be applied. A teacher who can recognize the stages of progression from physical properties to abstract mathematical entities—and who knows how to determine the stage the pupil has reached at a certain point of instruction—has a global view of learning mathematical concepts that results in great satisfaction to both himself and his pupils.

A careful review of Chapters 2 through 15 will reveal the use of many mechanical aids applied in exactly the way described in the previous paragraph. However, it must be stressed that previously learned mathematical concepts also become, in a very real sense, aids in learning new mathematical concepts. Thus counting, when it is really understood as a mapping in which a number of a collection can be obtained, becomes a genuine aid in learning addition as the act of associating a number of a union of two disjoint collections of objects. Once addition has been developed as a concept (a function or mapping $[(a, b) \xrightarrow{+} c]$), it may be used in a physical situation to develop the concept of subtraction or the concept of multiplication. It is only when pupils use acquired concepts to construct new concepts that the structure of arithmetic is built in their minds.

The number of sensory aids is almost limitless. To describe the myriad of helpful devices would be too space-consuming. However, a note on not cluttering the class with too many gadgets may be in order. Frequently aids can be made from cardboard or other available material which can be discarded after their purpose has been served. Thus a numbers pocket, made from a manila folder with half of the one sheet cut off

Hundreds	Tens	Ones

lengthwise and then cut into thin unit strips and the rest folded as shown in the diagram, can be easily created in a few minutes and thrown away as soon as children understand numeration to 1000.

Among the useful but inexpensive manipulative devices, let us mention the following:

Markers or counters (all of same shape and size)

Ten-beaded abacus

Flannel board or magnetized board with steel counters

Felt and cardboard circular disks in fractional parts

Measuring instruments both for chalkboard and pupil desk use: straightedge, compass and protractor, both English and metric rulers (foot, yard, meter, and tape in tenths of a foot), containers (pint, quart, liter, cup)

Lattice point and cross-sectioned paper

Cardboard, scissors, paste

Common physical geometrical models: regular solids, prism, pyramid, cylinder, cone, sphere

Among visual aids the film strip is to be recommended. It can be easily reversed to an earlier frame, and the frame can be used as long as necessary for most children to understand what it portrays. Moreover, these frames are usually prepared by experts who create a picture far superior to that which a teacher could draw. Motion pictures, on the other hand, tell a story and may motivate learning but seldom *teach* the topic under study. At present programmed instruction has some value for practice, and in the future, as electronics and computers enter into this type of instruction, it will be important for teachers to acquaint themselves with the contribution that these aids to learning may make.

An empty classroom, in itself, is a mathematics laboratory for anyone aware of its potential, and when the classroom contains furniture and some people, it is already a gold mine of opportunity for splendid mathematics lessons. Special equipment enriches the lode.

Unless the classroom is extraordinarily crowded, it should contain a mathematics table, or a mathematics corner. The specifics of what belongs in this area depend on the grade level, of course, but the general contents should include equipment for making models and drawings and charts, models already made or purchased, samples of the children's work, games which involve mathematical concepts and skills, reference books which the children can use and perhaps a few for the teacher (which selected children may share), and anything else which the children or the teacher consider appropriate.

Physical considerations aside, the teacher has two major responsibilities with regard to mathematics (or to any other subject). The first is to see to it that the general atmosphere of the classroom is conducive to happy and productive activity. This requires human and material resources. There is no prescription for meeting this requirement, but almost all elementary school teachers are possessed of large measures of human warmth, common sense, ingenuity, and genuine dedication to the education of their pupils. It would be nice if everyone possessed the wisdom of Solomon. A teacher needs wisdom when, for example, a youngster who has done nothing all year presents a smudged drawing and says he wants to put it up on the bulletin board. Possibly the wise response is, "You get the thumbtacks and I'll find a place," rather than "Let's see if it meets our standards for bulletin-board displays." He can improve it later.

The second responsibility is to devise ways of helping the children learn. This implies that the teacher knows something about children, something about ways of learning, and something about the subject matter. No one knows all about any one of these. There are ways of increasing what one knows already. For example, there are some elementary school teachers who have never had a course in geometry. This does not excuse them from teaching it. The teacher's guide for the textbook the pupils are using is one source of information about both subject matter and pedagogy. Beyond that, the teacher can consult a book on subject matter, preferably one written especially for elementary school teachers, and bolster his own knowledge. Even better, he can consult two or more such books. If he finds certain differences in the treatments of a given topic, he should not conclude that at least one of the books is necessarily wrong. There is always more than one mathematically correct way to treat a topic.

How does one devise ways to help children learn? Again, there is no prescription. Rigidity is stultifying. The teacher must have thought through each lesson and be forearmed against foreseeable difficulties. What should he do about unforeseeable difficulties, or about situations, within the lesson or at some other time, which he has not planned for? He should do *something*. He should not be afraid to say, "I don't know," especially if he follows this statement with "Let's see if we can find out." When a problem is pedagogical or psychological, rather than mathematical, frequently the best source of help is the other children in the class. Children usually have ways of communicating with one another. It is essential that a teacher have high standards for his own performance. It is tragic if he is such a perfectionist (or equivalently, so insecure) that he hesitates to do anything when there is any possibility of his making a mistake.

A teacher who gradually develops for himself a theory on the use of materials in teaching mathematics, modified from time to time, and sees how the use of such aids leads to mathematical understanding cannot help but develop a broader and more structured viewpoint on the whole of mathematical learning.

16–5 THE TEACHER'S KNOWLEDGE

To teach the program in mathematics outlined in this book with a feeling of satisfaction and security demands on the part of the teacher a sufficient study and understanding of the mathematical foundations of the material that is taught. What constitutes sufficient knowledge is difficult to say, but a number of commissions or committees have recently outlined this sufficiency in terms of high school and college study for the prospective teacher of elementary school mathematics. In terms of courses, all reports agree, more or less, that the preparation should include the following:

High school (ninth through twelfth grade)	College and university
1. A first course in algebra	1. A one-year course in foundations of arithmetic, including structure of the real number system
2. A course in high school geometry	
3. A course in intermediate mathematics, i.e., algebra extended and trigonometry (not required but recommended)	2. A basic course in modern algebra
	3. A course in informal geometry

Of course, it is not passing courses, but what the prospective teacher really *learns* in these courses that counts. Unless the person who teaches the college mathematics course frequently relates the mathematical foundation to the way correct concepts should be taught in the elementary school, very little of professional nature is gained. It is for this reason that courses in pedagogy, in which the mathematics can be directly related to the teaching process, should follow or be studied contemporaneously with the subject-matter courses. The pedagogy of mathematics makes sense only if the subject matter is thoroughly understood. In general, a good professional practice requires that pedagogy and subject matter be closely related. Further courses in pedagogy, such as given in this book, should always be accompanied by either observation or practice in elementary class teaching.

Today, knowledge in various disciplines, as well as in the psychology of learning, is increasing at an accelerated rate. Much that a teacher learns in college and in his first few years of teaching becomes obsolete in ten years because of new curricula and new techniques in teaching and learning. For this reason, a life-long career in teaching demands continued in-service study on the part of the teacher. This may be accomplished in several ways. School districts in increasing numbers are providing in-service courses, by competent consultants, on the most recent changes in content and teaching methods. New books are being written especially for the updating of teachers' knowledge, and these books can be expected to be produced for the teacher's self-study.

A teacher who teaches all day, in a self-contained classroom, all the subjects of the curriculum, can hardly be expected to attend conventions and conferences in each of the disciplines in which he instructs. But he can subscribe to, or have the school subscribe to, professional journals, and the reading of these journals can keep the elementary teacher abreast of most of what is happening in the teaching of elementary mathematics. At present, there are two outstanding English-language journals, one called *The Arithmetic Teacher*, published in the U.S.A., the other called *Teaching Arithmetic*, published in Great Britain. Besides these, journals devoted to elementary school education in general frequently carry articles devoted to the teaching of mathematics.

What should a teacher know? Enough! Enough to know that he is teaching correct concepts; enough to know that when he is in doubt he should consult textbooks, guides, or consultants before he develops the material for the students; enough so that he sees the whole of elementary mathematics instruction and not just his grade's small segment; enough so that he can develop the pupils' ability to observe and to be aware of what they are learning; enough to make the subject alive and interesting to his pupils; enough to enable him to help his pupils succeed, for success breeds further success; enough to know that he is doing a professional job of creating real mathematical understanding, and the ability to use it, in the minds of his pupils.

16–6 THE BALANCED PROGRAM

Mathematics is only one of the subjects taught in elementary schools. However, it contributes to the learning of other subjects—reading, social science, physical education, science, industrial arts, fine arts, music, linguistics—and these, in turn, contribute to the learning of mathematics. This is as it should be; mathematics (as well as most other disciplines) has its origin in the real world, and nothing in the ordinary everyday environment is clearly labeled *mathematics*. Children have to do all their learning in terms of their own ever-changing perception of the world they live in. In this sense, the modern classroom is a learning laboratory.

It is not possible to assign a grade level, or even a specific sequence, to most of the topics which belong in a balanced program in elementary mathematics. A concept is not an either-you-have-it-or-you-don't entity; it is a matter of degree. Descriptions are refined over a period of years until they can become precise definitions. The same pupil should learn more each year about topics he has already had, as well as about some topics which may be new to him. A long period of informal acquaintance with a topic should precede its formal presentation.

Once a concept or idea has been learned, a definition may be in order, but this alone is not the best mode of communication in mathematics. Usually we clinch the concept by creating a *symbol* for it, and mathematics becomes a symbolic representation of a piece of knowledge. Having learned what number is, we create numerals and a system of numeration: 3, 86, 204, and so on. Knowing what an operation is, the child learns to symbolize operations with the use of '$+$', '$-$', '$\times$', '$\div$', and writes, for example, '$3 \times 4 = 12$'. He also learns order relations, and is soon using the symbols '$<$' and '$>$'; for example, '$3 + 4 > 5$'. To these symbols he adds the geometric ones, A for a point, $\overleftrightarrow{BC}$ for a line, $\overline{BC}$ for a segment, $\angle ABC$ for an angle, and so on. By the end of the sixth grade the pupil will have a host of symbols, each of which connotes a unique concept which he can use in thinking, in solving problems, and in communicating results. A balanced program gradually develops the ability of each child to do this symbolic thinking. Such thinking is indispensable for further study of mathematics.

As the study progresses, the teacher builds a structure of interrelated concepts, such as indicated in the opening of this chapter. One concept leads to another, and several concepts show a generalization. At the start, $4 + 5 = 9$ and $9 - 5 = 4$ are distinct ideas, but at the end they are part of one idea: an operation and its inverse. Similarly, with $4 \times 5 = 20$ and $20 \div 5 = 4$, or $4^2 = 16$ and $\sqrt{16} = 4$. If a new concept of a shrinker is introduced and it is paired with the whole number as a stretcher, we create an entire new structure of fractions. And this goes on and on throughout the entire study of mathematics. A balanced program develops in the minds of the pupils a recognition of structure both in the subject and in the way it is learned.

But a knowledgeable structure is not sufficient for the further study or application of mathematics. A reasonable skill in (a) manipulation of symbols (computation) and (b) manipulation of ideas, reasoning with them and using them to solve problems, is needed by all citizens. So we develop algorisms from an understanding of the structure of number systems and systems of numeration; we practice a refined, mature algorism until it becomes an efficient tool for all pupils. We reason with definitions and concepts until the pupils sense how to draw correct conclusions and avoid errors of logic. We help the pupils practice this manipulation of ideas until it becomes a sought-for way of getting and checking solutions to problems. A balanced program does not neglect skill in computation nor skill in reasoning. It stresses ideas and manipulations equally.

Application of mathematics to the solution of problems (quantitative and spatial) does not come about automatically. A few children can make the transfer of a mathematical system to a physical, business, or social situation by reason of high intellectual ability, but most children must be shown and led to discover how to do this. A child may know ratios and how to treat them mathematically in a proportion, and at the same time not recognize how this idea is related to percent, or to comparison of physical quantities. A balanced program not only abstracts the mathematical ideas from a real-life situation, but it also teaches the child how to put the abstract mathematics back into other real-life situations. A balanced program enables a child to describe or organize a situation in terms of mathematics, i.e., to mathematize a situation.

To teach all things to all pupils is a recognized impossibility. To teach essential things to all pupils, to enrich the learning of those with greater cognitive intelligence, and to prolong the study of topics for children with less-than-average ability is good educational philosophy. In elementary school, we are not developing particular professional or career persons. We are concerned with developing the best minds possible from the raw material with which the children are endowed, so as to make of *all* children reasonably educated dignified persons in a democratic society. A balanced program adapts the instruction to the child's inherited ability, his rate of growth, and his ultimate needs as a free responsible citizen.

In general, what can we expect a balanced program of mathematical education to produce by the end of Grade 6? We can expect a young person, aged about 12 years, who has successfully passed through the preoperational and concrete operational stages of mathematical learning and has begun the type of formal learning so necessary to a real acquisition of mathematical knowledge. He has well-developed concepts of whole number, fraction, and rational number, and can carry out the four rational operations on these numbers by efficient computational procedures in the decimal system of numeration. He understands ratio, simple proportion, and percent, and can apply these concepts to the successful solution of practical problems in social, business, and science situations.

He has a fairly comprehensive knowledge of physical space—point, line, plane, and three-dimensional—and the various configurations occurring frequently in this physical space as he sees it. He can describe fundamental figures in terms of segments, angles, paths, the operations of union and intersection, parallelism and perpendicularity. He has developed some skill in constructing drawings of figures with the use of a straightedge and a compass, or a ruler and a protractor. He distinguishes among line regions, plane regions in space, and has a basic understanding of the theory of measure applied to length, area, volume, and angular regions. He senses the way in which arithmetic and geometry are related, both by measures and by graphical representation. He uses less-than-formal, but correct, language and symbols in communicating his knowledge.

He uses the words *set* and *subset* properly and has met on occasions (Venn) diagrams illustrating relations among sets and their subsets. He has been introduced to place-numeration systems to bases other than ten, and to the type of generalizations that lead to the study of algebra by using first frames and then letter symbols for expressing universal laws as formulas. He has had a taste of number theory in the study of the properties of certain number fields, prime and composite numbers, LCD and GCF, and divisibility. Above all he has gained a scientific spirit of inquiry in the way he studies and comes to know his mathematics, and sees its role in the culture he lives in. And hopefully, he enjoys the subject and is motivated to continue its study with enthusiasm as he enters secondary school.

EXERCISES

1. Select one year of study, any year from kindergarten through Grade 6, and list the broad objectives of the study for that year. Select one topic to be studied during that year and list the special objectives to be attained by all pupils through its study.

2. Select one year of study from the years from kindergarten through Grade 6, and for this year prepare a chart, similar to that in the beginning of this chapter, showing the interrelation of the fundamental concepts and structure to be attained during the year's study of mathematics.

3. List at least three desirable purposes that a class test should serve. How can test results enable each purpose to be achieved?

4. To test computational skill the teacher may give (1) a written test, (2) observe pupils in practice work, (3) interview the pupil, (4) have pupils make a self-evaluation report. List the test situations you might use to test problem-solving ability.

5. Tell what each of the following types of tests should evaluate: (a) diagnostic, (b) inventory, (c) achievement, (d) prognostic, (e) attitudinal. Select one of these types and describe how you would develop a test for the evaluation.

6. Tell what the term "sensory aids" conveys to you with regard to teaching mathematics. Select at least two such aids for use in teaching multiplication of whole numbers and describe how you would use them in the classroom.

7. A teacher in the elementary school at any grade should have a comprehensive view of the entire program of mathematical education from kindergarten through Grade 6. Defend or rebut this statement.

8. In terms of your present knowledge of *what* and *how* to teach in elementary school, review the contribution (or noncontribution) that your college professional study has made to your preparation. What changes in this study would you advocate?

9. All learning, of mathematics as well as of other subjects, should be approached with the spirit of scientific inquiry. What does this sentence mean to you with regard to teaching in the elementary school?

10. Teaching of elementary school mathematics should be dynamic, not static. List at least five attributes that characterize each of these types of teaching (dynamic vs. static). Then characterize a psychology of learning that you think is adaptable to teaching mathematics to children aged 5 to 12 years.

REFERENCES

ADLER, I., "The Cambridge Conference Report: Blueprint or Fantasy," *The Arithmetic Teacher* **13,** 3, March 1966, pages 179–186

BROWNELL, W. A., "The Evaluation of Learning under Dissimilar Systems of Instruction," *The Arithmetic Teacher* **13,** 4, April 1966, pages 267–274

BUROS, O. K., *Mental Measurements Yearbook*, Highlands Park, N.J.: Gryphon Press, 1959

DUTTON, W. H., *Evaluating Pupils' Understanding of Arithmetic*, New York: Prentice-Hall, 1964

KLAUSMEIER, H. J., and C. W. HARRIS, editors, *Analysis of Concept Learning*, New York: Academic Press, 1966, Chapter 14

MAYOR, J. R., "Issues and Directions," *The Arithmetic Teacher* **13,** 5, May 1966, pages 349–354

NATIONAL COUNCIL OF TEACHERS OF MATHEMATICS, *Evaluation in Mathematics*. Twenty-Sixth Yearbook, 1961

SCOTT, L., *Trends in Elementary School Mathematics*, Skokie, Ill.: Rand McNally, 1966

general bibliography

RECENT BOOKS ON TEACHING

BANKS, J. H., *Learning and Teaching Arithmetic*, revised edition, Boston: Allyn and Bacon, 1964

COPELAND, R. W., *Mathematics and the Elementary Teacher*, Philadelphia: W. B. Saunders, 1966

CORLE, C. G., *Teaching Mathematics in the Elementary School*, New York: The Ronald Press, 1964

GROSSNICKLE, F. E., and L. J. BRUECKNER, *Developing Meaning in Elementary School Mathematics*, New York: Holt, Rinehart, and Winston, 1963

HEDDENS, J. W., *Today's Mathematics—A Guide to Concepts and Methods in Elementary School Mathematics*, Chicago, Ill.: Science Research Assoc., 1964

HOWARD, C. F., and E. DUMAS, *Basic Procedures in Teaching Arithmetic*, Boston: D. C. Heath, 1963

KRAMER, K., *The Teaching of Elementary School Mathematics*, Boston: Allyn and Bacon, 1966

MARKS, J. L., C. P. PURDY, and L. B. KINNEY, *Teaching Elementary School Mathematics for Understanding*, New York: McGraw-Hill, 1965

NATIONAL COUNCIL OF TEACHERS OF MATHEMATICS, *Arithmetic in General Education*, Sixteenth Yearbook, 1941

NATIONAL COUNCIL OF TEACHERS OF MATHEMATICS, *Instruction in Arithmetic*, Twenty-Sixth Yearbook, 1961

General bibliography

SCHOOL COUNCIL FOR THE CURRICULUM AND EXAMINATIONS, *Mathematics in Primary Schools*, Curriculum Bulletin No. 1, London: Her Majesty's Stationery Office, 1965

SHIPP, D. E., and S. ADAMS, *Developing Arithmetic Concepts and Skills*, New York: Prentice-Hall, 1964

SWENSON, E. J., *Teaching Arithmetic to Children*, New York: Macmillan, 1964

RECENT BOOKS ON SUBJECT MATTER FOR TEACHERS

BANKS, J. H., *Elementary School Mathematics: A Modern Approach for Teachers*, Boston: Allyn and Bacon, 1966

BELL, C., C. HAMMOND, and R. HERRERA, *Fundamentals of Arithmetic for Teachers*, New York: John Wiley, 1962

BYRNE, R. J., *Modern Elementary Mathematics*, New York, McGraw-Hill, 1966

CROUCH, R., and G. BALDWIN, *Mathematics for Elementary Teachers*, New York: John Wiley, 1964

CROUCH, R., G. BALDWIN, and R. WISNER, *Preparatory Mathematics for Elementary Teachers*, New York: John Wiley, 1965

CROZES, Y., *Arithmetique*, Masson et Cie, Paris, 1956

FEHR, H. F., and T. J. HILL, *Contemporary Mathematics for Elementary School Teachers*, Boston: D. C. Heath, 1966

HACKER, S. G., W. E. BARNES, and C. T. LONG, *Fundamental Concepts of Arithmetic*, New York: Prentice-Hall, 1963

KEEDY, M. L., *Number Systems: A Modern Introduction*, Reading, Mass.: Addison-Wesley, 1965

KINGSTON, J. M., *Mathematics for Teachers of the Middle Grades*, New York: John Wiley, 1966

KOVACH, L. D., *Introduction to Modern Elementary Mathematics*, San Francisco: Holden Day, 1966

MESERVE, B., and M. SOBEL, *Introduction to Mathematics*, New York: Prentice-Hall, 1964

MITCHELL, B. E., and H. COHEN, *A New Look at Elementary Mathematics*, New York: Prentice-Hall, 1965

MOISE, E. E., *The Number Systems of Elementary Mathematics: Counting, Measurement and Coordinates*, Reading, Mass.: Addison-Wesley, 1966

NATIONAL COUNCIL OF TEACHERS OF MATHEMATICS, *Topics in Mathematics for Elementary School Teachers*, Twenty-Ninth Yearbook, 1965

OHMER, M., C. AUCOIN, and M. CORTEZ, *Elementary Contemporary Mathematics*, New York: Blaisdell, 1964

PAGE, D. A., *Number Lines, Functions, and Fundamental Topics*, New York: Macmillan, 1964

SCHAAF, W., *Basic Concepts of Elementary Mathematics*, revised edition, New York: John Wiley, 1964

SCHOOL MATHEMATICS STUDY GROUP, *Studies in Mathematics*, Volume 9, "A Brief Course in Mathematics for Elementary School Teachers," Pasadena, Cal.: A. C. Vroman, 1963

SHORTT, R. F., *Fundamental Concepts of Mathematics*, Boston: Ginn, 1965

SMART, J. R., *New Understandings in Arithmetic*, Boston: Allyn and Bacon, 1963

SMITH, S. E., JR., *Explorations in Elementary Mathematics*, New York: Prentice-Hall, 1966

SWAIN, R., and E. NICHOLS, *Understanding Arithmetic*, revised edition, New York: Holt, Rinehart, and Winston, 1965

VAN ENGEN, H., M. HARTUNG, and J. STACHL, *Foundations of Elementary School Mathematics*, Chicago: Scott, Foresman, 1965

WARD, M., and C. E. HARDGROVE, *Modern Elementary Mathematics*, Reading, Mass.: Addison-Wesley, 1964

WEBBER, G. C., and J. A. BROWN, *Basic Concepts of Mathematics*, Reading, Mass.: Addison-Wesley, 1963

WIRTZ, R. W., M. BOTEL, and B. G. NUNLEY, *Discovery in Elementary School Mathematics*, Chicago: Encyclopaedia Britannica, 1963

WREN, F. L., *Basic Mathematical Concepts*, New York: McGraw-Hill, 1965

index

index

Index

Index

Index